TUFTED DUCKS
IN A
ROYAL PARK

by

ERIC GILLHAM

Photographs by the author except for the two reproduced through the courtesy
of the *Daily Mirror*.
Sketch-maps and figures drawn by R. Steer.

© 1986 Eric Gillham

ISBN 0 9511556 0 1

First published in 1987 by the author

31 Coast Drive, Lydd-on-Sea, Romney Marsh, Kent TN29 9NL

Printed by Hythe Printers Limited, Hythe, Kent

Photographic prints prepared by K. Holdom, Lydd, Kent

To Joan

Contents

ACKNOWLEDGMENTS . . . . (ix)

INTRODUCTION 1

CHAPTER
1 St. James's Park 3
2 A general description of the
    Tufted Duck 19
3 Tufted Ducks in and around London 27
4 Autumn to Spring 41
5 Pre-nuptial courtship and pairing 49
6 The nesting season 69
7 The brood season 111
8 The post-breeding season 157
9 Food and feeding habits 169
10 Future prospects 189

LIST OF SKETCH-MAPS

1 The St. James's group of waters 36
2 St. James's Park Lake 37
3 Location of Tufted Duck nests on Duck Island from 1961 to 1970 inclusive 78

LIST OF FIGURES

1 Time-span of attacks by male Tufted Duck on other Tufted Ducks in the
   breeding season 70
2 Time-span of Tufted Duck nest site searching activity and the laying season 76
3 Time-span of the commencement of the flightless period of adult Tufted
   Duck on the St. James's group of waters (excluding Buckingham Palace Lake) 159
4 Total span of the flightless period of Pochard in St. James's Park and
   Tufted Duck on the St. James's group of waters (excluding Buckingham
   Palace Lake) 162

LIST OF TABLES

1 Breeding season population of Tufted Duck in St. James's Park between
   1954 and 1984 inclusive 193
2 26 approximate return dates to the St. James's group of waters (excluding
   Buckingham Palace Lake) of colour-ringed male Tufted Duck which
   were not present in St. James's Park in the breeding season and which
   completed their wing moult elsewhere 194
3 15 approximate return dates to the St. James's group of waters (excluding
   Buckingham Palace Lake) of colour-ringed female Tufted Duck which
   were not present in St. James's Park in the breeding season 195
4 50 approximate departure dates from the St. James's group of waters
   (excluding Buckingham Palace Lake) of colour-ringed male Tufted Duck
   which were not present in St. James's Park in the breeding season 196
5 30 approximate departure dates from the St. James's group of waters
   (excluding Buckingham Palace Lake) of colour-ringed female Tufted Duck
   which were not present in St. James's Park in the breeding season 197
6 Approximate sex ratios of Tufted Duck on the St. James's group of
   waters (excluding Buckingham Palace Lake) based on counts in period
   November to February inclusive 198
7 Composition of 162 close-knit pre-nuptial courting parties of Tufted
   Duck in St. James's Park in period 1959 to 1970 inclusive 199
8 Timetable of pairing of Tufted Duck in St. James's Park in period 1960
   to 1970 inclusive 200
9 Percentages of females paired in some small Tufted Duck populations 201
10 Copulation, attempted copulation and soliciting (without eventual
   copulation) by Tufted Duck in period April 13 1954 to June 6 1970 202
11 Analysis of precopulatory display by paired and unpaired Tufted Duck
   in period April 12 1961 to July 20 1967 204
12 Analysis of post-copulatory display and behaviour of paired and unpaired
   Tufted Duck in period April 12 1961 to July 20 1961 205
13 Some apparent reasons for the shortening or absence of the usual
   sequence of post-copulatory display and behaviour of Tufted Duck 206
14 Latest dates on which Tufted Duck were observed in pairs in St. James's Park 207

15 15 approximate return dates to St. James's Park Lake of colour-ringed
    male Tufted Duck which had been present in the breeding season
    but which left to complete their wing moult elsewhere........................ 208
16 38 approximate return dates to St. James's Park Lake of colour-ringed
    female Tufted Duck which had been present in the breeding season
    but which left to complete their wing moult elsewhere........................ 209
17 Breeding season attacks on various species of duck and hybrids by paired,
    or lone, male Tufted Ducks in St. James's Park............................. 210
18 Nuptial behaviour of Tufted Duck 211
19 Male Tufted Duck guarding his mate while she engages in feeding............... 212
20 Behaviour preceding copulation by paired Tufted Duck in period
    March 27 to July 13... 213
21 Nest site searching activity of Tufted Duck in St. James's Park 213
22 Nest sites of Tufted Duck and Pochard in St. James's Park (mainly on
    Duck Island) between 1954 and 1970 inclusive 214
23 Male and female Tufted Duck simulating nest building in a spot
    completely unsuitable for a nest 215
24 Number of Tufted Duck nests found on Duck Island, North Bay islets,
    Palace end island, and in mainland edge cover between 1954 and 1970 inclusive 215
25 Tufted Duck clutch sizes in St. James's Park between 1954 and 1968 inclusive 216
26 Communal calling warning behaviour of adult female Tufted Duck in
    the nesting season 216
27 Breeding age of female Tufted Duck.. 217
28 Loner female Tufted Duck seen ashore in an egg-laying condition
    (i.e. droopy at the rear end) 217
29 Apparently hungry female Tufted Duck coming ashore to be fed in the
    breeding season 218
30 Gesture of repulsion behaviour by female Tufted Duck........................ 218
31 Success of Tufted Duck nests in St. James's Park............................. 227
32 Eggs left in Tufted Duck nests after departure of those young which hatched 228
33 Examination of contents of 146 left-over Tufted Duck eggs taken from
    nests after the departure of the female and those of the brood which hatched 228
34 Some comparisons concerning Tufted Duck biology over two
    consecutive eight-year periods in St. James's Park 229
35 Hatching date analysis of 287 Tufted Duck broods in fourteen years
    in St. James's Park.. 230
36 Rearing success of Tufted Duck in fourteen years in St. James's Park............ 231
37 Analysis of Tufted Duck brood sizes when newly-hatched broods were
    first seen on water in fourteen years in St. James's Park 233
38 Numbers of newly-hatched tufted ducklings reaching water annually
    in tufted broods and in broods of other species in St. James's Park............. 234
39 Fledging period of young Tufted Duck...................................... 235
40 Dates on which adult Tufted Duck were first seen to be flightless on the
    St. James's group of waters (excluding Buckingham Palace Lake)
    between 1953 and 1969 inclusive.. 235
41 Commencement of the flightless period of adult female Tufted Duck 237
42 Distribution of flightless adult Tufted Duck on the St. James's
    group of waters (excluding Buckingham Palace Lake) in the years
    1953 to 1969 inclusive 238
43 Approximate departure dates from St. James's Park Lake of colour-ringed
    adult Tufted Duck which were present in the breeding season but which
    left to complete their wing moult elsewhere 239

LIST OF APPENDICES

1 Examples of pairing data of 4 colour-ringed Tufted Duck 241
2 Water area preferences of colour-ringed female Tufted Duck within their home ranges 245
3 Homosexual behaviour of female Tufted Duck 248
4 Evidence of nesting by loner female Tufted Duck 249
5 Summary of 19 records of the reactions, mainly by paired male tufted, to rape attacks by other male tufted 259
6 Time-span of a tufted brood female's stay with her young during the ducklings' fledging period together with available details of a brood female's wing moult 260
7 Duration of a brood female's stay with her young during the ducklings' fledging period 263
8 Overlap between a brood female Tufted Duck's wing moult and her brood duties 265
9 Voice of the Tufted Duck 266
10 A list of Aythya and other hybrids, considered to involve Tufted Duck parentage, in St. James's Park and elsewhere between 1963 and September 1984 268
11 Aberrant plumage 272
12 Birds breeding in St. James's Park in period 1961 to 1984 inclusive 275
13 Nomenclature 276

BIBLIOGRAPHY 279

INDEX 293

ACKNOWLEDGMENTS

It is for certain that this study would have been reduced in scope but for a welcome offer of field assistance from the newly-appointed St. James's Park Bird Keeper early in 1958. For the next seventeen years the late Mr. Arthur May provided me with important information on the Park's waterfowl which I most gratefully acknowledge. Besides marking the position of almost all Tufted Duck and Pochard nests on my maps he showed me the actual sites. Among other things he organised the catching of young to be colour-ringed and, for a decade afterwards, notified me of colour-ring combinations on the legs of live and dead birds seen or found by himself or reported to him. I am also indebted to Mr. Malcolm Kerr, the present Bird Keeper, for additional data covering the past nine years.

Throughout the past thirty-two years the Royal Parks Division of the Department of the Environment has always been helpful in providing important information relating to these studies. In the early 1950s this was given by Mr. W. G. Teagle, then by Mr. F. E. E. Fox, and, later still, by Mr. J. Norley. To these successive secretaries of the former Bird Sanctuaries Committee I record my thanks. During their respective periods of office both chairmen of this committee were sympathetic to a number of my requests. I am grateful, therefore, to the late Lord Hurcomb and his successor, Mr. Stanley Cramp. To the latter I am additionally indebted for his records of Tufted Ducks frequenting the lake in Buckingham Palace Gardens for the past quarter-of-a-century. I also extend my thanks to Miss I. Cavellini and Mrs. G. M. Morris of the Bailiff of the Royal Parks Office for dealing with my enquiries since the retirement of Mr. Norley.

I am greatly obliged to Mr. Peter Oliver for providing me with many records of London's Tufted Ducks and, since 1979, for meticulously keeping up-to-date my file on the populations of all known breeding waters of this species within twenty miles of St. Paul's Cathedral.

In the course of writing this book invaluable help and criticism from the following were greatly appreciated. Mr. Jim Allen not only read through the first manuscript but also translated for me some 12,000 words of German waterfowl literature. Dr. Al Hochbaum's numerous comments on the first typescript influenced the ultimate presentation of this book. Mr. Geoffrey Chapman also advised at this stage while Mr. Harry Cawkell made many recommendations on the final draft and kindly corrected the proofs.

Throughout my work on Tufted Ducks members of my family, former Official Observers for St. James's Park and other friends and acquaintances have, at times, assisted in a wide variety of ways. To the following, therefore, I am especially indebted:

Mrs. M. Abel	B. L. Gillham	Prof. G. V. T. Matthews
M. Anderson	M. A. Gosling	A. B. M. Mills
G. E. Andrews	G. A. Griffiths	A. R. J. Paine
P. Barnard	The late Dr. J. G. Harrison	Miss H. M. Prophet
The late T. L. Bartlett	The late Dr. J. M. Harrison	H. K. Reichbach
W. J. Breed	Dr. P. Harrison	Mrs. S. Rice
H. Chittey	A. Heaton	J. Rogers
C. M. Chapman	K. Holdom	R. Sanderson
Dr. S. Christmas	Lord Hollenden	R. Steer
Dr. T. Christmas	Lady Holman	Mrs. S. Swan
Miss S. Cox	C. J. Jolley	P. Voller
Mrs. J. Gillham	A. L. Lovibond	H. Wylie

INTRODUCTION

This book is about Tufted Ducks in the heart of London.

These lovable little diving ducks have always fascinated me since first getting to know them over fifty years ago in Beckenham's charming Kelsey Park, situated on the southern outskirts of the capital.

On August 1, 1953, I made what was probably about my third visit to St. James's Park since childhood. There, to my unforgettable delight, were eight to ten tufted mothers busily shepherding tiny ducklings about the lake. These families stimulated such a strong desire to learn more about them that my study of this species in St. James's began on that day. This enjoyable task continued annually until the autumn of 1984.

Throughout sixteen of the past thirty-two years it has been my good fortune to watch Tufted Ducks for part of most days between February and November. Observations were fewer in winter as well as in the remaining sixteen breeding seasons.

To a lesser extent I studied these birds in Hyde Park and Kensington Gardens. I have not visited the lake in the grounds of Buckingham Palace but have been kept informed about tufted there by Mr. Stanley Cramp who has been privileged to record the bird life of Her Majesty's gardens over many years.

The Department of the Environment, responsible for the care and maintenance of the Royal Parks, watches over the welfare of waterfowl. From 1947 until 1979 this state organisation was advised on bird protection and other aspects of natural history by a Committee on Bird Sanctuaries.

With the drastic pruning of national expenditure the government has dispensed with the services of this independent panel along with many others. It is hoped that new arrangements, introduced in 1979, will continue conservation of wildlife as before. Happily, in spite of this procedural change, wild birds have continued to prosper.

St. James's Park has a number of advantages as a study area for Tufted Ducks. Most important is that waterfowl become confident in the presence of human beings, behaving as if people are friendly members of their own community. Thus, only a few steps from some of Inner London's busiest thoroughfares, I was able to observe wild ducks in a manner that would have been difficult or impossible as an intruder on their natural environment.

Also highly advantageous, especially in the first decade, were the opportunities afforded for identifying a small number of individuals mainly by distinctive plumage markings. Then, from 1962 onwards, recognition on a greater scale was achieved by coloured leg-bands placed on nearly 150 birds.

Almost all of the tufted population are full-winged birds free to come and go at will. Pinioned ones observed on the lake rarely exceeded five in any one year and for some fifteen years averaged three annually.

To enable me to scrutinise Tufted Ducks day after day all waterfowl needed freedom from disturbance. Fortunately, no aquatic sports or associated activities are allowed in St. James's, so the only commotion on the lake resulted from the occasional authorised work of the Royal Parks Division's staff or its contractors.

Counting tufted was an important priority on practically every visit. The accuracy of figures was greatly enhanced by the openness of both lake and shorelines.

Basically the Park provides a haven for two distinct populations of Tufted Duck. There are the breeding birds, and larger wintering flocks coming from nesting grounds further afield, even from distant parts of Russia. Both local and immigrant birds share a doting public. As with the feeding of pigeons in nearby Trafalgar Square, the provision of food for waterfowl occurs unfailingly throughout the year. The trusting nature of so many of London's birds seems a lasting guarantee of future meals.

What part food from people has contributed to the success of Tufted Ducks breeding in St. James's can only be speculated upon. But, from a dozen nesting pairs in the middle 1950s, there has been a steady increase to over five times as many in 1984.

Of course the breeding population declined in some years, but from one decade to the next there has been an upward trend. On the other hand, winter numbers varied according to the severity of the weather. Fewer were present in mild seasons but between 300 to 600 could be relied on in mid-winter.

Looking back, I have been unbelievably lucky to have studied so many tufted at extremely close range in such a beautiful and tranquil setting.

Lydd-on-Sea, Kent
October 1985

CHAPTER 1

ST. JAMES'S PARK

Francis Willughby (1678) on the Tufted Duck:—

"We saw a bird very like this, perchance the same, in His Majesty's Pools in St. James's Park.

Its bill and legs were a lead colour; its head black. Its wings little, but above the wings the sides white. A long crest hangs down backward from behind the head. To me beholding the bird at a distance, the whole wings seemed white . . ."

Long, long ago the site now occupied by London's oldest Royal Park was marshy ground on the outskirts of a huge forest. Towards the end of the eighth century, in the days of the Saxon King Offa, there was a pool called Cowford, roughly in the middle of the Park as we know it now. This pond was fed by the Eya-burn (= Tyburn), a little stream issuing from meadows adjoining the ancient settlement of Tyburn, a village once situated about half-a-mile from the present Marble Arch. For several hundred years Cowford was linked to the Eya-burn, but some time before the dawn of the thirteenth century part of this watercourse became choked and the pool ended up as little more than a swamp.

I have referred to Larwood (1872) and to Official Records of the Royal Parks Division of the Department of the Environment for much of the historical background.

Before the latter part of the thirteenth century, some well-intentioned citizens of London founded a hospital on the site where St. James's Palace now stands. Its isolated position in those days was, no doubt, considered ideal for the purpose of housing fourteen poor young ladies all suffering from leprosy. This hospital, called "The Sisters of St. James's in the Field" and dedicated to St. James the Great, Bishop of Jerusalem, was endowed with 160 acres of land. Further gifts of land in other parts of the capital were similarly bestowed in later years. Edward I confirmed these gifts in the year 1290 and authorised a fund-raising six-day fair to be held in St. James's Fields, starting, appropriately, on July 24, St. James's Eve. All the charges and profits from the fair were for the benefit of the leper hospital. Probably to ensure that citizens of London arrived with spending money still in their pockets the King wisely decreed that all shops in the City of London were to be kept closed for the duration of the fair.

With the coronation of King Henry VIII things were soon to change. It is said that he objected to the view of the hospital whenever he looked out of the back windows of the Royal residence in Whitehall. The result was that Henry acquired much of the site of St. James's Park about the year 1532 by agreement with the authorities of Eton College, who were the custodians of the hospital from the time of Henry VI. The deal made by Henry VIII appears to have taken the form of an exchange of land in Suffolk. The King also granted a small life-pension to all of the sisters evicted from the hospital (Stow, 1603). The year before this transfer took place Henry also exchanged some other land with the Abbot and Convent of Westminster, thus acquiring a further 100 acres, part of which was added to the Park. Within a very short time the Monarch's new estate was made into a manor and enclosed by a large brick wall. From these beginnings evolved St. James's Palace and a Royal Park. About this period many improvements soon followed, such as planting, draining, and the construction of ponds. The new enclosure, called St. James's Park, was also stocked with deer.

In Elizabeth I's reign the Park continued to be reserved for the Royal Family and its retainers. At the western end, on some ground known as Rosamond's Land in 1531, a circular pool called Rosamond's Pond appears to have been formed by 1593. Though altered in shape this water remained for about the next 200 years. In the late sixteenth century St. James's Park seems to have been largely an open grass field except for an avenue and an orchard. Deer continued to be kept there and the ponds were stocked with fish and waterfowl.

When James I succeeded to the throne the Park is said to have resembled a meadow or common with a few scattered trees. By July 1612 His Majesty was making improvements. Water was channelled from Hyde Park to fill Rosamond's Pond, which was cleared of mud. James loved animals for, with the introduction of a new water supply, he soon established his own zoo. The 'Panda' diplomacy adopted by the People's Republic of China in the last two decades would have earned this King's hearty approval. George Villiers, 1st Duke of Buckingham, while on a mission to Spain sent a letter to his Sovereign telling how he had secured some animals, including camels and an elephant, from the king of that country to add to the growing collection. Other monarchs were just as obliging. The Czar of Russia sent hawks and sables, the Great Mogul obliged with two antelopes and the King of Savoy produced a leopard. Loyal subjects were also contributors, for a wild boar and two young crocodiles were presented by a Captain Newport, while the Virginia Company donated some flying squirrels.

Among the water birds, cormorants appear to have been kept for the purpose of catching fish for the Royal table. James seems not to have bothered too much about expense, for the elephant, on the advice of the keepers, was allowed a gallon of wine a day from September until April! Along with various deer, ducks, and pheasants, kept for the King's pleasure, the menagerie included a beaver and a cassowary.

Pollution of the atmosphere evidently became a topic in James's reign. This occurred through the first use of coal on any scale in London. Apparently, smoke from the Westminster breweries so contaminated the air in the Park that the King considered closing down the offending enterprises.

With the advent of Cromwell, Hyde Park and other Royal establishments were sold off for the benefit of the Commonwealth. St. James's, however, was spared, its only loss being the *Saint* which the republicans deleted from its title. James Park, as it became called, was still not open to the public in general. Oliver Cromwell's courtiers were granted free access, as were a few house owners whose back doors led into the Park. One improvement recorded was that deer, which seem to have disappeared in the Civil War, were reintroduced from Hampton Court and Bushey Park.

The Lord Protector's frugal wife is said to have kept cows in the Park for the supply of butter and buttermilk for her dairy in Whitehall. Cows appear to have been kept in St. James's over a period of several hundred years at least until late Victorian times. Antonia Fraser (1979) relates that in Charles II's reign women sold fresh warm milk to visitors in summer.

Mr. Jack Norley of the Royal Parks Division kindly researched for further evidence on this subject. He tells me (*in litt.*) that in 1770 much of St. James's Park consisted of grass plots where milkwomen grazed their cows at a charge of two shillings and sixpence (later raised to three shillings) per week. Twice daily these cows were taken to Whitehall where their milk fetched one penny a mug. Jack Norley also points out that Milkmaid Passage, situated off Queen's Walk, which forms the eastern boundary of Green Park, may have had associations with this enterprise. He also discovered that there was one cow left in the Park in 1880 and that the mother of one of the Inspectors of Police in the Park saw milkmaids there when she was a small child. This lady was born in 1884 and it seems, therefore, that the tradition of keeping cows had ended by the year 1900.

The Restoration heralded a fascinating period in the Park's history. Charles II got off to a flying start for, in September 1660, some 300 men were engaged in joining up the different pools and springs to form one straight canal. Trees were planted around Rosamond's Pond which was connected to the canal by a sluice. Two-and-a-half years later General George Monck, the newly created Duke of

Albemarle, then residing at the Whitehall Cock Pit on the edge of the Park, was
made Keeper. Though nothing more than a sinecure, the post entitled the holder
to appoint his own staff (Ashley, 1977). It is doubtful if this great commander
and adminstrator, who had invited Charles to return from exile, had any say in
the construction or siting of the decoy or in the introduction of the many species
of birds which were exhibited on the canal or in cages and pens in the vicinity of
the present thoroughfare we know as Bird Cage Walk. In view of Albemarle's
close association with both his Sovereign and the Park, one can imagine his
satisfaction in 1666 when, as joint general-at-sea with Prince Rupert, the King's
cousin, he engaged and defeated a huge Dutch fleet on St. James's Day.

Since those times many other famous men have been appointed Keeper or
Ranger by the Monarch. Queen Anne, however, decided to hold the Office
herself.

Charles II had the decoy and some duck ponds situated on an island. This
place was under the supervision of a salaried Pond-Keeper who, in turn, was
answerable to a person with the grandiose title Governor of Duck Island. After
the death of the first holder, the Office remained vacant for some time until the
Chevalier de St. Evremond had the audacity to obtain the post from the
Monarch by trickery. A number of other officials were appointed to look after
the King's various kinds of birds. There was a Keeper of Hawks, a Cormorant
Keeper, besides Falconers, Clerk of the Aviary, and a Bird Keeper. The last
position was held by Edward Storey who, according to Payne-Gallwey (1886),
was responsible for the decoy, and whose name lives on today as a street called
Storey's Gate on the south-east corner of the Park. Records show that this first
Bird Keeper put out 100 waterfowl nest baskets on Duck Island, a tradition
revived on a larger scale by a successor, Mr. Arthur May, some 300 years later.

Though Charles II ordered the closure of the Park for a while on several
occasions, it was usually open to everyone as it is today. His Majesty, who
incidentally was born in St. James's Palace, loved to saunter through the Park and
sometimes went for a swim in the canal. Charles seems to have been engaged in
one of his favourite daily pastimes, feeding his beloved ducks, when in the
summer of 1667 news of the Dutch incursion into the Medway was brought
to him.

Pelicans were among the first large water birds acquired by the King. Evelyn
(1641-1706) records seeing a pair in 1665 that had been presented by the
Russian Ambassador. Perhaps the most distinguished bird in the collection at
that time was the Canada Goose. It was from the specimens in St. James's Park
that Willughby (1678) gave us the first description of this introduced North
American goose which has prospered in many parts of the British Isles over the

past 300 years. Although Canada Geese, pelicans and cormorants have not been kept continuously since Stuart times, they have a long tradition and the first two species may be seen in the Park now. It is nice to know that the Tufted Duck was among the waterfowl kept by the King.

Though William III is said not to have fed the ducks himself, like the pleasure-loving Charles, he was, none the less, interested in their welfare. Because of poaching William issued strict orders for the protection of waterfowl and game within ten miles of the Court of Whitehall. His Majesty seems to have been happy relaxing in the midst of his ducks in a little summer house built for him on Duck Island. It is difficult to believe that anyone who sought amusement surrounded by waterfowl never fed the ducks personally. Possibly one is nearer the truth in surmising that while Charles fed the birds in public, William fed them in private.

Shortly after Queen Anne ascended the throne, a terrible storm, starting two hours before midnight on November 26, 1703, blew down a large part of the wall as well as over 100 elms. Two oaks which survived this disaster had been planted by Charles II from acorns taken from the historic Boscobel oak. These two trees were to live for another 130 years before being uprooted by a storm in 1833.

According to Larwood, George I contributed very little. Fortunately, the latter's alleged idea of turning the Park into a turnip field did not materialise. Department of the Environment records on the other hand state that the first King of the House of Hanover took a great personal interest in the Park throughout his *whole* reign. Indeed, he had good reason for close involvement after quickly encountering some cool impudence from his Keeper! On settling in at St. James's Palace His Majesty is said to have commented: "This is a strange country. The first morning after my arrival I looked out of the window and saw a park which they told me was mine. The next day Lord Chetwynd, the Ranger of my park, sent me a fine brace of carp out of my canal. At the same time I was told I must give five guineas to Lord Chetwynd's servant, for bringing me my own carp, out of my own canal, in my own park."

So-called improvements carried out by George III were the filling in of both Rosamond's Pond and the moat surrounding Duck Island in or about the year 1770. A few years later the canal was shortened by 140 feet to enlarge Horse Guards Parade. At the end of George IV's kingship, greater changes occurred and the Park was laid out by Nash in much the same form as we see it today.

One much loved bird, whose life in St. James's is said to have spanned four reigns, was a Mute Swan known to many Londoners as Old Jack. He was raised in the gardens of old Buckingham House, the site now occupied by Buckingham Palace. For many years this graceful bird was a favourite of George III's consort,

Queen Charlotte, who frequently fed him. Jack, normally a well-behaved bird, was said to have drowned many a dog and once dragged a twelve-year-old boy into the water by his trousers. In old age Jack was unable to cope with newly-introduced foreign waterfowl and, soon after being attacked by geese, died in 1840 aged close on seventy years.

Throughout Georgian times the lake's ornamental fowl appear to have been neglected. It was largely on the initiative of Queen Victoria's future husband, Prince Albert, that waterfowl collections in several Royal Parks were revived during 1837. The same year the Ornithological Society of London was formed under the Prince's patronage. After this association had provided a large number of water birds in 1841, Albert's powers of persuasion led to the construction of a delightful little cottage for the Bird Keeper beside the entrance to Duck Island. The bills for the dwelling, and the keeper's remuneration, were paid for equally by the government and the society.

Besides various geese and ducks, the collection, about this time, included some unspecified kinds of storks, cranes, herons, bitterns and spoonbills. After enduring for over three decades, the Ornithological Society of London foundered in 1869. The cottage, which showed increasing signs of disrepair from the 1960s, was meticulously restored by early 1983. During the past fifty years both wild and ornamental water birds have thrived in many of London's parks. Long may they continue to do so for, to the many thousands of visitors, these exciting, colourful birds add immeasurably to the pleasure of a lakeside stroll.

Only two important changes in the topography of the lake have been made in the past thirty-two years. To improve the flow of water, the Duck Island causeway and all of the minute North Bay islets were removed during 1982, and replaced by two bridges in January 1983.

A short history of the water areas in Hyde Park, Kensington Gardens and Buckingham Palace Gardens

Once again it is necessary to draw heavily on the researches of Larwood (1872), who tells us that before the Norman Conquest the site of the future Hyde Park lay within the ancient forest which, for more than a millennium, encompassed London to the north and west. At the time of the Norman invasion, the site formed part of an estate held *ex officio* by a high personage of the Saxon court named Asgar. King William I removed him from office and appointed one of his own nobles, Geoffrey de Mandeville, to succeed to all of Asgar's officially held lands including the Manor of Eia. Towards the end of the eleventh century the estate of Eia was divided into three manors called Neyte, Eubury and Hyde. The last-named was destined to become a Royal Park.

Whether or not it was through a troubled conscience that de Mandeville parted with the whole of the Manor of Eia to the Abbey of Westminster is open to speculation. But these lands were given by him to the monks in whose possession they were to remain for close on five centuries. Henry VIII's new order brought irreversible changes in ownership. In 1536, five years after the King's acquisition of land which was to form part of the site of St. James's Park, the Abbot and Convent of Westminster were again exchanging land with their Monarch. This time the Manor of Hyde was surrendered in return for a dissolved priory in Berkshire. With the transaction completed Henry was then able to extend his hunting grounds through to the Royal estate of Marylebone Park (later to become Regent's Park and the surrounding district) and thence to Hampstead Heath. A Royal proclamation of 1536 stated that anyone hunting or hawking His Majesty's hares, partridges, pheasants and herons was likely to suffer imprisonment or worse. It was in this period that the Manor of Hyde, or part of it, was fenced and made into a Royal Park.

Hyde Park continued to be used as a Royal hunting ground in the reigns of Edward VI, Elizabeth I and James I. From the early 1600s, the Park's springs or eleven separate pools provided some Londoners with piped water. Charles I generously opened Hyde Park as a pleasure ground for the public about the year 1635. Between 1730 and 1736, Queen Caroline, wife of George II, implemented plans for improvements. The many pools were drained and the main watercourse, Westbourne Brook, was transformed into a more extensive stream and became the Serpentine and Long Water.

King William III bought the Manor of Kensington from the second Earl of Nottingham and, with alterations, converted the house into Kensington Palace. About fifty years later George II and Queen Caroline acquired another 200 acres of land adjoining the Palace and employed Bridgeman to carry out improvements. This famous landscape gardener's contribution included, among other things, the construction of the Round Pond (Ward, 1912). After the Court ceased to reside at Kensington Palace, the public were admitted to the grounds during the summer months. A few years later the time was further extended, but it was not until the early years of Queen Victoria's rule that Kensington Gardens were opened to visitors all the year round.

The site now occupied by Buckingham Palace and its grounds was mainly fields divided by hedges at the beginning of the seventeenth century. Harris and his collaborators (1968) mention that when the gardens of Buckingham House were laid out in the early part of the eighteenth century Henry Wise was paid a large sum for constructing a canal. Coats (1978), in his detailed account of the

Palace Gardens' history, states only that Wise created a sunk lawn or bowling green and makes no reference to a water area at that time. However, a detailed plan of part of London produced by John Pine and John Tinney in the period 1737-1746 shows the lay-out of the gardens including a canal and, on the western boundary, a single small lake. Possibly the latter water was originally the sixth pond in an adjacent brickfield. With the transformation of old Buckingham House into Buckingham Palace Coats tells us that two existing ponds were made into one lake by 1828 and that an island was added seven years later.

It appears that the lake, as most people know it from a Central London street map, was formed about 150 years ago at the same time as alterations to St. James's Park were being finished. By a strange coincidence the completion of work on both waters heralded the breeding of full-winged Tufted Ducks in London.

A View of the Canal in S.t James's Park, Buckingham House, &c | Vüe du Canal et de la Maison de Buckingham dans le Parc de
taken from the Parade. S.t James.

The St. James's Park Canal in the 18th century (from an original print belonging to the author)

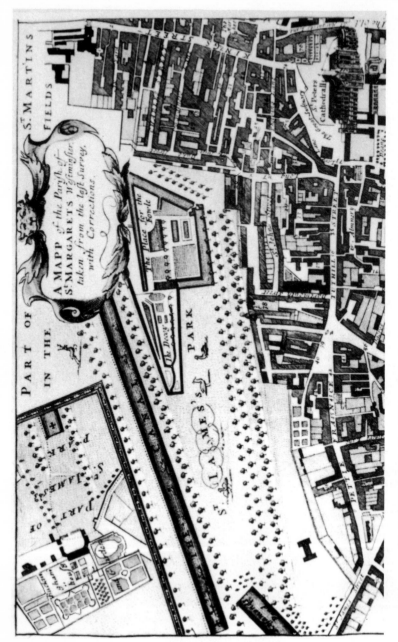

St. James's Park in the 18th century (from a map dated 1755 belonging to the author)

The principal bird subjects of all photographs are Tufted Ducks unless otherwise stated. References to males and females concern adults. Younger birds are clearly indicated.

Male in full plumage

Female in winter

Male Ring-necked Duck in full plumage

Female in worn summer plumage (August). Note the absence of a crest

Female's underparts in winter   Female with dark underparts (July)

Female with light underparts (late June)

Fledged duckling slipping beneath the surface

Female taking a header

Male surfacing from a dive

Male walking

CHAPTER 2

A GENERAL DESCRIPTION OF THE TUFTED DUCK

"There I saw tufted ducks for the first time – neat elegant little birds, black and white with brilliant yellow eyes and a permanent cowlick of plumelike crest rising slightly off the back of the head."
— *Dillon Ripley (1959) concerning a visit to St. James's Park in 1935.*

The Tufted Duck, *Aythya fuligula*, is a member of the genus *Aythya*, a class of twelve species of diving duck including the Ring-necked Duck, Pochard, Lesser Scaup and Scaup.* Despite plumage similarities between the adult male Ring-necked Duck of North America and the male tufted, the two species are no longer considered so closely related as was once supposed. The former has strong links with the true pochards but the latter has affinity with the scaups (*vide* Johnsgard, 1965).

The tufted is a compact duck with rounded head, a well-defined crest, and a broad bill which is a little shorter than the length of the head. Through commonly adopting a squat profile it appears short-necked, but this is shown to be not so when alerted to an erect posture. It is a much smaller bird than the ubiquitous Mallard and is about the size of the familiar Coot. The following plumage details, along with other descriptions of feathering in this book, are based on observations and not on an examination of museum specimens.

So that a visual record was available during the preparation of plumage descriptions, I took over six hundred colour and black and white photographs of Tufted Ducks throughout the whole year. From the onset it was realised that close-up shots of underparts were likely to be few. Therefore, sketches of the breast and belly were made instead. These feather patterns represented birds in all months of the year and totalled 1,700.

Come to St. James's with a bag of bread if you wish to study the plumage of Tufted Ducks. Feed them and they will lean over backwards to let themselves be

---

* See Appendix 13 for nomenclature.

inspected closely from various angles.

Adult male – full plumage and bare parts

For nearly six months of the year the distinctive male in breeding plumage is mainly black glossed with purple on the head and neck. In some lights the cheeks and sides of neck are glossed with dark green, much more noticeably than the dull green cast elsewhere on the upperparts. The pure white belly and flanks contrast sharply with the black body. The two to three inches long black drooping crest, at the back of the head, is usually visible at close range. Further away it is especially eye-catching when blown by the wind. In flight a broad white stripe extending the whole length of the wing becomes less conspicuous on the primaries. The underwing and axillaries look white.

The bill is grey-blue tinged with slate, commonly with a prominent white band behind the black tip. This characteristic is particularly noticeable at close quarters. Viewing a bird head-on, the black on the bill tip extends over the nail and is, normally, like an inverted fan in shape. At its widest this black stops short of the lateral edges, thus differing from that on the bill of an adult male Pochard. The eyes are bright yellowish-gold. The lead blue legs and feet look a little darker than the bill and show up against the blackish webs and joints.

It is nearly Christmas before most drakes assume this breeding plumage. Based on hundreds of birds seen within about a dozen feet an insignificant number were in full dress between late October and late November. An approximate timetable with percentages of drakes seen in nuptial splendour is as follows:— ten by November 30; twenty-five by December 7; sixty by December 15; and seventy-five by December 22. At some distance a higher percentage of drakes appeared to be in breeding plumage by the beginning of December. However, on closer examination, the opposite was the case. The majority had (1) crests less than one inch long or none at all; (2) varying amounts of dusky markings on the white flanks; (3) blackish patches down the centre ridge of the bill. A bird with any of these three characteristics was not considered to be in full plumage.

Adult female – full plumage and bare parts

The less conspicuous but more variable female is, in general, a browner bird throughout the year. Unlike the adult drake, who is in one plumage for winter and much of the nesting season, the female has one dress for winter and another for the breeding period. In winter her dorsal and stern areas look blackish with a dull green gloss. The head and upper neck are blackish-brown, often with a purple gloss. In strong light these colours appear browner, the purple sheen adding richness to the feathering. The lower neck and breast are dark-brown, the latter usually with some white flecking just above the waterline. The drab flanks are the palest of the brown parts on a swimming bird. These side panels vary from a more even colour to a variable mix of yellowish-white, white, grey, and pale-brown, producing an effect of vertical barring which is sometimes quite strong. In a few birds the colours of breast and flanks blend to a more uniform brown slightly paler than the head, neck and upperparts.

A proportion have tiny or large white speckles on the forehead at the base of the bill. In an extremely small number this white forms either a small but well-defined white patch or a prominent white 'mask' extending onto the chin. The lower breast and belly are white. In a few birds there is a small amount of brown flecking on these white underparts. The under tail-coverts are whitish, with or without varying amounts of grey-brown markings. Sometimes purer white under tail-coverts are separated from the rest of the underparts by a narrow pale-drab band. Females with brownish under tail-coverts frequently have a little white around the vent. These feathers can be seen well when a bird rolls on its back to preen.

The stand-off crest is not only shorter than in the adult male but is more variable. In some females it is well-tapered, in others it is bushy at the end, while in a few it is short and spiky or rudimentary. Most females have a crest of sorts for a time in winter. The black-tipped slatey-grey bill is darker than in the male. Behind the black tip is a narrow bluish-grey (sometimes bluish-white) line. Often this bluish-grey extends as a narrow strip along the sides of the upper mandible. The eyes are variable in colour. A trifling number have brilliant yellowish-gold eyes like those of an adult male. Many have bright reddish-gold irides, while in others these bare parts are dull reddish-gold. A minority have extremely dull brownish-yellow eyes. Although the eyes of most colour-ringed females tended to brighten with age, a small number had dull brownish-yellow irides for up to two years after fledging. One had this eye colour throughout the first five years of her life, after which she disappeared. The legs and feet look a similar colour to those of the adult male but match the female's bill more closely.

Summer or breeding season plumage is also subject to variation. The female is a warmer brown than in winter due to golden-brown edges to the upperparts, breast, and especially the sides of the body. The breast and flanks tend to merge through being the same tone while the much darker stern area, wings, back, and head, all look similar, too. A narrow area around the base of the bill is paler than the head. In some birds a small white or whitish spot either side of the base of the lower mandible may be seen between May and September.

The underparts, below the waterline, differ markedly from winter. In some females the dividing line between dark breast and white belly is obscure or jagged. Many have heavy horizontal barring on the belly, while in others the underparts from bill to tail are wholly and intensely dark. In a few the lower edge of the dark breast is neater and below it the belly is lightly barred. Sometimes the barring on the belly is divided into two by a dark central portion extending downwards from the breast. At the beginning of June it is not unusual to see as many as six breeding females all with completely different belly patterns. Once a brood female had clean white underparts as in winter. The crest is usually absent or poorly developed and the bill becomes darker than in winter.

A broad white stripe like that of the male shows in flight. When a resting bird flaps its wings the brilliant white axillaries gleam against the whitish underwing and dark flanks.

The two females in summer on plate 88 of *The Handbook of British Birds* (Witherby *et al.*, 1948) are good examples of this sex between May and July. On the other hand the adult female summer on plate 79 of *The Birds of the Western Palearctic* (Cramp and Simmons, 1977) has characteristics of a bird in new plumage in September. Never have I seen such an excellent crest together with a clean bill in a breeding female in summer.

Details of other male and female plumages will be found in succeeding chapters while the calls of this duck are given in Appendix 9. Descriptions of aberrant plumages are given in Appendix 11.

Locomotion, feeding, and resting

Often when dozing or idling on water Tufted Ducks sit high with their tails cocked up at angles of about forty-five degrees from the surface. Other resting birds carry their tails flat on the water as most do when diving.

In several important works this species is said to swim buoyantly but rather low in water with tail on the surface. In particular, Peterson *et al.* (1974) tend to stress this point in their account of the Ferruginous Duck. Emphasis on a tail-down posture is misleading because swimming tufted commonly reveal their under tail-coverts like Ferruginous Ducks. Moreover, I have frequently seen the latter species with its tail flat on the surface in between dives. Carriage of the tail, therefore, depends largely, but not exclusively, on what these ducks happen to be doing when under observation. Ogilvie (1975) points out that diving ducks are able to control their buoyancy, which must have a bearing on swimming and diving postures.

When diving for food Tufted Duck swim low, often with the tips of the tail-feathers trailing just beneath the surface. They either slip under or leap upwards almost out of the water and, with bill pointed vertically downwards, plunge headlong below. As they dive, wing tips are crossed, the tail slightly fanned and depressed, while a kick from both feet together is an all-important aid to submersion. Downy ducklings dive similarly, depressing their fluffy sterns as they go under.

Beneath the surface, continued submersion and propulsion is maintained by the legs and feet. Instantly, these limbs are moved sideways out from the body in line with the flanks instead of being held below the belly as occurs when birds are walking, swimming on the surface, or commencing a dive. Driver (1974) found that Eider, Old Squaw, and Red-breasted Merganser ducklings manoeuvred under water in a similar fashion with their legs and feet moving in a horizontal plane. Personal observations on underwater activity were of Tufted Duck and Pochard in two or three feet of clear water. Invariably both species swam with their wings closed.

At the diving limit Tufted Ducks swim obliquely to the bed of the lake holding their position with legs and feet. They travel along with their bills just clear of the bottom searching for food from side-to-side. To surface, the head and feet are drawn back to their normal position and the bird shoots up like a cork released under water.

Although several hundred birds have been watched searching for food along the bottom, none was seen to probe deeply into the mud. Nevertheless some did so, as silt adhering to their bills and foreheads testified. One female surfaced with an unusually large mud facial extending well up the forehead and almost to both eyes. Pochard, and pinioned Canvasbacks in captivity, were much more commonly seen with muddy bills and foreheads than tufted.

The posture of a duck diving and swimming beneath the surface is seldom referred to in waterfowl literature. Therefore, Ederic Slater's fine underwater photographs of Musk and Blue-billed Duck in Australia are of special importance (vide Frith, 1967). The position of the legs and feet of the latter species is similar in the Tufted Duck.

On land Tufted Duck are not always ungainly. On firm, flat ground they can walk quickly and easily with the body held horizontally, the head drawn back, and the bill inclined downwards. When moving slowly, hesitantly, or stopping, a more upright carriage is assumed. On occasions while ashore for food, female tufted became partially hemmed in between low iron fencing on one side and members of the public on the other. In these circumstances they sometimes rose straight into the air two to three feet and flew towards a wide enough gap back to water. There was a loud whirring from powerful wing beats as birds lifted. In contrast a drake Ferruginous Duck cornered under similar circumstances rose vertically fifteen to twenty feet with greater ease. The noise of its wings was a silken rustle quite different from Tufted Ducks.

Taking off from water is sometimes accomplished by springing clear, though usually by pattering along the surface for varying distances. The 'run' needed to get airborne often depends on the space available as well as on wind and weather. Once under way this species flies fast with rapid wing movements and a manoeuvrability equalling that of the Teal. Alighting on the water is usually more spectacular than taking off. Once I happened to glance upwards in time to be thrilled by a female tufted hurtling helter-skelter at a terrific speed towards the surface some fifty feet out from the bank. To my astonishment her seemingly uncontrollable descent was checked perfectly only inches above the water, onto which she settled causing only a few ripples on the calm surface. Within seconds her bill was tucked out of sight in the dorsal area and she commenced dozing. More normal methods of alighting involve thrusting the feet forward and skidding along the water on belly or tail. Some plane down slowly, lower their feet into the water, and come to a halt almost immediately. With those flying in, a few at a time, to join an increasing assembly on water, a short splashing skid of about six feet is usual.

Tufted Ducks flying down to settle on tiny fenced-in ponds are skilful at pulling up abruptly in flight. One moment they are coming in fairly fast and in the next they are fluttering twenty feet up. Then, with much flapping, they make a slow descent straight to the surface.

On land Tufted Ducks and Pochard most commonly rest in sitting rather than standing positions, with their heads turned round to the back so that their bills nestle among the scapulars with the tip tucked under one wing. Some doze with the back of the neck drawn down to the mantle, the nape close to the folded wings and the bill a little above or just touching the breast. Resting is similar on water and feathered ducklings adopt postures like those of adults. Downies, however, tend not to move their heads so far round to the rear but hold them to one side so that the depressed bill rests on, or with larger downies under, the growing wing stubs. Occasionally adults rest with their heads to one side like small downies.

Hybrids

The occurrence of male crosses in full plumage resembling a species of duck different from either of an individual hybrid's parents often leads to incorrect identifications by inexperienced observers. With the increase of waterfowl collections, especially those visited by wild Tufted Duck, Pochard, and other species, hybridisation is likely to happen more frequently than before the 1950s.

Eighteen years ago six distinctive drake hybrids resulting from interbreeding between ducks of the pochard family were described in the *Wildfowl Trust 17th*

Annual Report by the late Doctors James and Jeffery Harrison and myself (Gillham *et al.*, 1966). The crosses detailed were the progeny of various combinations of four species: Pochard, Tufted Duck, Ferruginous Duck, and Scaup. For future identification and discussion they were loosely defined according to the male of a species each one was thought to resemble, *viz.* (1) 'Lesser Scaup type'; (2) 'Pochard type'; (3) 'Tufted Duck type'; (4) 'Baer's Pochard type'; (5) 'Scaup type'; and (6) 'Ferruginous or Paget's Pochard type.' One parent of the first five hybrids was considered to be a Tufted Duck but the sixth was a cross between a Pochard and a Ferruginous Duck. In the dim distant past this last type was regarded by some as having been a distinct species called Paget's Pochard, for which reason it is the only one with an original and an alternative name. If warnings had been handed down through the years regarding points of difference between 'Paget's Pochard type' and a Ferruginous Duck, especially concerning irides and bill tips, one may wonder whether the Sutton Courtenay 'Lesser Scaup type' hybrid would have caused such an ornithological stir a little over twenty years ago. Towards the end of the 1950s a school of observers, among them some of great experience, either claimed, or supported the claims of others, that the bird was a male of the North American Lesser Scaup, a species not yet recorded in a wild state in the British Isles. Eventually the bird was obtained, critically examined, and confirmed as a hybrid (Perrins, 1961), probably of Tufted Duck x Pochard origins. This last dispute proved beneficial in focusing attention on the problem of identification posed by hybrids generally. From time to time strong divisions of opinion still occur over 'Scaup type' crosses, two varieties of which are extremely difficult to tell from a drake Scaup except at the closest range.

A presumed Ring-necked Duck x tufted hybrid drake was observed in the West Country in the winter of 1976 and spring 1977 (Vinicombe, 1982). It had features of both species, the principal Tufted Duck ones being a short distinct crest and white secondaries. Though bill differences are described in detail there is no reference to the black tip. Sketches, however, show this characteristic as typical of a male ring-neck. The absence of further published records of this 'Ring-necked type' cross is a little surprising in view of the large influxes of Ring-necked Ducks in 1977, 79 and 80 (*vide* Rogers *et al.*, 1982).

A list of hybrids is given in Appendix 10. Most of these birds were recorded in St. James's between 1963 and 1984. In each case one parent was thought to be a Tufted Duck. Since hybrids within one of the described types sometimes differ in varying degrees from one another, the possibility of an occasional back-cross cannot be ruled out.

It should be mentioned that crosses have, of course, occurred with some frequency in other parts of the London Area within the past twenty years. Records of these birds proved such a problem to the London Natural History Society's ornithological records committee in the 1960s that a paper (Osborne, 1972) was published in the *London Bird Report* providing guidance on the field identification of several ducks of the pochard family in relation to similar crosses.

The study of hybrids, especially females, is still in its infancy. Only with close co-operation between owners of waterfowl collections, museums, field observers, and photographers, will our knowledge of these birds be quickly advanced. I hope that waterfowl breeders will help speed up this process by observing, photographing and recording the plumage of all progeny resulting from pairings between two different species of duck.

CHAPTER 3

TUFTED DUCKS IN AND AROUND LONDON

The Tufted Duck is a plentiful Eurasian species nesting from Iceland eastwards to the Kuriles in lands between the forty-fifth and seventieth parallels. Winter limits extend far southwards, to Nigeria, Eygpt, Arabia, Burma, Thailand, Vietnam and the Philippines.

These wildfowl have greatly increased in the western part of their range this century. Wild ones are first said to have bred in the British Isles in 1849. By the end of the 1920s Coward (1929) was already describing them as our best-known diving ducks, a status which, following further considerable population growth in the past sixty years, stands firmer than ever today.

Tufted Ducks nest in most English counties. Breeding pairs numbered about 4 to 5,000 in Britain and another 2,000 in Ireland by the middle 1970s (Sharrock *et al*, 1976). According to Ogilvie (1975), up to 50,000 birds wintered annually in the British Isles in roughly the same period. Based on a waterfowl survey in 1980, Tuite and Owen (1984) estimate the British breeding population at about 45,000 birds. Unlike the vast majority of Eurasian Tufted Ducks, which migrate long distances, those nesting in southern Britain are mainly resident moving primarily within that region.

The population of the London Area

Tufted Ducks were common ornamental waterfowl in the nineteenth century breeding freely in captivity under suitable conditions. Small numbers were turned down near Edenbridge, Kent, in the early 1900s (*cf.* Ticehurst, 1909) and in Surrey prior to 1925 (Walpole-Bond, 1938). They bred successfully and their offspring flourished.

Within the London Area,* a region covering a radius of twenty miles from St. Paul's Cathedral, the first nesting report this century was in 1901. It is possible that the initial foothold was aided by introductions. However, the population

---

* The London Area referred to in the text is the arbitrary boundary for London Natural History Society recording. This area, in excess of 1,200 square miles, includes all of Middlesex and parts of Buckinghamshire, Essex, Hertfordshire, Kent and Surrey. One of the annual journals of the society is the *London Bird Report*.

increased slowly in the period 1900-1960 reaching over 100 pairs by 1961 (Homes *et al.*, 1964). In the next decade there was a substantial rise to 300 pairs by 1972 (Montier *et al.*, 1977). Ten years later I estimated at least 550 pairs in the nesting season of 1982. Mr. Peter Oliver has provided me with details of a breeding survey carried out by members of the London Natural History Society in 1984. Ninety-six out of 129 sites visited held between them a minimum of 713 pairs and a maximum of 957 pairs. After allowances for sites not visited, and one observer's difficulties in distinguishing pairs among large numbers resting ashore close together, he considers that the total number of pairs in the London Area was between about 800 and 1,000.

Based mainly on published records Tufted Ducks have bred in approximately 200 sites this century, mostly on waters in gravel-pits, parks, or on commons.

The fortunes of this species have been closely associated with London and the surrounding districts' twentieth century demands for more and more fresh water. The construction of reservoirs around the capital, and the numbers of waterfowl frequenting them, have been fully discussed in *The Birds of the London Area*.* Figures given in that work show that the surface expanse of these man-made lakes was increased from 200 acres in the year 1870 to 500 by 1900, 1,350 by 1910 and 3,300 acres by 1962. A further increase to over 4,000 acres resulted from the opening of two more reservoirs by the late 1970s. Perhaps of equal importance with total acreage is that the number of reservoirs has multiplied from three to fifty in a little under one hundred years.

Up to the middle 1940s, the extraction of sand, gravel and brick-earth, for building materials, had been continuing for over a century in the London Area (Fitter, 1945). With the expansion of the construction industries following the Second World War flooded gravel-pits have become more numerous, especially along the Thames and its tributaries, thus providing tufted with additional nesting habitat. Considering the surface acreage of the reservoirs they do not support a large nesting population of Tufted Ducks. More would breed on these waters if the majority possessed islands. The importance of the latter may be appreciated by the seventy-eight years' history of those nesting on several islands at Walthamstow Reservoirs.** This long established colony was the largest in the London Area in 1984 holding between ninety-two and 125 pairs (Peter Oliver *in litt.*).

These pleasant little divers winter on waters of all sizes but, normally, the

---

* This revised book by a committee of the London Natural History Society was published in 1964 (Editor, R. C. Homes).

** Five reservoirs of this group, shown on maps as possessing islands, have a combined water area six or seven times larger than St. James's Park lake.

largest concentrations occur on reservoirs and on a few gravel-pits. Before 1900 Tufted Ducks were rather spasmodic winter visitors, and even by 1910 flocks of twenty, thirty and ninety were the kind of numbers reported in the London Area. Twenty years later groups of 400 and 500 were observed, while the first count of 1,000 was made at Walthamstow in 1932. In the winter of 1938-39 numbers reached 3,000 for the first time, half of them on Barn Elms Reservoirs alone.

Since the winter of 1947-48, the London Natural History Society has carried out synchronised winter duck counts on certain specified waters as part of the national wildfowl count scheme.

Homes (1976), in summarising the results for the first twenty-five years, shows that Tufted Duck numbers multiplied. In round figures the average winter maximum for five-year periods increased from 2,600 by 1951-52 to 4,600 by 1971-72. Oliver (1983) reviews these and more recent counts of this species for the same waters down to 1981-82. His findings for the past decade indicate that the numbers have been much more constant. The mean winter maximum for this period stands at 4,800. The most Tufted Ducks recorded on any of the counts in thirty-five years was a little over 7,000 in 1979-80. Those wishing to see the results of certain wildfowl counts expressed as an index should consult *London Bird Reports* 39 and 47.

Both Homes and Oliver emphasise that these wildfowl censuses are primarily to determine trends. The annual *London Bird Reports* not only give the averages of the November to February counts but the varying winter populations for a selection of individual waters as well.

Figures in these journals for the years 1970 to 1983 show that Tufted Duck numbers, at eight important reservoirs, ranged mainly between 500 and 2,000. At a ninth reservoir the winter population fluctuated from 300 to 4,000 over the years. For the same number of important gravel-pits the winter flocks varied between 250 and 900 at eight pits and between 500 and 1,500 at a ninth site. Of the many small lakes and ponds not referred to I know of thirty, mostly in parks or on commons, where fewer than fifty tufted occur in winter.

The Tufted Duck remains the commonest diving duck within twenty miles of St. Paul's Cathedral, a position it has held for many years.

While the storage of fresh water for domestic and factory use has greatly benefited wintering tufted, the digging of materials for the construction industries has tended to assist the breeding population.

The population in St. James's Park

Unpinioned Tufted Ducks are first known to have nested in St. James's Park nearly 150 years ago. The earliest reports for Inner London's* waters are sketchy. Glegg (1935) tells of the breeding of an introduced pair in St. James's in 1838. That year, the four ducklings reared, together with adults, flew regularly to the Serpentine, while in 1839 three large broods also reached maturity. Hudson (1898) recorded eight to twelve full-winged birds remaining in one London park between spring and autumn for three years up to his time of writing. Nothing else seems to have been known until 1913 when full-winged tufted were nesting in several London parks.

Regular breeding by unpinioned birds has occurred in St. James's since 1925. A hundred ducklings were seen there in 1929 and over eighty young were reported in six out of seven years up to 1936 (*vide Bird Life in The Royal Parks* reports from 1930 onwards**). Throughout the late 1940s Tufted Ducks continued to breed in St. James's. 1948 was a bad year but several broods reached the flying stage. 1949 appeared better since nine broods with eighty-six young were recorded. 1950, however, was a complete disaster. No young were reared and the blame for this was placed on predators. 1951 and 1952 proved similar to the last two years of the 1940s.

From then on the colony has steadily increased and shown encouraging signs of stability (*cf.* Table 1). In 1953 there were approximately ten pairs and by 1960 thirty. Fifty pairs were recorded for the first time in 1969. That year St. James's qualified for inclusion among those lakes having the largest breeding concentrations in England. Sharrock *et al.* (1976) list only three waters, one each in Somerset, Huntingdonshire and Essex, with populations of between fifty and sixty pairs, in the period 1968-72. For the fifteen years after 1969 there were only three seasons when the number of nesting pairs fell below fifty in St. James's.

Peak breeding season counts in the Park, including pairs and non-breeders, first exceeded 100 in 1962, and were always over 150 after 1973. The highest numbers occurred in four out of five years between 1980 and 1984 when the breeding season population was between 190 and 200 birds.

Population of Hyde Park, Kensington Gardens and Buckingham Palace Gardens

Before the Second World War this species bred regularly in Hyde Park and Kensington Gardens from 1924 until at least 1938. Forty-nine ducklings were

---

* The term "Inner London" refers to a rectangular area, four miles east and west, and two-and-a-half miles north and south of Charing Cross, as used by the London Natural History Society.

** Refer to bibliography, for these reports were published under three different titles between 1928 and 1977.

counted in 1933. During most of the war years nesting apparently ceased and there are no records until 1954, when twelve pairs were present and three broods subsequently seen.

Three pairs bred in 1956, after which the population varied from one or two to about eighteen pairs. 1961 was among the best of the earlier years with at least nineteen young reared. On July 30, 1975, I counted thirty-four young, two-thirds of them well-grown. The following year in the middle of August there were thirty-six sizeable ducklings.

Above the level of the northern extremity of the Long Water are situated the fountains whose basins have been used by Tufted Duck in some breeding seasons during the past half-century. Over twenty years ago, when aquatic plants supported in underwater containers added a touch of elegance to these basins, tufted nested at least once in the thickest clump of vegetation. On a number of occasions since 1933, however, females have led their young up from Long Water and reared them on these apparently suitable nursery areas. The Department of the Environment's predecessors, the Ministry of Works, thoughtfully provided wooden ladders for downies to get into the basins and wooden rafts on which they could be brooded by their mother or rest during fledging. Among the largest numbers on these tiny artificial ponds were five broods in 1933, while counts of actual young totalled seventeen in 1934, sixteen in 1961, and thirty-one in 1976.

At long intervals usually single broods of small young have been seen on the Round Pond. An absence of typical nesting habitat in the vicinity indicates that ducklings were, almost certainly, conducted by their mother from Long Water to this pool.

Tufted may have nested beside the lake in Buckingham Palace Gardens in most years from 1925 onwards (Cramp and Teagle, 1952; Cramp and Tomlins, 1966). Stanley Cramp informs me (*in litt.*) that he saw young in sixteen out of twenty years in the period 1961 to 1982. He considered three or four pairs may have bred annually and that some young were taken by their mothers to St. James's Park. In the *Bird Life in The Royal Parks* report for 1935, there is an account of a tufted female with eleven downies who were let out of the north door of the Palace. They then crossed the forecourt to the roadway where police held up traffic until the family got to St. James's. Another incident received wide publicity in 1969. This time the Press were on hand so that countless thousands were able to enjoy the *Daily Mirror's* photographs of the female leading her line of eight ducklings across the Palace forecourt together with the plain clothes officer who saw them safely to St. James's. Apparently they were trying to get from the Park to the lake in the Palace Gardens.

It seems likely that over the past thirty years the Palace Gardens' annual breeding population has varied between one and six pairs, possibly a few more on occasions. The most young seen at one time by Stanley Cramp was twenty-two downies on July 4, 1969.

Since the middle 1970s the average number of Tufted Ducks nesting in the four Royal Parks and Gardens discussed was in the order of seventy to ninety pairs.

Pinioning in the London Area

Ever since full-winged tufted first began breeding in the capital a few pinioned ones have, from time to time, been kept in a number of London's parks. But it is doubtful whether ornamental stock boosted breeding numbers to any great extent because of this species general increase and spread throughout the Home Counties this century. During this study I knew of only two pinioned females, and one accidentally crippled female, which got broods to water in St. James's. Between them they had eleven ducklings but, at most, only one downy reached maturity.

A greater contribution from pinioned tufted has been their usefulness as live decoys and through infecting wilder companions with a trust in man.

A pair or two of pinioned Pochard have been kept in several London parks in the past four decades. Throughout a period of fifteen years, Arthur May released more pinioned and unpinioned birds of this species than tufted in St. James's. In spite of this there was a marked decline in the Park's breeding population of Pochard after the middle 1970s.

Tameness in the London Area

A tantalising question: how many of the London Area's Tufted Ducks are tame enough to accept food like those frequenting some of the central Royal Parks and Gardens? Over several weeks I visited eighteen of the capital's many ornamental waters before the cold spell in the winter of 1982-83 and fed in close 691 out of 785 birds seen. I believe, therefore, that at least 1,000 different tufted are fed within a few yards range in London and its suburbs in a mild winter.

Some observers have suggested that truly wild birds never approach the shorelines of the waters of Inner London's parks as closely as those reared locally. If this is true then one has to accept that the great majority of the tamer tufted are of park bred origins. Furthermore, one might have to conclude that birds caught by hand and ringed on these lakes, and later recovered in other parts of Britain and on the Continent, are of similar stock. There is a case for believing that some tufted, perhaps those wintering for the first time in St. James's and Hyde Parks, and in Kensington Gardens, are wilder than others. Sooner or later they learn the ropes and mingle with other waterfowl at the traditonal feeding points.

Immediately following spells of bad weather which kept all but a few of the bread-bringing public from St. James's, most tufted have come to the feeding points. It seems, therefore, that the shyer ones, either through hunger or the prospects of an easy meal, eventually join the eager majority. Another reason for not assuming that all birds avoiding the feeding points are exclusively the more timid ones is that some groups of Tufted Duck spend many daylight hours dozing well away from the places where people normally feed the waterfowl. They, and Pochard of similar behaviour, are often the night or dawn feeders, many of which leave St. James's at dusk between autumn and spring.

At times members of the public have strayed over the boundary fences, crossed forbidden ground to the water's edge, and fed some of these isolated parties of resting waterfowl in winter. On such occasions both tufted and Pochard behaved as if they were at the regular feeding points.

Tufted Ducks frequenting public parks where there are no experienced birds of their own species to demonstrate the safety of approaching human beings to be fed may take several winters to shed their wariness. This was the position at Orpington Priory, in Kent, twenty years ago. By the winter of 1963-64 the main lake there had just been wonderfully transformed from a neglected weed-covered swamp into a nicely landscaped open pool attracting many water birds. Among them were ten tufted.

Throughout the four winters to, and including, that of 1966-67, I was unable to throw bread pellets within the tufteds' limits of approachability because they always kept at a much greater distance from the shore than the tame Mallard. In a few instances when bread fell near a bird it was regarded as a missile inducing evasive action.

By December 1967 a few of the twenty-two birds present recognised bread as food and either ate some from the surface or dived to retrieve small pieces. Two months later fifteen out of twenty-five came within my throwing range and six were fed. Nevertheless, some Tufted Ducks still regarded thrown bread as a danger and swam rapidly away from scraps even when swimming and diving less than six feet from the bank. On March 16, 1968, fifteen were fed without difficulty, and the following December, fourteen out of twenty-two came within three yards to take food thrown to them. At long last most of the Priory's wintering tufted had become tame. On a visit there sixteen years later twelve out of thirteen quickly assembled to be fed almost at my feet.

Some effects of Park regulations and the geography of water areas on populations

Returning to discussions on Inner London, it seems that differing regulations governing usage of the Royal Parks by visitors, together with the geography of the water areas, influence the seasonal distribution and numbers of Tufted Ducks. For example, St. James's has minimal disturbance all the year round because boating, bathing, and fishing are prohibited. Combine these rules with the highly suitable and protected nesting facilities provided on one of the lake's two main islands and we have the ingredients of an ideal waterfowl reserve.

On the much larger Serpentine the recreations not allowed in St. James's are catered for, though fishing and bathing are restricted to clearly defined areas. This lake's one small island is far less attractive for nesting water birds than Duck Island in St. James's Park; moreover, it lacks the latter's constant protection.

No sporting activities are currently allowed on Long Water. Boating was permitted as far as the bird sanctuary's barrier until the middle 1970s, when it was banned.

The sole pastime authorised on the Round Pond is sailing model boats, excepting the high-powered and noisy types, some of which are capable of killing or maiming waterfowl. This water differs from the others through being completely open without either bordering shrubs, flower beds, grassy verges, or an island. Here the public may walk on firm ground at the water's edge around the whole perimeter of this pleasant pool. A moderately-sized central island or several islets with ground cover would, unquestionably, transform this lake into a suitable breeding area.

Water birds are also fed regularly by visitors on the Round Pond and on the Serpentine and Long Water. It appears to me that a smaller number of Tufted Ducks fare better for bread on these lakes than their more numerous counterparts in St. James's. Certainly there is less competition from other kinds of duck, especially as pinioned ornamental birds are extremely few.

Screeching Black-headed Gulls compete for food on all of these lakes and are able pirates, too. Few miss a chance of robbing waterfowl, often snatching a morsel from a bird's bill. Possibly site fidelity rather than food from the public is the stronger factor governing the winter distribution of several kinds of duck in London parks.

Boating is an activity which tufted need to adjust to if they are to share some lakes with human beings. Stand beside the Serpentine, near the Lido, on an August day and watch these divers moving almost lazily out of the way of passing rowing boats and a few swimmers. This experience may create an impression that small craft in parks are always acceptable to this species. But events proved otherwise. When the work-boat was taken out, periodically, on St. James's lake, it so alarmed *all* waterfowl that many tufted flew off and stayed away for hours on end. In one breeding season the work-boat was used over several days west of the bridge, resulting in tufted and other ducks being absent from the Palace end of the lake for much of that time.

The presence of a floating weed cutter on the Round Pond one year halved the population even on a day when the machine was not operating.

Though most Tufted Ducks soon come to terms with man's regular activities on some water areas even the boldest ones are disturbed by the unusual.

The acceptance of rowing boats occurs on less spacious waters than the Serpentine. On a hot summer's day the narrow circular channel forming Finsbury Park lake was often crowded with both dinghies and Tufted Ducks. It was difficult to decide whether the latter's tolerance of many small craft in a restricted area would have been so great if the large central island had been unattractive for nesting and unprotected. Islands have a magnetic appeal for breeding tufted. It cannot be overstressed that the one dominating Finsbury Park lake has, for some years, possessed the best ground cover among over twenty islands in waters of parks and commons around London.

The Tufted Duck's tolerance of pleasure boats on the Serpentine, and on a few other waters, is not characteristic of this species throughout the whole London Area. For instance, Parr (1974) records that the effect of summer sailing on wilder waterfowl frequenting Island Barn Reservoir, in Surrey, was to greatly reduce the numbers of tufted between July and September.

Recognition of individual birds

Before exploring the life-cycle of this little diving duck in St. James's, it is necessary to elaborate on the recognition of individuals which have commanded so much of my attention.

Until 1964 separate identity on a small scale was achieved by watching birds possessing aberrant colouration, injuries or deformities, besides a few that had been pinioned by the Bird Keeper. For example, some tufted had distinctive flecks of buff or white feathering on various parts of their plumage. Some, less fortunate ones, had either a wasted tail, a damaged wing or foot, or even a missing leg. Sadly there were those, too, with either a deformed bill, a missing eye, a noticeable scar, a tumour on the head or neck, or fish hooks in the wing, body or bill. Though some of these unlucky birds became subjects for regular observation, efforts were made to catch those hampered by fishing tackle in order to free them from their predicament.

During a visit to St. James's Park with Dr. Al Hochbaum in March 1961, I

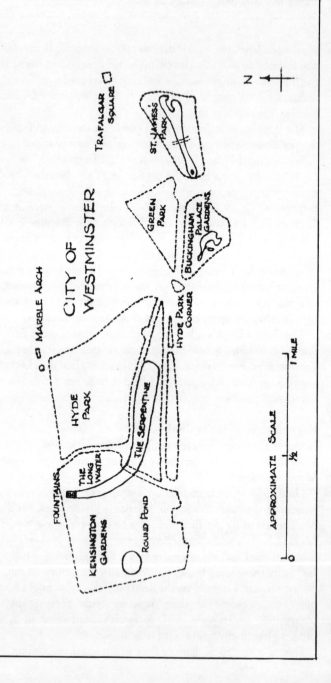

MAP 1 THE ST. JAMES'S GROUP OF WATERS

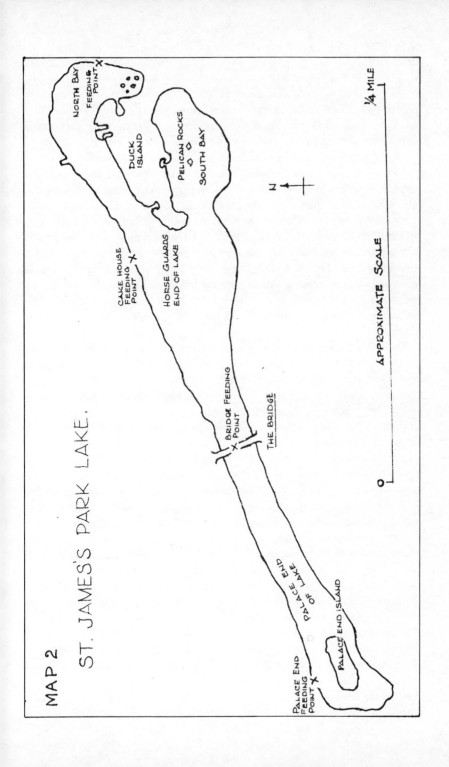

MAP 2

ST. JAMES'S PARK LAKE.

North Bay

Feeding Point ✕

Duck Island

Pelican Rocks

South Bay

Cake House Feeding Point ✕

Horse Guards End of Lake

N

Bridge Feeding ✕ Point

The Bridge

Palace End of Lake

Palace End Feeding Point ✕

Palace End Island

0   ¼ Mile

Approximate Scale

learned that American ducks often lost coloured plastic bands placed on their legs to aid individual recognition. This information was to prove particularly useful when sixteen months later a small programme for colour-ringing Tufted Duck in St. James's was begun with the co-operation of Arthur May.

If too many were colour-banded, and ring losses were high, there seemed a possibility that one might end up with several birds of the same sex bearing the same colour-ring combination, thus preventing recognition of many individuals. Accordingly, only 148 Tufted Duck were caught by hand and ringed with coloured plastic leg-bands between 1962 and 1969. Of these, 115 were almost fully-grown, but still flightless, young of the year; seventeen were hand-reared young; two were pinioned young; eight were adult females trapped on their nests; and one was a female caught with her brood as she made her way up the grassy ramp beside the Prime Minister's residence in Downing Street. The remaining five were an assortment of adults and juveniles, two of which were pinioned.

The 115 ducklings ringed just before they could fly represented a third of all young to reach the flying stage in those years when colour-banding took place. Seventy-eight per cent of these 115 tufted (forty-five of each sex) were seen again after release and sightings of colour-ringed birds totalled 4,190 up to the end of December, 1970. Loss of rings and fading of colours was on a small scale and therefore resulted in the loss from observation of comparatively few ringed birds.

To identify individuals it was necessary to feed in as many swimming birds as possible around the lakesides and then to concentrate on those bearing one to three coloured leg-bands. Thus, numerous Tufted Ducks were rewarded with food during the processes of recognition. Other sightings were usually of birds resting or walking about on the shore. Some of these colour-ringed ducks were destined to yield much useful data for up to a decade.

Throughout these investigations one or two tufted flew regularly between St. James's Park and Buckingham Palace Gardens, in daytime, most of the year round. Colour-ringing showed that there was some interchange of birds between the Round Pond and the continuous Serpentine and Long Water. Moreover, known birds also occurred between these water areas and St. James's lake. An absence of diurnal movements in the direction of, or from, Regent's Park, and the infrequency of colour-ringed birds recorded there, suggested that the tufted of this more northerly Royal Park were a separate breeding group.

The study area

The fifty-three well-tended acres of St. James's Park consist mainly of grassland

and lawns, with many scattered trees, shrubberies and magnificent seasonal flower-beds. Lying in a hollow and running full length, the attractive lake possesses two wooded islands. In addition there are two bare rocky islets. The exposed stone or concrete faced banks, combined with an absence of tall aquatic vegetation, allow visitors unhindered views of the many waterfowl.

For close on 130 years the lake has had a solid bottom commencing with nine inches of lime concrete in 1856. Because of the loss of human life through drowning, a decision was taken at that time to limit the water level to two-and-a-half feet within five yards of the margins and to restrict the maximum depth to five feet.

The lake was drained in 1914 and remained empty until refilling in 1922. But a substantial leakage led to further draining and reflooring with reinforced concrete in 1923. Since then, constant water levels have been maintained, except during cleaning operations which have been regular in the past fifty years.

On account of recurring movements of Tufted Ducks between St. James's and the neighbouring lakes in Buckingham Palace Gardens, Kensington Gardens and Hyde Park, it is convenient and appropriate to regard them as one population. This study primarily concerns the tufted inhabiting St. James's, which constitute the largest assembly on what is hereinafter called the St. James's group of waters (Map 1). These shallow lakes have a combined coverage of about sixty-three acres:—

Water area	Approximate expanse in acres*	Approximate depth in feet*
St. James's Park lake	11	3 to 5
Serpentine – Long Water	41	16 in places
Round Pond	7	4 to 6
Buckingham Palace Gardens' lake	3¾	Maximum 6

---

* Details of acreages and depths have been provided by the Department of the Environment.

CHAPTER 4
AUTUMN TO SPRING

The onerous summer task of clearing rubbish left by visitors tails with the passing of autumn. But scarcely have the park toilers paused for a respite than nature herself litters paths and greensward with myriads of fallen leaves. Yet again, men, brooms, and machines are busy removing the withering foliage to leaf yards or enclosures, one of which forms a valuable little bird sanctuary bordering Bird Cage Walk. Here, in a nicely landscaped corner with peripheral trees and shrubs, most of the Park's nineteen familiar species of land-birds occur throughout winter.*

Though tourists are fewer than in summer, pleasant autumn and winter days draw scores of employees from nearby offices for a lunch-time constitutional. Even these walkabouts are not without historical associations, since adjacent to the north-west corner of the Park lies Constitution Hill, which Antonia Fraser (1979) says may have been so-named through Charles II's daily sauntering in that area.

The autumn and winter population
Throughout October the numbers of Tufted Duck are at their lowest ebb. The average for this month is usually about thirty, increasing to around ninety during November. In recent years up to 150 have occurred in October and 200 by mid-November. These higher numbers in mild weather are due to the dispersal of some birds from their moult areas, probably those in the London Area (*cf.* Chapter 8). At this time of year a male tufted in full plumage is uncommon. Some adult males superficially resemble females while many are in various stages of moult into breeding dress. A short or rudimentary crest, dusky patches on whitening flanks, and dull blackish upperparts characterise a large proportion of adult males in these months.

One needs close views of young males to separate them from adults. The most advanced three-to-four months old males are usually distinguishable from adult drakes by their duller eyes and darker bills in autumn.

---

* For list of breeding birds see Appendix 12.

By the middle of December further increments swell the total to 250. But the full mid-winter complement, ranging from 300 to 600, is seldom reached before the middle of January. The build-up to peak numbers, however, is dependent on the severity of the weather further east, particularly in the Low Countries. When bitter winds and snow come early the largest influxes may occur at any time from the second week of November onwards. A proportion of adult Tufted Duck reared in the Park return to the St. James's group of waters only as autumn and winter visitors. They arrive back between late August and mid-January, eighty-five per cent returning about mid-November (*cf.* Tables 2 & 3).

Severe weather in the London Area, from whatever quarter, influences the numbers of tufted in St. James's, though seldom so spectacularly as in the hard winter of 1962-63. With the onset of that cold spell most of the lake was frozen over at Christmas and remained so for the first seven weeks of 1963.

Initially the tufted departed, fewer than ten remaining on December 27. By January 7 twenty to thirty had returned and, as conditions around London worsened, there was an increase to 170 five days later. From then on previous records were surpassed, culminating in 700-800 on January 26 and 1,800-2,000 on February 2. All of these birds were packed into South Bay which, at that time, was probably one of the few sheltered ice-free pools for miles around the capital. Until the third week of February about twenty-five per cent of the London Area's tufted were concentrated in St. James's.

Assessments of the Park's winter population before 1953 differ little from those recorded throughout most years of this study. From about 1939 to 1950 between 300 and 400 Tufted Ducks were normal (Homes *et al.*, 1964), though Cramp and Teagle (1952) considered that 400 was often exceeded.

My winter counts for the St. James's group of waters, excluding Buckingham Palace lake, in the four years 1967 to 1970 range from 400 to 700 birds. Information for the last-named water is scanty and the maxima recorded there by Stanley Cramp were twenty-four on March 10, 1961, and twenty-eight on March 24, 1962.

Movements between autumn and spring

The main evidence concerning the migration of Tufted Ducks to or from St. James's lies in the increase and decline in numbers between October and April. Not once in daytime have I observed the arrival or departure of groups suggesting that I was witnessing other than local movements. Indeed, apart from an occasional courting party from March onwards, it was extremely unusual to see more than about five tufted leaving the Park unless waterfowl were provoked by a major disturbance. Likewise, birds arriving were equally infrequent, and they, too, seldom exceeded five together. Almost without exception the directions of flight were to or from the other lakes of the St. James's group of waters.

At dusk the situation was different. The numbers involved were considerably larger and the flight paths lay in another direction. Many times between autumn and spring I have stood on the bridge as daylight faded, awaiting the evening flight of Tufted Duck and Pochard. Suddenly, out of the gloom around Duck Island, they lifted in a succession of small parties or one or two large flocks. Then, clearly silhouetted against a pale but darkening sky, they passed directly overhead at a height of fifty feet. Halfway down the Buckingham Palace end of the lake the fast-moving formations climbed higher, veered sharply left of the Royal residence, and vanished towards the south-west. Within fifteen minutes as many as 300 tufted left and the whole movement was over. In strong north-easterlies departing Tufted Duck and Pochard flew into the wind, circled over Horse Guards Parade, and headed into the gloaming in a southerly direction.

I was seldom in the Park around dawn to check on return movements. Nevertheless, counts on the day after evening departures showed that tufted were present in their former numbers. Probably the destinations of those involved in flights at dusk were reservoirs situated up to eighteen miles to the west and south-west. At the appropriate time one of these night movements may have become the first leg of a migratory journey to distant breeding grounds.

There were occasions when not a single Tufted Duck left the Park at dusk. Even when large numbers departed a proportion always stayed behind, especially in the vicinity of the bridge. With the shortest evenings up to ninety tufted, together with a few other water birds, assembled regularly near the bridge to be fed after dark. They were seldom forgotten, for among homeward bound commuters, crossing towards Victoria, there were usually a few thoughtful ones who paused to throw them food. It was not only the remains of packed lunches that were fed to the ducks but large quantities of left-over bread and cakes presumably contributed by canteens or restaurants. One memorable good Samaritan was a crippled down-and-out who came frequently at dusk one cold winter. Weighed down by a large wooden box piled high with thrown-away fruit, most probably gleaned from hotel waste-bins, he dragged himself to the waterside to dispense his gifts to waiting geese.

As spring approaches Tufted Ducks commence leaving St. James's. In mild winters some are gone before February is out. These early departures are followed by another marked drop in numbers in the second half of March. A further noticeable reduction takes place between mid-April and mid-May.

Ringing recoveries and sightings of colour-ringed birds between autumn and spring

Colour-ringing has shown that some wintering tufted lingered until the third week of May and that males tended to leave ahead of females. In fact, seventy-four per cent of colour-ringed drakes were gone before April 15 whereas sixty-three per cent of females quitted after that date (*cf.* Tables 4 & 5).

Undoubtedly most Tufted Ducks which winter come mainly from other parts of Britain or from abroad, since the combined numbers on all four lakes are normally far in excess of the total breeding population of the St. James's group of waters.

Individuals caught and banded with aluminium rings in St. James's Park and Kensington Gardens in winter, and found overseas between spring and autumn, total sixteen (Homes *et al.*, 1964 and *Brit. Birds* ringing reports). These Tufted Duck were recovered in Denmark (1), Russia (10), Sweden (3), and Finland (2). Single birds were recorded from as far east as western Siberia and as far north as Novaya Zemlya, some 300 miles beyond the Arctic Circle. All of the foregoing London-ringed tufted, excepting the Danish and one Russian bird, were reported before December 31, 1954. They fit well into the distribution pattern of about another seventy which were ringed in the British Isles and notified from abroad between January 1, 1955, and December 31, 1964. Recoveries were mostly from places between 55° and 70°N and 10° and 70°E in Scandinavia, Finland and Russia (*cf. Brit. Birds* Vol. 58 ringing supplement 1965).

Atkinson-Willes (1963) states that immigrants to S.E. England emanate mainly from Finland and N.W. Russia from 56°N to the Arctic coast and eastwards to 75°E and that the large Icelandic breeding population of tufted migrate mainly to Ireland. It is not surprising, therefore, that the sole St. James's Park recovery from a northerly foreign breeding area west of the Greenwich Meridian was of a juvenile banded in Iceland. A bird ringed in the Park on September 4, 1952, was reported in France on January 6, 1954. Between 1955 and 1964 only seven out of the seventy foreign recoveries mentioned above were from Europe to the south of the British Isles.

What proportion of Tufted Ducks wintering on the St. James's group of waters originate from other parts of our country is impossible to assess because so few published ringing returns have been informative. However, a bird banded in St. James's Park in winter was found 160 miles north at Castleford, Yorkshire, on the following May 29. No less interesting was an adult female ringed in Essex about forty miles north-east of London on June 21 and recovered in the Park in August two years later. Both birds were probably breeding season residents, the latter at least initially, in the localities where banded.

Of fourteen more tufted banded with aluminium rings in the Park, mainly in winter, and recovered in succeeding winters, seven were reported where ringed. Singles were found in the London Area and three others met their end between thirty and thirty-five miles east on the Thames and Medway estuaries. The thirteenth was recovered about 100 miles north in Nottinghamshire, while the fourteenth was found within thirty miles of the latter at Burton-on-Trent.

A further eight birds reared and colour-ringed in St. James's were found dead mostly in winter or spring where banded, except for one recovered in Hyde Park and a first-winter juvenile reported from Dunstable at no great distance beyond the London Area. Single sightings of St. James's reared colour-ringed birds came from nearby lakes in Regent's and Finsbury Parks and Kew Gardens in winter and spring.

Since 1975 Mr. Roy Sanderson and Drs. Stephen and Tim Christmas have been engaged in a long-term ringing project on Inner London Tufted Ducks. Between them they have caught and banded over 600 birds, mainly on the St. James's group of waters. By November, 1983, they had kindly sent me details of forty-five recovered dead and fifty-four recaught and released alive. These ninety-nine birds, ringed mostly in autumn and winter, consisted of eighty males and nineteen females.

The pattern of these recoveries, which bears a similarity to that of the early 1950s, is now outlined with an interpretation of the birds' movements prior to being found dead or retrapped:—

Recoveries of 99 live and dead Tufted Ducks

Foreign = 28 and British = 71

Male	Female	Period when reported suggestive of breeding, wintering, migration, etc.	Number of birds	Localities where recovered or recaught and released	Remarks
	Sex				
17	–	Dates suggestive of birds in countries where they breed	17	Russia – 8 Finland – 3 Sweden – 4 Norway – 2	
–	1	Ditto	1	Czechoslovakia	
10	–	Dates suggestive of birds in wintering areas or on migration	10	Denmark – 3 Holland – 4 West Germany – 1 France – 2	

6	–	Dates suggestive of birds in breeding or post-breeding areas	6	Essex (Abberton)	Includes 1 ringed at Abberton and recaught on the St. James's group of waters.
–	1	Date suggestive of a bird in breeding area or on migration	1	Essex (Abberton)	Ringed at Abberton and recaught in St. James's Park. See section on Longevity.
43	17	Dates mainly suggestive of birds in wintering areas	60	London Area	Includes 5 females ringed in winter and subsequently caught on nests in St. James's Park.
4	–	Ditto	4	N. Ireland – 1 Cambridgeshire – 1 Essex – 1 Kent – 1	The Essex bird was ringed at Abberton and recaught and released on the St. James's group of waters.
80	19		99		

Among the ninety-nine recoveries are three interesting retraps of males. One ringed in St. James's on January 16, 1977, was caught at Abberton on June 10, 1977, then retrapped a second time in Hyde Park on January 2, 1979. The second, ringed in Kensington Gardens on October 19, 1977, was recaptured in Regent's Park on December 23, 1980, before finally being shot in the Netherlands on November 10, 1981. The third was ringed at Abberton on May 16, 1977. Then, on December 31, 1981, it was caught in Kensington Gardens and shot the following year on October 26, in the U.S.S.R.

There is now clear evidence that some tufted from Hyde Park and Kensington Gardens regularly visit the lake in Regent's Park. Roy Sanderson tells me that this knowledge is due to Mr John Widgery who, on dates between November 30 and March 31 in three recent winters, has caught fifteen males which had been ringed in autumn and winter in the first two localities. A sixteenth drake, ringed on St. James's lake in winter, was retrapped early in March in Regent's Park.

Sex ratios between autumn and spring

In St. James's I found that though sex ratios differed between three groups centred around (a) the Horse Guards end, (b) the bridge, and (c) the Palace end, females were more numerous on the lake as a whole in the years 1967 to 1970 inclusive (Table 6). In the past decade, however, males have exceeded females in mid-winter. As recently as January 30, 1983, there were 300 present, drakes predominating by over two to one.

Figures for the same water supplied to me by Stanley Cramp show that males outnumbered females nearly forty years ago. Among mid-winter populations of between *ca.* 300 and *ca.* 500 tufted, the excess of males reached a maximum of between two and three to one on February 16, 1947, and two to one female on February 29, 1948.

Counts on the Serpentine and Long Water and on the Round Pond from 1967 to 1970 inclusive revealed that an excess of drakes was the rule (Table 6). Roy Sanderson confirms that the preponderance of males in Kensington Gardens and Hyde Park between 1975 and 1982 was the reason for his catching and ringing many fewer females.

Sex ratios of tufted wintering within twenty miles of the capital have been discussed in *The Birds of the London Area*. While the proportion of males on London Natural History Society censuses was between fifty and sixty per cent, the surplus of drakes varied considerably on different waters.

In the winter of 1982-83 I found that among close on 800 tufted counted on eighteen ornamental waters there were two males for every female.

Preferences for particular water areas and particular sections of one water area

The preponderance of males on the St. James's group of waters raises a question whether segregation arises through a greater attraction to a water area or for the company of their own sex. Of the forty-five of each sex colour-ringed tufted seen again after fledging, more males than females were attracted to the Round Pond and the Serpentine and Long Water between November and February. Over eight years sightings on these two lakes, in this mid-winter period, involved thirty different birds, of which twenty were males compared with ten females. Since the concentrations of males undoubtedly contained a proportion from north-west European breeding grounds it seems likely that St. James's reared tufted drakes tended to be drawn more to their own sex at this time of year. The earlier departure of males, already referred to, strengthens this supposition.

A strong liking for a particular portion of St. James's lake was evident among wintering Tufted Ducks long before the colour-ringing programme was begun. Some known birds could be found for weeks on end inhabiting certain sections of shoreline. Confirmation of this attraction was provided in the five years up to and including 1970. On average, each year, twelve out of twenty-four colour-ringed birds kept to one part of the lake for periods ranging from fifteen to eighty-eight days between January 1 and March 31. The duration of their stay, mainly in one area, averaged seven weeks for forty females and half that number of males. On two occasions when for up to ten days the water was two-thirds frozen over most tufted left the Park. But immediately the lake was ice-free they returned and colour-ringed birds were back in their favourite spots.

These preferences were maintained by some individuals for three or more successive winters. The same was equally true of a smaller number of colour-ringed birds more strongly attached to the Round Pond and the Serpentine and Long Water than to St. James's. One male, for example, was sighted over six consecutive winters on Long Water. Most years he returned between late September and November and left by mid-March. He was usually to be found at the feeding point opposite the Peter Pan statue in Kensington Gardens. Three other males favoured the last-named lake and the Round Pond for three winters running.

CHAPTER 5

PRE-NUPTIAL COURTSHIP AND PAIRING

Throughout winter Tufted Ducks lead a peaceful life on the St. James's group of waters. From early autumn the only sign of any conflict between them is their weak defence of individual spacing. Look closely at flocks on water and it will be seen that within the densest concentrations all birds are spaced at least one to one-and-a-half feet from those immediately around them. When circumstances cause intermingling and closer bunching this spacing is constantly maintained with a minimum of threat, thrust, or pursuit. Sometimes a duck of about equal size is rammed when it comes too close. This behaviour consists of bumping an intruder with the breast and riding up over its back or tail either from one side or from behind. Defence of individual spacing is activated when bread is thrown to a gathering of tufted and other ducks at one of the lakeside feeding points. Then other waterfowl are often threatened and geese and swans may be pecked beneath their tails.

On land the situation is similar. A bird going ashore and approaching nearer than a foot or so to one sitting down is usually repulsed by an open bill from a head and neck thrust forward. In the female this defence gesture may be accompanied by a rattling KER KER KER note. At times, a dominant intruder adopts a reciprocal threatening attitude and takes over another's resting place, causing the occupier to move and resettle roughly the same one foot or more away. A minimum spacing or 'elbow room' between birds seems to be of great importance, for it allows individuals to dive, take to the wing, or, if ashore, to rush to water without the risks and consequences of frequent collisions.

Apart from defence of individual spacing the few Tufted Duck pairs formed in the latter half of winter show no hostility either to other pairs or to the unmated birds which so greatly outnumber them. Occasionally, these early pairs seek isolation but, even then, the male allows strangers to approach without attacking or intimidating them.

With lengthening days the pleasant whistles of the tufted drake are heard more often. Among the many unpaired birds sexual activity accompanies calling as an increasing number of these ducks indulge in pre-nuptial displays.

To get to grips with pre-nupital courtship station yourself on St. James's Park bridge on a mild day after the middle of March and scan the tufted as they ride buoyantly on the water for some fifty yards in each direction. This area, together with the south-western half of the lake, is usually a good place for observation, since numbers of waterfowl thin out and, where the water narrows, birds can be closely observed with little difficulty.

Each year the pattern is similar. One or two pairs can be clearly recognised through the male and female resting side by side at a distance from other tufted. Most of the remaining birds, in loose assemblies of varying sizes, consist of mixed sexes with males usually predominating. Periodically, these groups indulge in pre-nuptial display. Between the nearest feeding birds and the more distant dozing ones a company of eight males and one female catches the eye through the drakes' busy manoeuvring with necks erect, at the same time making occasional attempts to drive away a companion to reach the female's side. As the group passes quickly beneath the bridge a pleasant chorus of soft bubbling whistles is heard. These calls, combined with the distinctive wide spacing of the participants, tell us that it is a close-knit courting party in action.

Beyond the courting birds a pair drifts slowly towards the centre of the lake. The male carries his neck erect and, raising his bill above a horizontal position, flicks it rapidly from side-to-side. Within a minute or two the female stops preening and performs likewise. Suddenly she is up and away, followed immediately by her spouse, and the pair fly off towards Buckingham Palace. These chin-lifting movements are pre-flight signals given by paired and unpaired birds of both sexes at any season and are not associated with pair formation. Males of isolated pairs may make these flight intention movements for up to ten minutes or so before the female responds and leads her mate into the air. Sometimes the female ignores the drake's continuous signals and neither bird takes to the wing. Less frequent in pre-flight situations is a side-to-side head-shake.

Pre-nuptial display

The courtship of the tufted, like that of many species of duck, is divided into two separate phases. Pre-nuptial wooing precedes the formation of a pair. Then, after a period of non-display, the nuptial courtship of the mated couple begins. Since the latter is closely associated with nesting, it is described in Chapter 6.

Johnsgard's (1965) observations on the aquatic posturing of Tufted Duck are an obvious starting point for comparisons, since his extensive studies have embraced almost all of the Pochard tribe besides most of the *Anatidae* as well. The display terminology which follows is that used by Johnsgard in his *Handbook of Waterfowl Behaviour* (*cf.* pages 247 to 249).

Pre-nuptial courtship in St. James's consists mainly of a daily repetition of ten different displays, nine of which are given by males:—

(1) *Neck-stretch*	(6) *Preens-behind-the-wing*
(2) *Headthrow*	(7) *Preens-dorsally*
(3) *Kinked-neck call*	(8) *Upward body-stretch*
(4) *Cough*	(9) *Turning-the-back-of-the-head*
(5) *Crouch*	

The commonest displays of the female are the *Neck-stretch* and *Inciting*. Occasionally females assume the *Crouch* and the *Upward body-stretch* but I have not seen them give the *Headthrow* when courting.

Inciting display is given by females in courting parties and by paired females when approached by strange males. This comprises upward *Neck-stretching* from the normal swimming posture, alternated with chin-lifting movements and slight threatening gestures to one side. Often these hostile actions are performed by the female from the normal swimming posture, though this is less usual after the pair bond is fixed. During pre-nuptial courtship either a single note TACK or TARR, or a double call TACK-TARR, is heard from females. *Neck-stretching* is frequent and occurs independently of *Inciting*.

There is little of the token *Preening-behind-the-wing* by either sex in close-knit courting parties.

Much pre-nuptial display by males is preceded by side-to-side head-shaking, as has been recorded by Johnsgard before the *Headthrow* in Baer's and White-eyed Pochard, and in the New Zealand Scaup. The *Kinked-neck call*, a double mellow WHEE-OU, is sometimes given by drakes from the normal swimming posture, but more frequently occurs with the upwards *Neck-stretch*. In this display the neck is less erect than in pre-flight movements and a slight body shake often accompanies this call. The *Headthrow* of the male, normally given when a courting party is relatively static, may be accompanied by the *Kinked-neck call* or performed in silence.

The *Cough*, a triple call, WHA WA WHEW, is given by males either from the normal swimming, or from the *Neck-stretch* postures. The accompanying wing-and-tail flick (or body shake) is usually much more noticeable than that given with the *Kinked-neck call*. Males sometimes switch from the *Cough* to the *Kinked-neck call* or vice versa during courtship. The former, triple call, is the commonest note heard in close-knit courting parties and is equivalent to the KIL KIL KIL note of male Pochard.

In March and early April, as darkness settles over St. James's Park, this soft music of many displaying male Pochard drifts in from the centre of the lake between Duck Island and the bridge; but the comparable call of the male tufted is less audible at the same range.

Though not a posture of the Tufted Duck *Sneaking* is common with Pochard and seems to be so with the Canvasback (Hochbaum, 1944). In the last two species one *Sneak* posture is like that of the male Rosy-bill, consisting of the head and neck extended low or flat on the water. The second *Sneak* attitude, of the Pochard, is similar to that depicted by Johnsgard (page 229) for the Canvasback. Both species assume a crouching posture with head held slightly foward and bill carried roughly parallel with the surface.

Hochbaum's threat posture of the Canvasback appears analogous to the *Crouch* in Tufted Duck. The main difference between the two is that in the latter the head rests back on the shoulders and does not protrude beyond the line of the upper breast.

When a close-knit courting party of Tufted Duck becomes less mobile, and the birds temporarily bunch together, the *Crouch* is adopted by all of the males at the same time. The female, who responds with the upward *Neck-stretch* and inciting movements, is then the tallest member of the group. From the closeness of the males it seems by their crouching posture that each lays claim to the female and is defending her against the others. In other courting situations only the nearest drake crouches in defence of the female, in which circumstances he appears to be the one most acceptable to her. After a pair bond is fixed similar behaviour is commonplace. When other males approach a couple in the *Neck-stretch* or give the *Headthrow* to the female, the paired male usually *Crouches* in defence of his mate, who makes *Inciting* movements. Similarly, when two pairs meet, often both drakes adopt the *Crouch* in defence of their respective mates. In this posture the crest lies close to the back of the head.

Turning-the-back-of-the-head is a common activity among males of close-knit courting parties, though the head feathers are not always strongly depressed as described by Johnsgard. Another frequent pre-nuptial display posture, the *Upward body-stretch*, is similar to that recorded for the Common Scoter. The infrequency of this standing upright on the water by either sex outside of courtship suggests to me that it cannot be dismissed solely as a comfort movement when so commonly given by males and occasionally by females during pre-nuptial display. Three behaviour patterns referred to by Johnsgard, *Bill-dipping*, the *Sneak*, and the *Nod-swim*, have not been observed.

Courtship flights, the aerial equivalent of aquatic courtship, have been little recorded among Tufted Duck populations. This is somewhat surprising because in North American diving ducks these distinctive flights were frequently observed in the Canvasback, Redhead, Lesser Scaup and White-winged Scoter

(Hochbaum, 1944). Less spectacular aerial behaviour was also reported for the Ring-necked Duck (Mendall, 1958). Since courting parties move restlessly about the St. James's group of waters it is possible that courtship flights occur high up in the air-space above and between the various water areas. These flights, however, were infrequent in St. James's Park.

Of the ten aquatic displays of the Tufted Duck, I have seen all but the *Headthrow* and the *Upward body-stretch* given on land. Only the *Crouch* of the drake calls for comment because when performed ashore it becomes a kind of grovelling posture as the male creeps slowly along with his lower breast and belly touching the ground.

In the first half of this century pre-nuptial courtship of Tufted Duck was studied by early British pioneers like Lascelles, Brock, Legge, Wormald, Millais and Boase (*cf.* Witherby *et al.*, 1948 and Bannerman, 1958). Since those days further information has stemmed from the writings of Steinbacher, Lebret, Bezzel, Bengtson, McKinney and Johnsgard (*cf.* Cramp and Simmons, 1977), all in the 1960s. Though my own observations add nothing particularly new to the combined studies of these twelve observers, the individual display patterns recorded in St. James's and elsewhere were subject to more variations than descriptions seem to imply.

Pre-nuptial courting groups

Though a few Tufted Duck show signs of sexual awareness from early in November there is little serious courtship before the end of February. Throughout March pre-nuptial display is less sporadic and increases in intensity as the two types of courting groups become noticeable. At first, *loose assemblies* of ten or so males and half that number of females are formed. For up to ten minutes there is much calling and displaying, after which activity ceases and the groups disperse. Following a short interval a party re-forms, but this time there may be fewer birds though males still predominate. From late March until June the second group, the mobile *close-knit courting party* consisting of two to eight males but only *one* female, tends to replace the informal gatherings of earlier on (*vide* Table 7).

It is within the second grouping that display is concentrated and more aggressive. Even when not engaged in courtship the males and the single female keep close company, flying, feeding, dozing, and preening together. Some of the threatening and scuffling observed during display is due more to infringement of individual spacing than to the selection of a mate. At intervals, as display ceases, tranquillity prevails through members of the group maintaining a noticeably wide distance between one another. Since individual spacing is defended in winter when Tufted Ducks form their densest concentrations it would be remarkable if the boundaries of tolerance were relaxed in the heat of competitive pre-nuptial courtship. When a courting party is inert one or two drakes may swim off and join a more active group. Sometimes a male or two are attracted from one hectic courting party to another.

From my observations on certain individual males and the female in close-knit courting parties it is clear that some members stay together for up to fourteen consecutive days, presumably until the female becomes paired to the male of her choice. The most unusual case was of a courting party in which several males participated for nearly seven weeks until the female paired with a particular drake. Even after pairing, and in spite of the male's defence of his mate, the couple were unable to rid themselves of two former members of the group. Throughout the six to seven weeks the number of drakes varied from three to nine, averaging six in the first two weeks, and four throughout the remainder of the period. Had not some males and the female been recognised individually one could have been misled into believing that over this long period several different females had been the mainstay of a similar number of different courting groups.

It seems that for some females to leave close-knit courting parties there must come a period when she ceases to respond in any way to the overtures of the drakes, causing them to lose interest. However, even sexually inactive females receive persistent attention from courting males. In fact, so strongly are drakes attracted to females in the nesting season that Rogers (1964) built a trap with a compartment. In the latter he put a succession of female Lesser Scaup as decoys and caught thirty-five males and one female of the same species for ringing between May 19 and June 10, 1958.

Close-knit courting parties of mixed species
It is not uncommon for single male tufted to be members of close-knit Mallard and Pochard courting parties. Likewise, a single male Pochard was a performer in Tufted Duck, Red-crested Pochard, Mallard, and Wigeon courting groups. Once lone male tufted and Pochard were seen together in the same Mallard courting party.

On two occasions drake tufted participated in thrilling twisting and turning Mallard display flights around the tree tops at dusk. Likewise, a single male Red-crested Pochard had a place in Mallard courting sessions on water and in flight.

Other strangers seen at various times in three separate close-knit courting parties of Tufted Duck were a Ferruginous drake and males of 'Baer's Pochard type' and 'Lesser Scaup type' hybrids. One spring day two other 'Lesser Scaup type' crosses were each seen in different Pochard courting parties at the same time.

Temporary pairs

While two to three close-knit courting parties are active on the lake one can often watch a greater number of lone males seeking isolated females. Unaccompanied drakes swim to these detached females and begin following them in the *Neck-stretch* posture interspersed with dorsal or behind-the-wing preening movements. Within a short while many a female yields to this persistent soliciting and copulation occurs usually well away from others of their own species. With the sexual act completed the male and female either stay together as a pair or immediately split, each bird going its separate way. Some of these pairs which are not seen to copulate may well part later in the day, or within a few days, since temporary pairings are frequent and seem to form an important stage in the process of true (= fixed) pair formation. It is not unusual to watch three or four of these isolated females being solicited at the same time.

When soliciting the male commonly *Preens-dorsally* or *Preens-behind-the-wing* but these displays are infrequently given by females. A female Scaup, paired temporarily to a male tufted, gave more *Preens-behind-the-wing* in thirty minutes than I had observed in female tufted in one period of seven years. Frequently a female fails to respond to a male's soliciting and continues swimming along or preening genuinely.

Temporary coupling is not a new concept in waterfowl behaviour, for the editors of *The Handbook of British Birds* state in *Vol. III* p. 234 under Mallard "Display . . . serves as a kind of introduction leading to association of individual pairs, which may be loose at first, but gradually becomes fixed." This is equally true of Tufted Ducks with a qualification that one or both partners may be temporarily paired, once or twice to others, before settling down to a fixed relationship (for examples see Appendix 1).

In winter, on the North Kent marshes, I often found individual pairs of Shelduck, Pintail, Wigeon, Shoveler, Teal, and Goldeneye in isolation far from their respective gatherings. On two or three occasions copulation was observed, and with the Goldeneye the male and female parted immediately after coition and the female flew off and rejoined the flock. Similarly, on Staines Reservoir in Middlesex, I have observed pairs of Smew and Goosander well isolated from others of their kind in winter. Adams (1947) mentions copulation by an isolated pair of Wigeon on February 25, 1945, and records that coition was observed between mated Red-breasted Mergansers in each month from December to March, in Devon.

A noticeable aspect of pre-nuptial courtship is the contrasting behaviour between males of temporary pairs and those in close-knit courting parties. With the former the male and female come together casually, associate for a while and then, presumably because of the drake's waning interest, go their separate ways. With a close-knit courting party both its mobility and the time limits of the various display sessions are set by the female. When she swims to the other end of the lake the males are in close attendance. When she dives the males tend to follow. When she flies the drakes become airborne too. When she no longer stimulates their overtures and adopts a resting or dozing posture most males follow suit, only one or two of them sometimes departing. Although the female is the leader of the group she seems a prisoner of her admirers for so long as some remain attracted to her.

Never was a female seen to leave one of these courting parties either by diving, by going ashore or taking to the wing. The drakes of the courting party shadowed her every move.

Chronology of pair formation and fixed pairs
Turning to the months when the pairing of Tufted Ducks takes place in St. James's, I found that few pairs were formed before the end of March (*cf.* Table 8). In the eleven years 1960 to 1970, on average only four per cent of the females were paired by mid-March; six per cent by March 31; thirty-two per cent by April 15 and forty-six per cent by April 30. Independent confirmation was provided by colour-ringed birds between 1963 and 1970 and it will be seen from the same table that they followed a similar time-table, though only thirty-six per cent of the females were paired by April 30. This low percentage of pairing among known individuals by the end of April is to some extent reflected in the temporary nature of many associations. Males seek out females and remain in their company for a short period, often only leaving them *after* copulation has taken place. From May onwards there is less splitting of pairs after copulation and the *fixed pair* is more noticeable than the *temporary pair*.

Out-of-season warm weather may speed up the process of pair formation, as occurred in 1961, a year remarkable for temperatures of 60° to 73°F in London between March 4 and 25. Under these unusually advanced summer conditions, forty-one per cent of the females were paired by March 24 and sixty-four per cent by March 29. On the other hand, the extraordinary mild winter of 1974-75 (hailed by the news media as the mildest of the century) had no effect on early pairing. From the beginning of 1975 flowers were a common sight, but temperatures, though much higher than usual, were not comparable with those of March 1961. In the last week of March 1975, when the first wintry weather arrived, paired birds did not exceed the average nine per cent out of the 150-200 birds present (*vide* Table 8).

For comparison, the following published information on the chronology of pairing is quoted by Bauer and Glutz (1969). On the authority of Bezzel these authors state that, in the Ismaning Ponds area in South Bavaria, West Germany, some thirty-four per cent of the females were paired by the first half of March; seventy-nine per cent in the second half of the month; and 100% by the second half of April. March, therefore, was the month when most pairing took place, and if the Ismaning Ponds constitute a relatively large breeding area for tufted, like St. James's, then it seems that regional differences occur in the pattern of pair formation. In some small populations in and around London I found a high percentage of females paired between mid-March and mid-April (*cf.* Table 9).

The speed with which some colour-ringed Tufted Duck became a partner in fixed pairs, coupled with the fact that they had not been observed in close-knit courting parties beforehand, suggests that pairing is achieved by some without much competition or delay. If the only avenues leading to pairing lay through a close-knit courting party, I would have expected to see far greater numbers of these groups in the course of a week than was ever the case. Incidentally, it must be borne in mind that not all compact groups consisting of several males and *one* female are close-knit courting parties. Two or more wandering sexually active males may, for a while, attach themselves to, and display to, any lone female (*cf.* an example in Bannerman, 1958) or a pair. Even lone, sexually inactive, females are unable to escape the attentions of these drakes, but respond to advances by defending their individual spacing.

With pairs, the male and female keep close together, the former frequently crouching in a threatening posture while all the displaying males are spaced at a greater distance from each other and from the pair. Pairs are often no more successful than unaccompanied females in avoiding, or even freeing themselves of, unwanted males which pester them for several days on end.

Many Tufted Ducks are known to remain in their winter quarters in May and June (Dementiev and Gladkov, 1952; Bauer and Glutz, 1969). It might, therefore, be thought that many first year birds fail to pair. This, however, has not proved to be the case among yearling colour-ringed females of which ninety-four per cent (34 out of 36) paired compared with only sixty-two per cent (10 out 16) of yearling colour-ringed males.

While almost all first year colour-ringed females mated they tended to do so later in spring than older birds. Out of thirteen couplings of yearling females only twenty-three per cent were paired before April 16. In contrast fifty-two per cent of two- to five-year-old females were paired before the same date. This is not unexpected because first year birds, generally, assume their full plumage later in winter than older birds, some even showing marked signs of immaturity well into, and occasionally throughout, the nesting season. Also, it is in line with

Weller's (1965) findings on some species of diving ducks of a general correlation between acquisition of breeding plumage, pairing and initiation of nesting.

Leaving aside temporary pairings which are often formed quickly, the period for an unpaired bird to be seen alone before becoming a partner in a fixed pair was three to four days in respect of thirty pairings involving colour-ringed birds (for examples see Appendix 1). The actual time required for pair formation was probably less than this since in twelve of the thirty cases birds were 'loners' for only two days or less. The ultimate duration of the pair bond of the thirty pairings referred to averaged seven weeks. In only six of these couplings were colour-ringed tufted seen in close-knit courting parties preceding fixed pair formation.

Interspecific pairings and associations

Drake tufted sometimes pair with Mallard, Pochard and Red-crested Pochard in the Park. It is probable that many interspecific unions arise either because of imprinting as newly-hatched ducklings or through the rearing of small downies of different species together in captivity. Two hand-reared and colour-ringed male tufted, who as adults were attracted to a female Chiloé Wigeon and a female Red-crested Pochard respectively, would have reached the flying stage at least partly in company with young of the last two species in the Bird Keeper's rearing pens.

Single male tufted consorted closely with Mallard on many dates between February 15 and June 22 in eleven out of thirty years. Over eight breeding seasons these interspecific relationships lasted from thirty-one to 123 days, averaging sixty-five days. One aluminium-ringed drake's fixation spanned at least six consecutive years; and two other tufted each had associations for two years running.

While accompanying Mallard, these male tufted adopted some of their companions' habits, such as walking and resting on grass far from water and feeding off the surface.

In five nesting seasons partnerships did not end when a male and female Mallard became paired. Instead, the drake tufted were accepted by the couples and with them formed close-knit trios. One group of three flew onto the creeper-covered roof of the Duck Island cottage accompanying the female Mallard in her search for a nest site. In three other breeding seasons a drake Tufted Duck paired with a female Mallard.

The strength of an interspecific attachment is demonstrated by the following incident. On May 14, 1965, a male tufted with a number of Mallard friends, including a female, wandered into a Duck Island pen through a door which had been left open. Arthur May and I caught, colour-ringed, and released the tufted

A pair dozing

Male resting

Male resting

The Cake House feeding point in St. James's Park

The bridge over St. James's Park lake looking north

Buckingham Palace and the Palace end island from the bridge over St. James's Park lake

Duck Island and the South Bay fountain from the bridge over St. James's Park lake

Part of Long Water in Kensington Gardens

One of the small fountain basins in Kensington Gardens

Part of the Round Pond in Kensington Gardens

Unpaired male defending his individual spacing

Unpaired male defending his individual spacing

on the lake, but the Mallard were retained as captives in the enclosure they had entered. To our amazement the tufted was back with his associates within a week. Careful examination of the cage revealed a small gap in the wire netting through which he must have squeezed in an overwhelming desire to rejoin his companions. This male appeared to have reverted to a true Tufted Duck on becoming sexually inactive as I found him alone in a flightless condition on the Round Pond on August 21, 1965. Two weeks later he was once again in St. James's still keeping to himself.

A second colour-ringed male Tufted Duck was paired to a female Red-crested Pochard in the breeding seasons of 1964 and 1965.

Copulation

Copulation and attempted copulation were observed between March 1 and July 23, ten per cent of all instances taking place in March long before tufted begin to nest. Soliciting, which is part of the sequence leading to coition, covered the same time-span but started at the beginning of February. One third of all soliciting was witnessed in February and March (cf. Table 10).

Soliciting and copulation are most often performed in isolation and invariably take place on water. Until the end of April the former is normally a prolonged affair lasting for up to ten minutes or more. The male assumes the *Neck-stretch* and follows the female closely with his bill held either horizontally or depressed by about 45°. His crest stands away from the back of the head and appears to be introduced into the display. The *Neck-stretching* posture is frequently punctuated by *Dorsal-preens* or *Preens-behind-the-wing* (cf. Table 11). In pre-flight movements the crest tends to hang limp close to the back of the head.

Throughout the early stages of soliciting the female adopts a normal swimming posture and shows little interest in the male's behaviour, thus making his display a drawn-out affair. Eventually the female, too, adopts the *Neck-stretch* posture, then lies prone on the water and copulation follows quickly (cf. Table 11). The male mounts the female from one side then, turning so that both are facing in the same direction, grasps her nape feathers with his bill. With the female mostly, or wholly, submerged coition lasts for less than half a minute. Post-copulatory behaviour usually consists of both birds bowing, after which the male frequently swims away from the female in a rigid bill-down posture (cf. Table 12). Occasionally the post-copulatory ritual is shortened or absent (cf. Table 13).

Interspecific copulation

Three times male Pochard have been seen copulating with female Tufted Ducks. In one case the Pochard mounted a female tufted immediately after the latter's mate had finished doing likewise. A not dissimilar instance involved a pair of Red-crested Pochard which was about to copulate when a passing male Red-crested Pochard x Rosy-bill hybrid got in first and trod the unsuspecting female. These last two examples, together with a number of records of interruptions to copulation, demonstrate a necessity for the sexual act to be performed in isolation.

Duration of the pair bond

The span of the pair bond period extends over seven months of the year. The earliest that tufted were seen in couples was January 23 (colour-ringed birds not before February 16) and the latest August 9 (colour-ringed birds not after July 23). Most colour-ringed tufted which breed in the Park pair on the lake following the first days of spring.

For individual fixed pairs the duration of the bond ranged from as short as fourteen days to 111 days. The average length of time for nine colour-ringed males to remain paired was six-and-a-half weeks and the average for fifty-one colour-ringed females seven weeks. I believe that most pairs are formed five to seven weeks before the first egg is laid. The latest dates for tufted to be seen in pairs are set out in Table 14.

Two males behaving as a pair

There were six instances of two males, well away from any other ducks, behaving as a pair in the breeding season. The sole record for tufted was of a male soliciting his companion as he would a female. In another case a male Red-crested Pochard dived and brought up vegetable matter fifteen times. He then moved towards another drake to share his food on most occasions just as occurs between male and female of a pair in this species. Once two male Mallard were seen behaving as though copulating together.

CHAPTER 6

THE NESTING SEASON

Spring seldom comes dramatically to London's scene. There is no general period of time as in colder countries when, after weeks of freezing temperatures, melting snow gives way to a warmth that brings new life to a once icy land. With our frequent mild winters a spell of colder weather is just as likely to come after the early days of spring as before them.

Though the weather may be unpredictable the visual signs of early spring abound, and in St. James's Park evidence is on every side. In places the greensward is carpeted with crocuses and daffodils which, together with flowering bedding plants, blend new colours with drab winter tones. A Mistle Thrush, atop a lofty plane tree beside the Mall, together with a few Song Thrushes and numerous Blackbirds throughout the shrubberies, loudly proclaim their territories.

Statuesque pelicans doze on their favourite lawns or rockeries while scattered pairs of ducks glide peacefully on placid waters. Only the sudden clamour of bellicose Canada Geese, Coots, or Herring Gulls disturbs the waterside calm on many an early morning.

Return to the breeding grounds

Observations on my colour-ringed Tufted Ducks have shown that nesting and summering birds return to St. James's over a period of ten months lasting from early August until late May. Most males arrive between mid-December and mid-March, whereas nearly all returning females trickle back between early October and late May (Tables 15 & 16). However, some ninety per cent of both sexes combined return before the middle of March.

At the beginning of spring a number of winter visitors still mingle with the nesting season population. It will not be until the middle of May that the majority of the remaining tufted constitute the breeding season colony of the lake.

Non-breeding birds

Tufted Ducks frequenting St. James's between late April and the middle of June include many which fail to pair. Unmated males were more plentiful than

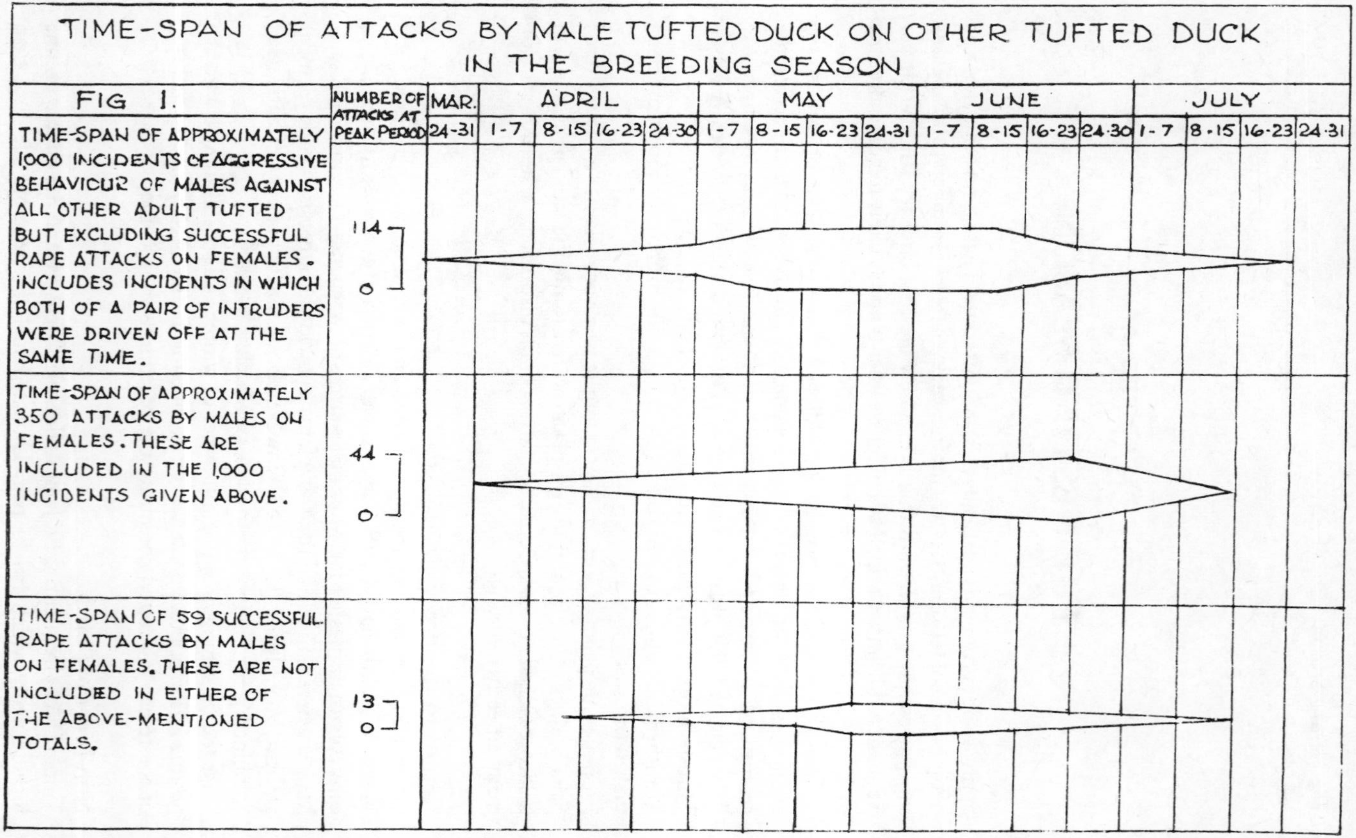

TIME-SPAN OF ATTACKS BY MALE TUFTED DUCK ON OTHER TUFTED DUCK IN THE BREEDING SEASON

FIG 1.

	NUMBER OF ATTACKS AT PEAK PERIOD	MAR. 24-31	APRIL 1-7	8-15	16-23	24-30	MAY 1-7	8-15	16-23	24-31	JUNE 1-7	8-15	16-23	24-30	JULY 1-7	8-15	16-23	24-31

TIME-SPAN OF APPROXIMATELY 1000 INCIDENTS OF AGGRESSIVE BEHAVIOUR OF MALES AGAINST ALL OTHER ADULT TUFTED BUT EXCLUDING SUCCESSFUL RAPE ATTACKS ON FEMALES. INCLUDES INCIDENTS IN WHICH BOTH OF A PAIR OF INTRUDERS WERE DRIVEN OFF AT THE SAME TIME.
114 — 0

TIME-SPAN OF APPROXIMATELY 350 ATTACKS BY MALES ON FEMALES. THESE ARE INCLUDED IN THE 1000 INCIDENTS GIVEN ABOVE.
44 — 0

TIME-SPAN OF 59 SUCCESSFUL RAPE ATTACKS BY MALES ON FEMALES. THESE ARE NOT INCLUDED IN EITHER OF THE ABOVE-MENTIONED TOTALS.
13 — 0

unpaired females, outnumbering the latter by three to one in the first sixteen years to between five and six to one throughout the remainder of the study (Table 1).

At Finsbury Park, another important breeding area for tufted, counts in seven years between late May and early June also revealed a large surplus of unmated birds with males predominating. In West Germany, Bezzel (Bauer & Glutz, 1969) reported that 100 per cent of the females were paired by the second half of April, indicating an absence of unmated birds of this sex.

In the four periods covering thirty-one years referred to in Table 1, males averaged between fifty-four and sixty-two per cent of the nesting season population.

It seems that in many other Tufted Duck breeding areas there are approximately three males to every two females. Tuite and Owen (1984) state that in the 1980 survey of breeding waterfowl on British inland waters males made up between fifty-nine and sixty-nine per cent of the tufted population recorded in May and June.

Figures provided by Peter Oliver for the London Natural History Society's survey of this species in 1984 show that drakes accounted for sixty per cent of all birds observed between May 19 and June 3. Similarly, in 1983 I visited twenty-five breeding sites, twenty-four of them in the London Area and one in West Sussex, plus another two sites in South Kent in 1985, and found 696 tufted. This total represented 250 pairs, 166 surplus males and thirty surplus females, the drakes making up sixty per cent of those seen.

An excess of drakes was also reported among Tufted Ducks breeding on Lake Mývatn in Iceland in 1975 and 1976 (Gardarsson, 1979). In the first year they amounted to close on fifty-seven per cent of approximately 4,800 birds and in the second sixty per cent out of about 5,300 birds.

The home range
In the last week of March the behaviour of the paired male tufted begins to change. He then becomes aggressive primarily to others of his own kind (Figure 1), but also to other species of duck as well (Table 17), and commences defending a minimum area of about three to four feet radius around him and his mate. This belligerency usually lasts from the beginning of nest site searching until the commencement of incubation. Hostility is not confined solely to one small water area but occurs ashore, or anywhere on the lake, should the pair's minimum spacing be intruded upon. Not all paired males are markedly antagonistic and individual behaviour varies. Some drakes take no action when other pairs swim close, while others make but a token gesture. For example, a

male dozing, bill in scapulars, beside his female, may swim a foot or two towards a passing pair without even removing his bill and waking up, so to speak.

Other males defend an area of over thirty feet around their females when at their favourite loafing spots. In these situations interlopers are common and often several pairs looking for nest sites intrude on many occasions in the course of a couple of hours. Time after time a male needs to leave his female to evict other tufted, besides a few other species as well. Regular trespassers get to know particularly hostile drakes and give them a wide berth.

Threatening behaviour is not directed solely at other individuals or pairs, for a paired male sometimes threatens his own female. Usually, he extends the neck forward, confronting his mate with a wide open bill, a gesture used in defence of individual spacing.

Coinciding with the male tufted's assertiveness the female starts searching for a nest site, thus providing the first positive signs that the breeding season is under way. Between late March and early June the male and female frequent certain stretches of water and shoreline where they doze and feed together in isolation from others of their own kind. At intervals they leave their loafing spot either to feed elsewhere or to search for a nest site.

When a pair's favourite loafing spot, principal feeding area and nest site all happen to be close together there is a strong resemblance to a *defended area* or *territory* such as Hochbaum (1944) describes for certain species of diving duck. The paired male tufted's more widespread aggressive behaviour, however, constitutes a mobile defence of the female on the lines reported by Mendall (1958) for the Ring-necked Duck. The area where hostility occurs is the *home range*. Sowls (1955), following his studies with colour-ringed ducks, writes that "pairs did not always establish definite boundaries to defended areas. Some drakes defended more than one area." He, therefore, adopts the broader concept of *home range* described as "the area in which a pair spends its period of isolation between the break up of spring gregariousness following spring arrival, and the re-formation of fall gregariousness." In the same year, Dzubin (1955), whose work was also based on colour-ringed waterfowl, confirmed this notion, saying "Home range is the area in which a pair is most active during the breeding season (*i.e.* during the pre-nesting, nesting, and incubation periods)."

Generally, these findings apply to tufted in St. James's, where their activities are seldom confined rigidly to a small corner of the lake. My colour-ringing has shown that while some pairs favour a restricted stretch of water, they regularly frequent at least one or two of the points where the public feed the waterfowl (Map 2). Tufted Ducks also visit other waters of the St. James's group and probably ponds and lakes a little further afield. Throughout the nesting season counts of birds on the lake are lowest in cold and wet weather when the bread-bringing public are minimal. It is then that many birds find it necessary to seek additional food beyond the Park.

Hochbaum (1944) considers that the territory of a pair of ducks is selected by the female. I found that the home range of a pair of Tufted Duck is chosen by the female. My study of colour-ringed females reared in St. James's revealed that long before pairing takes place, in fact before some females are capable of pairing, many already have strong preferences for a particular part of the lake (*vide* Appendix 2). Within this chosen section such females have one or more favourite bankside or open water loafing spots *to which they bring their mates after pairing.* Selection of a home range, therefore, frequently takes place when a female is between four and seven months old.

Some females have favoured one part of the lake and particular loafing spots for as long as three to six seasons. Colour-ringed female No. 110, for example, used the Palace end for three consecutive breeding seasons and four consecutive winters. Colour-ringed female No. 115, known to have been a non-breeding bird for the first five years, preferred the Horse Guards end throughout that period. Although her visits to St. James's got progressively fewer and more irregular afterwards, she remained faithful to that end of the lake for ten consecutive years. Colour-ringed female No. 136 was a devotee of the Horse Guards end of the lake for six winters and breeding seasons running.

When ashore in the nesting season unattached males and females often maintain a wider individual spacing between one another than in winter. The male and female of a pair commonly sit side by side with as little as a few inches between them, but it is not unusual to find them resting up to two yards apart. With these widely spaced couples it is impossible to recognise them as a pair when individuals around them are spaced at similar or even lesser intervals apart. Only when they join up in the air or on water, following disturbance, is one aware of their bond.

Nuptial courtship

After the formation of a fixed pair courtship ceases but is resumed from the time the female begins her quest for a nest site. This post-nuptial display and pair maintenance behaviour then involves only the male and female of the pair, usually in isolation. The principal joint post-nuptial posture is the *Neck-stretch.*

Another activity which takes place on water, and occasionally on land, is the *Nuptial jab* (Table 18). Frequently, this action by the male is followed by the pair taking to wing in *Nuptial flight* (Table 18). On water or ashore the drake, with partially open bill, gives his mate a swift sudden jab or several jabs at short intervals. These pecks, given from behind or to one side of the female, are almost always directed at her back, rump, or upper tail-coverts but rarely at the neck. The suddenness of the prod causes the female to make a brief spurt of a foot or so across the water. Such behaviour sometimes happens during the pair maintenance activity in which the male guards his female while she dives for food; in the course of, or following, nest site searching; during a spell of *Neck-stretching* display; or in between pre-flight movements given by one or both of the pair. Commonly, it is triggered by disturbance caused, for example, by human beings, dogs, or Carrion Crows. I believe that the object of the nuptial jab is to induce the female to indulge in a nuptial flight which helps strengthen the pair bond.

Flights are leisurely but frequently swerving in character due to occasional, momentary, evasive action by the female as the male's bill moves close to her stern or dorsal area. Once a drake was clearly observed to nip his female's tail and three times males were seen to pull at the upper tail-coverts of females.

Out of eighty-four nuptial flights only four were witnessed high above the lake. The rest took place at heights varying from four to fifty feet above the water. Occasionally the female was vocal, her calls being either soft or gentle (four times), normal (twice), or loud (once).

Sometimes the male attempts to fly in front of the female as occurs in pre-nuptial courtship with several species of surface-feeding ducks (*cf.* Gillham, 1951). Thrice single unaccompanied males and six times unattached females followed individual pairs on their nuptial flights without direct involvement. Once, however, three lone females, together, tagged onto a pair and joined in the paired female's occasional erratic aerial manoeuvres. On another date a single lone female joined in likewise. Unaccompanied, or unpaired, tufted were not the only ones to intrude on the nuptial flight of a pair. There were three instances in which other pairs joined in to make foursomes. One four-bird flight suddenly changed from a two-pair leisurely nuptial one to a more vigorous pursuit flight in which both males chased each other's mate. Once only, three pairs indulged in nuptial flight together. I have observed other species in these co-operative nuptial flights over the North Kent marshes. On several occasions two pairs each of Pintail, Shoveler and Teal made aerial foursomes.

I have also witnessed tail-pulling by male Pochard when single pairs engaged in nuptial flights. The most unusual instance of this aerial behaviour was observed within a flock of this species over a North Kent marsh in May 1953. It was just on three-and-a-half months after the tidal waters of the Thames burst through the sea-walls, flooding thousands of acres of grazing land for several weeks. By the 10th of that month the saline, stagnant, fleets and ditches were unsuitable for nesting Pochard, most of which were still in one compact group. On being flushed a flock of twenty-two were clearly in pairs. As the party levelled out at least three pairs indulged in nuptial flights, each male pulling at his mate's tail feathers but all of them keeping together in formation. It appeared to me that though many of the males had reached the nuptial stage of the breeding cycle the unsuitability of the nesting habitat had prevented the flock from breaking up.

The normal nuptial behaviour of Tufted Duck and Pochard seems parallel with that of the Canvasback. Hochbaum (1944) writes, "the drake sometimes approaches the hen from behind, tugging at her rump and tail feathers, when she evades him by rushing away in a quick dash across the water." A little later on he continues, "In nuptial flight the drake attempts to catch the upper tail-coverts, or the tail-feathers of the female with his bill . . . I have seen this same tail-pulling many times in nuptial flights of the Redhead and occasionally in the Lesser Scaup." Johnsgard (1965) considers that aerial chases involving male Canvasback attempting to catch the female by the tail, as described by Hochbaum, may be examples of attempted rape. Of the similar behaviour in Tufted Duck I am convinced that it is associated with the maintenance of the pair bond.

Guarding of the female

From the end of March one is accustomed to the drake tufted's attentiveness to his mate as the pair go about their daily lives, be it swimming, flying, or searching for a nest site. But the male's assiduousness is most marked from the final stages of nest site selection until the female has completed laying. Besides aggressive defence of his mate, and waiting nearby while she is at the nest, this new attentiveness is manifested through a distinctive behaviour pattern in which he is clearly guarding the female while she engages in feeding. Like the nuptial flights this behaviour also serves to strengthen the pair bond.

As the peak of the laying season approaches, more and more pairs, all noticeably well-spaced from one another, may be observed behaving in the same manner (Table 19). The male does very little diving, usually none at all, but remains on the surface in an alert posture with neck either erect or flexed slightly backwards. All the time he keeps constant watch over his mate as she dives repeatedly for food. Anxiously, he may pivot around on the water following the line of her air bubbles and watching for her to break surface. As she bobs up he swims quickly to the spot, by which time she may have slipped below once more. Commonly, this guard duty lasts for as long as the female continues feeding, though occasionally the drake joins in her activity. Even when she takes a brief respite for preening he is ever watchful.

An important advantage of guarding is that it enables the female to feed

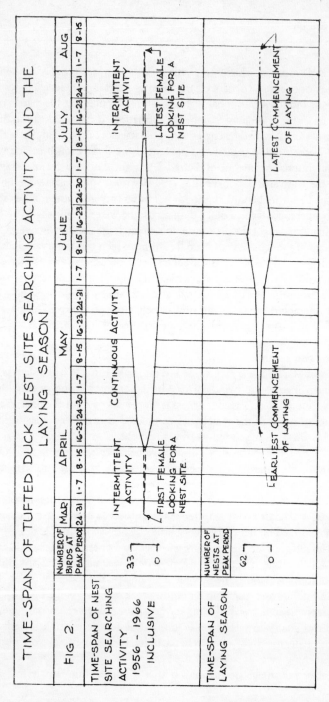

TIME-SPAN OF TUFTED DUCK NEST SITE SEARCHING ACTIVITY AND THE LAYING SEASON

FIG 2.

NOTE 1 NEST SITE SEARCHING ACTIVITY IS BASED ON FIELD OBSERVATIONS.
      2 TIME-SPAN OF LAYING SEASON IS BASED PRIMARILY ON BACK DATING OF NEWLY-HATCHED BROODS.

without interruption at the time when the eggs are forming in her body. Moreover, adequate food is essential because the approaching incubation period is, normally, the hungriest phase in the life of a female tufted in St. James's during the breeding season. Mendall (1958), in describing almost identical guarding for Ring-necked Duck, emphasises a pair's isolation from others. Among captive ring-neck pairs I have observed this behaviour on a number of occasions. Some drakes kept a wary eye on me all the time their females dived for food. Guarding of the female also occurs with Pochard in St. James's but is more irregular and less developed than in the tufted. In fact, it was not until the middle seventies that I observed any guarding at all by Pochard males. In June, 1982, a drake Pochard, paired to a female tufted, watched over his spouse while she dived for food.

I have also noticed similar protectiveness in Shelduck in May. In this species the male remained alert and guarded his mate while she swam along feeding off the surface.

There are circumstances when parallel, but quite differently motivated, behaviour occurs between unpaired birds. Single roving unattached male tufted often follow an isolated lone female which is busily diving for food. The male stays on the surface and courts the disinterested female whenever she reappears from a dive. In the *Neck-stretch* posture he moves beside her giving his double call as she bobs up.

Copulation

Although successful and attempted copulation was observed between March 1 and July 23, some ninety per cent of this sexual behaviour happened after March 31 (Table 10).

With nesting birds the sexual act occurs more casually than earlier on and with little preliminary display (Table 20). Brief *Neck-stretch* postures by the male and female together, or by the male only, followed by the female lying prone with neck extended on the surface, are common precopulatory behaviour (Table 11). The sometimes lengthy *Dorsal* or *Behind-the-wing* preening displays which precede copulation before April 25 tend to be briefer and less frequent after that date. Post-copulatory display is the same as described in the previous chapter (*cf.* Table 12).

The search for a nest site

The span of the nest site searching period of Tufted Ducks extends a little over four calendar months (Figure 2). March 29 is the earliest I have seen females looking for nest sites, but it is four to five weeks later that nest site searching commences in earnest. The preliminaries leading to site selection consist of (1)

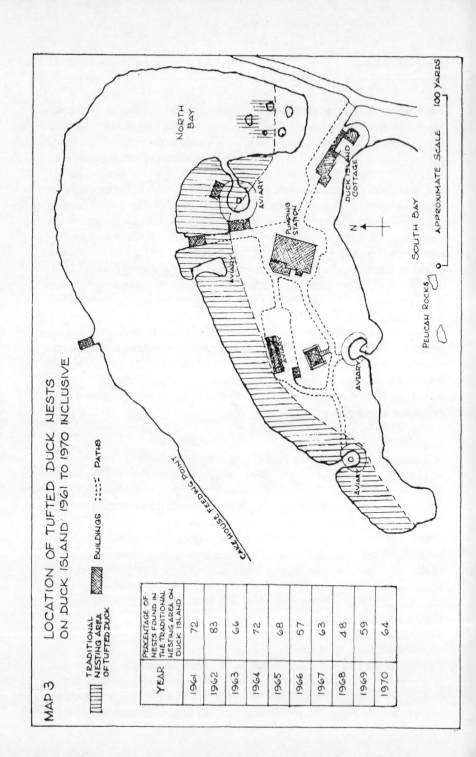

MAP 3   LOCATION OF TUFTED DUCK NESTS
ON DUCK ISLAND 1961 TO 1970 INCLUSIVE

TRADITIONAL
NESTING AREA
OF TUFTED DUCK

BUILDINGS

PATHS

NORTH BAY

AVIARY

AVIARY

PUMPING
STATION

DUCK ISLAND
COTTAGE

N

AVIARY

AVIARY

AVIARY

SOUTH BAY

PELICAN ROCKS

APPROXIMATE SCALE   100 YARDS

CALZ HOUSE FEEDING POINT

YEAR	PERCENTAGE OF NESTS FOUND IN THE TRADITIONAL NESTING AREA ON DUCK ISLAND
1961	72
1962	83
1963	66
1964	72
1965	68
1966	57
1967	63
1968	48
1969	59
1970	64

cruising along the shorelines, and (2) walking movements ashore into cover. Much time is spent on cruising. With fixed pairs almost always both birds take part. The male is alert and the pair, the relaxed female in the lead, swim slowly around the shorelines of large and small islands and parts of the mainland bordered by suitable undergrowth. Most of this activity, therefore, is observed in the vicinity of traditional nesting areas (Map 3). Where access ashore is unimpeded, the female appears to be looking either for suitable ground vegetation or artificial nest sites close to the water's edge, or for well-worn waterfowl paths leading further inland. Some landward routes are long-established ones, having been used by nest site searching birds for over twenty years. Along those parts of the shorelines bordered by stone or cement walls up to a foot or so high there is much swimming to and fro until the female decides upon a most desirable place up which to flutter and scramble to inspect the plant growth beyond.

It is clear that the female plays the dominant role, leading the male ashore on her inspection of cover (Table 21). Much less frequently this initiative is reversed and the male leads his mate into the vegetation. Rarely, the male leaves his female at, or near, the water's edge and goes ashore alone, appearing to search for a nest site by himself. Seeking a nest site is not a brief affair completed on one trip into cover. The majority of females take about seven days looking for a site, though a few spend as long as three or four weeks inspecting the undergrowth and artificial structures before depositing their first eggs.

Nest site searching takes place at any time of day and consists of many short excursions ashore by the female until an area has been thoroughly traversed. Each search, from the time the female goes ashore until her return to water, is usually completed within five minutes, but sometimes lasts fifteen minutes. When a potential site is located the female settles down and scrapes the ground or the material in a nest box with her feet, at the same time shuffling around, using her breast to fashion a shallow depression. A number of these nest bowls are scooped in different places and in different nest boxes before a final choice is made.

Nest site seeking often appears to be a social affair. For example, on June 26, 1957, two pairs were examining vegetation simultaneously on a tiny North Bay islet measuring about six feet in diameter on which a third female was already sitting on eggs. Again, on May 7, 1958, three females and a pair were prospecting in the same eight square yards of scanty grass and weeds. Shortly after, three of these females queued patiently around the opening of a large hollow log. Then, one after another, they entered the log, and settled down for a few minutes before leaving by the rear exit. Within a further few minutes four females, in turn, re-entered the log from the rear, scraped briefly, and left by the front opening. Similarly, on May 5, 1959, three females followed one another into the same log, each performing the scraping routine before leaving. These, and many other observations, suggest that the sight of one female searching for a nest site stimulates others to follow suit.

Site seeking females seem to be tolerant of each other. Only on three occasions were they seen to peck or thrust at one another, one such instance being when a female vacated a nest scrape and another settled onto it.

Males accompanying their females are usually much more aggressive to others and incidents like the following two are commonplace. When on May 4, 1959, a pair was chased off by the male of a second pair, the latter took over the first male's loafing spot while his mate settled onto the nest scrape just vacated by her opposite number. On May 25, 1965, colour-ringed female No. 100, accompanied by her mate, was investigating an artificial nest site in which another female was scraping. No. 100's male looked into the site, pecked at the occupant, and chased her as she rushed out.

The presence of males accompanying their females in a restricted area of cover sometimes causes an interruption of site search activity without developing into a scuffle or pursuit. On April 25, 1962, three females went ashore in the hollow log area. In minutes one female was on top of the log while the other two were at the front and rear openings respectively. At this point the males joined their females and, stationary, all three pairs looked intently, and somewhat nervously, at each other. After a minute or two further site searching in the log area was abandoned as the pairs drifted away to look elsewhere.

At the beginning of the nesting season encounters on water between site seeking pairs may lead to mild defence reactions by the males. In many cases the paired female gives the *Neck-stretch* and chin-lifting movements of incitement while her mate responds with the low crouching threat posture, approaching intruders with a slightly open bill, or with a rapid partial opening and closing of the bill. Sometimes the drake follows this with a brief rush of three to six feet across the water, sufficient to cause intruders to depart quickly.

The Tufted Duck's quest for a nest site involves searching in many places close to water, as the variety of the locations of known nests clearly suggests (Table 22). Besides these situations females have been seen inspecting the barest island rockeries, tiny islets with little cover, flower beds, the tops of dense shrubs six to eight feet high, and even a partially built Herring Gull nest. Several times they have been observed pulling at material, and scraping, on occupied Coot nests during an owner's temporary absence. Twice site searching females settled briefly on a deserted Canada Goose nest with eggs. One of these tufted females, apparently dissatisfied with an egg just outside the rim, tried to roll the Canada's egg back into the nest with the underside of her lower mandible.

Eggs of others have not always received such considerate treatment. For example, on June 9, 1956, a female tufted, on her fourth day looking for a nest site in a restricted area, returned carrying a light-coloured duck egg between the tips of her mandibles. Swimming out some thirty feet, she deposited the egg on the water and let it sink. Five minutes later this female returned to land and was back into cover continuing searching. In 1969, similar behaviour was observed with a nest site searching female Pochard, which briefly nibbled the egg before it sank beneath the surface. On April 22, 1961, one of several site seeking female tufted returned to water carrying an egg pierced through and held by her lower mandible. She swam out a few feet from the bank and began eating the contents before the remainder disappeared beneath the water. Unfortunately, one can only theorise on whether females took these eggs from nests on which they settled or picked them up along the trails as they walked through cover.

There is a widespread belief among students of waterfowl that the drake takes no part in the selection of a nest site. Be that as it may, the male's initiative in leading his female into cover (Table 21), and inspecting the undergrowth himself, suggests that his role in site searching is not always a completely negative one. Moreover, male tufted accompanying their females have been seen to settle down and scrape in vegetation, in a rock crevice, and in a hollow log.

Once, in Sussex, a drake tufted was closely involved in seeking a nest site. I first noticed him swimming slowly along the edge of some twenty feet of emergent rushes, stopping every yard or so to peer into them. On reaching an opening he passed through, staying in the vegetation for five minutes. All this time the female idled on open water. Eventually the male reappeared, looked towards his female, then pivoted to face the gap in the cover. This he repeated four times without stimulating the female's approach. Following this lack of response he swam ten feet in her direction then back to the trail entrance on four occasions. Finally, the female moved towards her mate and followed him through the rushes to thicker cover beyond. There they remained for about three minutes.

Loner females nest site searching

From the second week of May there is increased nesting activity among pairs. It is at this time that some unattached females begin site seeking. These *loner females* are not accompanied by a male when loafing, feeding, or when searching for a nest site.

Some form a loose liaison with pairs, since out of 228 instances that single females were seen associating closely with pairs they were tolerated fifty-six times and evicted by the paired male on 172 occasions. On five dates that trios were watched the two females indulged in a homosexual relationship (Appendix 3).

Observational evidence suggests that a female's association with one or several males is casual. Four out of five cases detailed in Appendix 4 have the following point in common. In the week or two prior to the estimated laying date of the first egg all females were alone when seen. A male was seen near the female once only in the fifth instance.

On occasions loner females have comprised one sixth of all females present in St. James's in part of the breeding season.

Were it not for their nest site searching activities loner females would be difficult to detect early in the nesting season. This is because other unattached females are present on the lake. These latter are sexually inactive ones which exhibit no sexual awareness, do not look for a nest site, keep to themselves and appear to be non-breeding birds. One sexually inactive colour-ringed female was never seen in close association with a male, and rarely even in the company of females, in any of her first five breeding seasons, so this category is not confined to a particular age group.

Males of other species nest site searching

Males of other species have also been observed nest site searching. On June 1, 1957, two male Mallard, apparently paired to one another, swam up to a hollow log at the water's edge. One male went inside, settled down and scraped a bowl as well as tearing at leaves at the log entrance. Similarly, on May 21 the same year, a male Pochard went into the same log and scraped, sending up a cloud of dust as he did so. Two years later, on May 16, the female of a pair of tufted was scraping on a Coot nest when a male Mallard evicted her, settled and did likewise. A parallel instance occurred on April 12, 1961. This time a male Mallard evicted a site searching female Mallard from a hollow log and scraped a bowl himself.

Token nest building in an unsuitable site for a nest

Throughout the nesting period both paired and unpaired male and female tufted fidget with small pieces of nest material while sitting ashore close to water (Table 23). This displacement nest building usually takes the form of stretching forward and pulling a few tiny bits of twig and leaves to the body or passing them over the back and placing them close to the stern. Among pairs the male may perform in this manner while his female dozes, or vice versa. Sometimes both of the pair go through these motions of nest building at the same time. Not infrequently a bird walks about picking up fragments of material and dropping them over its back. This behaviour is of regular occurrence with brood females and is also practiced by male and female Pochard.

On the North Kent marshes, in the breeding season, I often found small quantities of Shelduck down in neat heaps on flushing pairs from places unsuitable for a nest. Since many nests of this species consist almost exclusively of down it is probable that the Shelduck's behaviour is parallel with that of the Tufted Duck described above (*cf.* Gillham 1951A).

Nesting cover and artificial nest sites

Duck Island abounded with natural cover in 1954. Then most of the ground beneath the tall arboreal canopy was carpeted with ivy, providing excellent concealment for duck nests. Within five years, however, this vegetation had greatly declined, some eighty per cent of the ivy having died off. Except for a scattering of small trees and shrubs, large patches of ground became bare under the feet of an increasing number of pinioned waterfowl and the excreta of roosting starlings. By 1960 natural cover had reached its lowest ebb. Throughout the sixties there was a slow but steady improvement due to the interest of Arthur May, who built spoil banks and low fences and encouraged ivy to grow around the latter. He planted many bushes and shrubs and restricted the movements of pinioned waterfowl over parts of the island. New plants were protected with plastic sheeting or sacking and he drove off the Starlings at dusk, causing them to roost elsewhere.

Nest boxes were placed under low trees and shrubs, beside fences, and in other sheltered spots. Artificial nest sites located in less exposed situations were like magnets to Tufted Duck (Table 22). Before 1960 the few available man-made nest sites were, primarily, for the use of pinioned waterfowl. From the beginning of 1962, however, a drive to provide more nesting places for wild, as well as ornamental, duck was begun in earnest. Arthur May constructed an increasing number of boxes and shelters, while my own contribution that year was thirty-one drum-shaped wire frames covered with rushes especially for tufted. Each year more structures were provided until by the beginning of May, 1969, there were 344 artificial sites available. At last there was ample alternative nesting accommodation for pinioned and full-winged duck alike.

From 1962 to 1970, inclusive, some eighty-seven per cent of Tufted Duck nests found in the Park were in artificial sites (Table 24). This percentage, however, did not take into account the presence of up to about six nests annually in the limited natural cover on the Palace end island. After 1964 there was no regular check of nests on this island, nor were the few artificial sites located there maintained. This was because of frequent raiding by boys in search of waterfowl eggs. After taking these additional nests in natural cover into consideration, approximately three-quarters of all Tufted Duck nests in St.

James's from 1962 to 1970 were in artificial sites. Placing of man-made nest sites for ducks is not a modern practice in the Park, but one which goes back some 300 years. Evelyn (1641-1706) tells us how on a visit to the decoy area which existed in 1665 he found "withy-potts or nests for the wilde fowle to lay their eggs in, a little above the surface of the water."

Commonly, nests are located within twenty feet of the shoreline. Some eighty-five per cent of all those found up to 1970 were less than twenty yards from water; rarely a nest was over ninety feet inland.

Between 1962 and 1964 inclusive, a small number of the same wire and rush sites as provided for St. James's were put out on the traditional nesting islands at Hall Place in Kent. In this breeding area, where fifteen pairs nested in the first year and six pairs in the last, a single artificial site was used in 1962 and two in 1964. The high percentage of untamed Tufted Ducks using these man-made nesting places in the latter year was almost certainly due to their positioning in natural cover where nests had been located in previous years. In Central Europe this species is known to have made use of nest boxes placed on the ground (Dementiev and Gladkov, 1952; Bauer and Glutz, 1969).

On Duck Island a number of wooden nest boxes for use by Mandarin and Carolina Ducks were erected some three to four feet above ground. However, only once in seventeen years was one of these elevated sites used by tufted. At Hall Place, a female tufted was found dead in a similarly raised but completely empty wooden box, suggesting a possibility of her inspecting a potential nest site just prior to death. Until the middle 1970s one of several artificial nest sites for Shelduck, which qualified as a burrow rather than a recess, was used regularly by nesting Tufted Ducks in St. James's Park. Since 1980 the present Bird Keeper, Mr. Malcolm Kerr, has constructed a number of similar sites consisting of a two foot long section of six inch diameter drain pipe inserted into a rectangular wooden box. Some are placed under bushes and covered over with debris while others are situated underground, all with only the mouth of the pipe and the inspection cover of the box accessible. These have proved to be attractive nesting places for tufted.

On a few occasions late nesting female tufted used sites recently vacated by their own kind with newly-hatched broods. Once Arthur May put some deserted Tufted Duck eggs in a Mallard scrape holding one egg. Seven days later there were no additional eggs and no signs of nest building. About a month after this he found that a Mallard had taken over and obligingly hatched out the tufted eggs first.

Nest construction usually commences with the third egg and continues throughout the laying period; females building in ground cover crane forward to pluck leaves and other vegetation within reach and draw it to them. No female was ever seen walking to the nest with grasses or any other materials in her bill. However, one bulky, fairly open, nest on the bare concrete rim of a Duck Island pond was made of dead leaves and twigs. Much of this debris must have been brought to the site from at least four feet away.

To reduce disturbance the materials of most nests were never examined until after the female and brood had departed. It was then found that the down content varied, some nests having hardly any at all. Different publications describe the Tufted Duck's nest down as dark grey; dark brown; and very dark sooty with inconspicuous white centres. Similarly, published accounts of Pochard down give the colour as: brown; dark; and blackish with light or pale centres.

I find single down sprays of these two species overlap in colour. Pochard down varies from pale to medium brown and tufted down from medium to dark brown. Each spray of down has two tones of brown. In the tufted the browns are more of a contrast in many sprays, whereas in the Pochard the tones are a closer match. The light centres of Pochard down are best seen when a couple of egg-cups full of down of both species are placed side by side. Weller (1957) found much variation in the nest down of the Redhead.

Recorded descriptions of Tufted Duck eggs are equally variable. I found two distinct colour types, one of which was greenish-grey and the other brownish-grey. The latter resembled the hue of a normal Pheasant's egg. No eggs were measured but eight authorities give the average dimension of over 1,200 from elsewhere as falling between 57-59mm (length) x 40-42mm (breadth).

Each year Arthur May placed fresh straw in most artificial nest sites. The importance of this aid was best appreciated on inspecting these places towards the end of the season. It was then found that almost all sites not provided with nest material remained unoccupied. Also a few sites were unused through the straw having been stolen by other birds, especially Moorhens and Coots.

One year scores of Starlings were killed during heavy rainstorms in June. Shortly after Arthur May found a number dead in duck nest sites where they had sought shelter. One dead bird was discovered in a box occupied by a sitting tufted.

Clutch size

I made no daily check on nests during laying to determine clutch sizes with maximum accuracy. Much of the available information was provided by Arthur May who, in order to minimise disturbance, made but several visits to some of the nests found. The average size of ninety-two clutches was nine, the number of eggs ranging from four to sixteen per nest (Table 25). Although there was no certainty that all eggs laid in one nest were the product of a single female, we examined the largest clutches for any colour differences. For comparison, at Loch Leven in Kinross, Scotland, Newton and Campbell (1975) found that clutch sizes consisted of five to sixteen eggs. In round figures nine was the average clutch size of Tufted Ducks recorded by Havlín (1966) in Czechoslovakia.

Multiple clutches (or Dump nests) of the same species and defence of the nest

Multiple clutches of Tufted Duck eggs were uncommon in St. James's. In five seasons only three out of approximately 300 nests contained unusually large numbers of eggs indicating that they were the product of several females. In contrast, multiple clutches of seventeen to forty-two eggs were recorded annually at Loch Leven by Newton and Campbell (1975). These dump nests were considered due to a shortage of tufted nest sites in favoured areas.

Although breeding Pochard were always considerably fewer than tufted in St. James's they more often produced multiple clutches. For example, in 1970 alone there were three large dump nests of this species. As Pochard began nesting earlier than tufted they had the first options on available sites (*cf.* Table 22). A shortage of nest sites in favoured areas, therefore, is probably not the sole cause of several females laying in one nest. One explanation is the likelihood of several females merely selecting and using the same spot for a nest and none of them contesting ownership.

Following extensive studies of parasitic egg-laying in some North American ducks, Weller (1959) concludes, "The parasitic habits of the Redhead are a natural consequence of the deterioration of maternal instincts. The exact cause of parasitism is still unknown but the host, more than the parasite, may be of chief importance in the successful development of parasitic laying."

I do not know how closely most females defend their nests when laying or incubating eggs. However, I once witnessed an extremely fierce fight between two female tufted occupying nests about three feet apart in scanty vegetation. A third female sitting on her nest was seen to engage in a brief pecking duel with a Coot which came up to her. Similar behaviour occurred when a Moorhen stood beside a fourth sitting female.

When Arthur May was about to peer into one nest box a female tufted came out in a crouching posture. With neck extended low and wings drooped she pecked at Arthur's hand several times, then returned to her eggs. A minute later she came out briefly a second time and went back in again.

Nests shared between two different species

Laying by one kind of duck in the nest of another is as well known as intraspecfic nest parasitism. In the tufted I have called this behaviour nest sharing. This is because it was impossible to be sure who originally owned a particular nest. Most shared nests were in artificial sites containing straw provided as nest material. Thus one nest looked like another. Though five female Mallard and one female Garganey sat tight on nests containing their own and tufted eggs this was no guarantee of ownership. However, in all probability the first-named species initiated about half of the nests it occupied with tufted. Shared nests were more frequent than intraspecific dump nests (*vide* Table 22).

An interesting example of nest sharing was in 1968 when colour-ringed female No. 127 became the joint owner, with a female Wigeon, of a nest started by the latter. Twice I saw the female tufted on the nest with the female Wigeon sitting not more than two feet away, while Arthur May saw both females sitting almost side by side. When the day came for taking the brood to water, the two females apparently divided the product of their labours. Colour-ringed female No. 127 was accompanied by one downy Wigeon while her nest mate had two downy Wigeon. Clearly there must have been reasonable harmony between these females over a period of three to four weeks.

Shared nests have resulted in a female Mallard and a pinioned female Garganey reaching water with whole broods of tufted but none of their own ducklings. Another type of parasitism is the laying of one or two eggs in the nest of another species. This behaviour is frequent with female Mallard, Pochard, Red-crested Pochard and tufted.

Communal alarm behaviour

Throughout most of the nesting season tufted females have a distinctive communal alarm behaviour serving to alert both birds on their nests and those nest site searching ashore in cover (Table 26). First one female starts calling a strident KURR note and is followed, in quick succession, by others, until as many as ten or more, plus a few female Pochard, keep up a continuous clamour. This communal warning is given mainly by females on water in close proximity to the islands and dies away as danger is considered to have passed. It is most commonly triggered by human intruders walking through nesting areas, as well as by dogs, either drinking at the water's edge, or on a leash on the nearby public footpath. A cat lurking in bushes or pouncing on sparrows close to water is another signal for alarm, as are Carrion Crows or Magpies moving through the trees of the breeding islands. Perhaps not surprisingly, a dog chasing a female Mallard and brood and a Canada Goose seizing a Mallard have also set off the communal calling of female tufted. In populations of under five pairs in Kent and Sussex I have heard females of two pairs calling together when disturbed on their nesting waters.

The laying period and breeding age of females

At what age do females commence laying? Bauer and Glutz (1969) state that many, but not indeed all, breed *on completion* of the first year of their life. The same authors also quote a statement by Boyd (in Le Cren and Holdgate, *Exploitation of Natural Animal Populations*, Oxford, 1962) that females, in particular, are sexually mature only after two years. Colour-ringing in St. James's has shown that in all proven first season layings the females were *just under* one year old. Table 27 gives the ages (to within about seven days) and dates of the first egg of these females. In three out of the four cases nesting commenced early, so all young females are not necessarily late nesting birds.

The laying season in St. James's spanned 100 days (Figure 2). Dates for the first eggs of the earliest and latest clutches were April 25 and August 2, respectively. At Hall Place in the period 1957-65, inclusive, the laying season was much shorter, about seventy-two days (Breed, 1962, also W. G. Breed *in litt.*). Commencement was roughly the same as in St. James's but the first egg of the latest clutch was laid between June 26 and July 5. At Loch Leven between 1966 and 1971 the duration of the laying season of an extremely large population was approximately eighty days. First layings were between April 20 and 24 and the first egg of the latest clutch was recorded between July 4 and 8 (Newton and Campbell, 1975).

The laying season of Pochard in St. James's spanned sixty-seven days, a little shorter than that of the Hall Place tufted. Extreme laying dates were in periods April 4-10 and June 9-15. Similarly, with this species on one North Kent marsh between 1948 and 1956, the season extended over about fifty-four days, which compares closely with laying dates in the U.S.S.R. given by Dementiev and Gladkov (1952).

At Hall Place, the tufted population from 1957 to 1965 inclusive averaged eight or nine pairs. Here the height of the laying season occurred in the first week of June though in one year it was late in May (Breed, 1962; W. G. Breed *in litt*).

Millais (1913) wrote that most tufted on Loch Leven were paired by the end of March. The more recent intensive study of the large nesting population on the same loch (Newton and Campbell, 1975) indicates that the peak of the laying season is in the last week of May compared with the second week of June in St. James's. The main explanation for delayed pairing in St. James's is almost certainly correlated with the lateness of laying. Closer studies of populations, especially smaller ones, may reveal that early pairing results in early nesting.

While the female is at her nest the drake is in attendance nearby. At intervals he may visit a feeding point for a brief meal, then return to his favourite resting spot to await his spouse in her off-duty period. Commonly, five to ten of these drakes, all well-spaced from one another, may be seen dozing, preening, or idling in a restricted area. Waiting spots are frequently on water but they may be one particular yard or two of dry shoreline, or a corner of a rockery beside the lake. One male spent many weeks waiting ashore on top of a six-foot-high stone-faced earth mound four yards from water. From his vantage point he had a good view of his sitting mate. But more often than not the nest is out of sight of an attending drake.

At this time of year two types of unmated male tufted mingle with the breeding population. First there are *novice drakes*. These are sexually inactive birds, which associate closely with pairs. They do not arouse a paired male's hostility, thus preserving harmony within the trio. *Novices* tend to be rare in St. James's because few paired male tufted tolerate intruders approaching within a radius of three or four feet. Out of a sample of 104 occasions that lone males ventured close to pairs they were driven off 101 times.

Hochbaum (1944) drew attention to a paired male's tolerance of interloping drakes on his territory. In eight species of American duck he found intruders not uncommon, calling them *novice drakes*.

The second type is the *sexually active unmated male* whose behaviour is a common source of friction with paired males in the breeding season. Either singly, or in roving parties of up to half-a-dozen, these males display to a paired female, causing her drake to adopt his threatening *Crouch* posture, or make brief rushes across the water to drive them away.

Egg-laying loner females

There is mention earlier of the behaviour of loner females who devote time and energy looking for a nest site. In the laying season these females are still in evidence on their own but some are in an egg-laying condition in what Hochbaum describes for diving ducks as a "pot-bellied", or droopy at the rear end, appearance (Table 28). As when nest site searching, these sexually active females must have only casual associations with males (*cf.* Appendix 4).

It is possible that some loner females are responsible for the Tufted Duck eggs in shared nests and are parasitic. If this is the case then they differ from parasitic Redheads watched by Weller (1959). He found that not only did the male usually accompany his mate to the vicinity of the host's nest but kept with her during the parasitizing period until completion of laying or the beginning of incubation.

Defence of the female and other aggressive behaviour

As May wears on the paired male's mild defence of his female is replaced by much more aggressive responses to intrusions, especially in the vicinity of the traditional nesting islands. These quarrels involve nest site searching or loafing pairs, waiting males (whose females are at their nests), loner females, and sexually active unmated males. A waiting male continues to defend his three to four feet spacing even when the female is not with him. In St. James's most belligerency can be termed *the battles of the nesting area shorelines*.

Similar behaviour is noticeable at the traditional feeding points, suggesting that hostility arises through the necessities of a nest site and a food supply drawing tufted close together. Indeed, many times have I triggered defensive antagonism between peaceful pairs by feeding them bread until they were lured within their small areas of intolerance.

Away from the breeding islands and public feeding points pairs tend to space themselves at wider intervals, especially when diving for food, thus reducing friction to a minimum. Along the shorelines, at a distance from nesting cover, pairs are equally well-spaced even where small groups occur. These associations are made up of a pair or two and several single birds of both sexes all observing a minimum spacing of about three to four feet.

Pairs or loner females cruising in search of a nest site continually provoke hostility. As intruders approach pairs or waiting males along a shoreline, a defending male makes a rush, skitter, or short low flight across the water to drive away the intruding female or her mate. If singled out, the interloping female flees, diving quickly when an attacking male is about to seize her. On surfacing she may be rushed at two or three times, commonly diving in a flash to evade her pursuer. Often the unwelcome female, or both of the pair, take to the wing, either initially or on surfacing from an underwater pursuit. On water an intruding drake sometimes goes to the aid of his female, but when an aerial chase develops he seems to tag along more in the role of a spectator than as a defender of his mate. Should the intruding male be the initial target his female may, likewise, follow along in flight. Within about five minutes the defending paired male ends a pursuit and swims or flies back to his mate, or to his loafing spot if he was originally there on his own.

Females are largely passive and attacks are often, but far from exclusively, directed at them. Aggression is not directed solely at intruders. Not only do some males threaten their own mates but pursue them as well. On one occasion a waiting male joined a strange (incubating) female without attacking her. But when his own female swam towards him he promptly chased her for a short distance over and under the water. Finally the pair swam off together harmoniously.

Fighting along the nesting area shorelines and in adjacent cover is

A paired female defending her individual spacing

Paired female defending individual spacing

Close-knit courting party

Paired male giving pre-flight signals

Close-knit courting party: the male on the extreme right is *Leading* the female by *Turning-the-back-of-the-head* towards her

Close-knit courting party: furthest male is commencing the *Headthrow*

Males of a close-knit courting party adopting the *Crouch* posture while the female gives the *Neck-stretch*

Male performing the *Crouch* posture on land

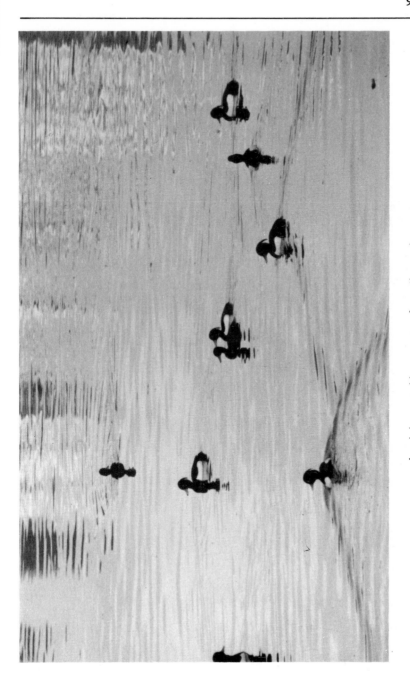

A pair harassed by a group of courting males

A male Pochard gives the *Headthrow* to a disinterested female Mallard

One *Sneak* posture of the male Pochard

The second *Sneak* posture of the male Pochard resembling that of the male Canvasback

Male with a fixation for a pair of Mallard

A male *Preening-behind-the-wing* to his mate, a female Scaup

independent of a large increase in the number of breeding pairs. This behaviour was no less apparent when the population was only a quarter of its present size. Because site seeking by one pair attracts several other pairs to the same spot, resulting in them prospecting for a nest site in company, scuffles have always been frequent.

As mentioned earlier in this chapter unmated males, either alone or in loose parties of up to half-a-dozen, display to paired females. These drakes behave in the same manner to sexually inactive females, sometimes staying with them for up to one or two days. With no drake of their own to protect them these females respond to advances by defending their individual spacing. No female, not even those which are incubating or with broods, is exempted from the unsolicited attentions of sexually active unmated males.

Usually females are approached in the *Neck-stretch* posture, the male giving his double call. Often the *Headthrow* posture, with or without the double call, is performed either initially or during a confrontation. Occasionally flights develop, some of which resemble aerial courtship, while others are aerial pursuits with the female an unco-operative participant. The status of the female involved has a bearing on her behaviour. Non-breeding and post-breeding females, and paired females which have entered the period of non-display, are least likely to respond to courtship overtures.

In the St. James's Park Pochard, hostility in the nesting season was negligible when compared with the amount observed in Tufted Ducks. While watching nest site searching pairs on small open pools in a large Sussex reed-bed, I found that lone male tufted and Pochard frequently flew from one open pool to another seeking females of their respective species. Lone male tufted were more aggressive than unattached drake Pochard, often pursuing females for short distances.

Mendall (1958) associated friction between Ring-necked Ducks with nest site searching activity, for he writes, "It appears as though there is mutual respect for each pair after nest sites have been selected." Writing on the Bufflehead, Erskine (1971) likens breeding season aggression to that of the Ring-necked Duck saying ". . . the mated female distance is maintained with little conflict after the initial shuffling associated with nest site selection."

The male Tufted Duck's mobile defence of his female includes the expulsion of other kinds of duck which intrude on the pair's minimum spacing. An analysis of species and sexes involved shows that male intruders outnumbered females by more than two to one (Table 17). This has no special significance other than that both male Mallard and Red-crested Pochard exceeded females through an imbalance in sex ratios. Moreover, these two species and Pochard start nesting much earlier than tufted, so the males are more prominent around the nesting islands and public feeding points when the Tufted Duck's battles of the shorelines take place.

Some drake tufted are selective concerning whom they expel. For example, one male allowed a few Mallard to come close but chased away other Mallard. Another male tolerated Red-crested Pochard and Pochard near him and his mate but ejected Mallard. A third male accepted the close approach of Mallard but evicted Red-crested Pochard and Rosy-bills.

In the Wildfowl Trust's collection at Arundel, two paired male Long-tailed Ducks, in May and June, could not bear the sight of wild Mallard on the ponds they shared with other pinioned long-tails and several species of captive duck. At least two or three dozen times in an hour one of them rushed at male and female Mallard causing the intruders to fly off or run ashore. Not once was there any friction between the long-tails and the other residents of their pens.

Nesting season chases involving other species are not unknown among diving ducks. Erskine (1971) cites instances of male Bufflehead driving away Pintail, Redhead, Lesser Scaup and Eider. In the shoreline scuffles and pursuits so far described there is seldom any physical contact. At times a wing or nape feathers are seized, but no bird gets hurt and feathers rarely fly.

Before dealing with rape pursuits of female tufted it is advisable to recall the main flight situations with which confusion may arise. Most perplexing can be those involving only three or four birds at a time. Thus one needs some experience of the various behaviour patterns from beginning to end, not just the aerial sequences.

Three or four Tufted Ducks indulging in slightly erratic aerial manoeuvres may be engaged in:—

(1)	Pre-nuptial flight of a close-knit courting party.	(only one female in the group)
(2)	Nuptial courtship flight.	(always one pair plus one or two male or female hangers-on)
(3)	Defence of the female expulsion flight	(one or both of a defending pair plus one or two intruders of either sex)
(4)	Rape pursuit flight.	(one or both of the pair plus the victim, which may be alone or accompanied by her mate)

Rape

The most determined and sexually motivated attacks are those which end in the female being caught and ravished. While many writers on waterfowl have referred to these assaults on females, I have not found one who has clarified exactly what rape means. My definition, therefore, is the rough seizure of a female by a drake, followed immediately by enforced copulation without the normal ritual of precopulatory display by both sexes.

These sexual attacks by a male tufted on a strange female, which occur most often in May and June, commonly involve energetic underwater and aerial pursuits. Rape is frequently triggered by a strange female intruding on the spacing of a pair. This invasion of privacy leads to a two-bird pursuit in which the paired male leaves his own mate to chase an interloping female. Identical two-bird rape pursuits occur when a strange female closely approaches, or is approached by, a waiting male whose female is on her nest nearby.

Another situation leading to an assault involves three birds. This happens when one pair encroaches on another pair's spacing and the male of the latter pursues both intruders into the air but concentrates on catching and raping the female when all three return to water. As with two-bird chases, a waiting male may put to flight a pair and force them back to water in an endeavour to seize the female.

A third set of circumstances concerns four-bird pursuits which take place when two pairs swim close together. This sometimes results in the two males flying after each other's mates and ending in one female being ravished by the other female's drake.

So far, these two-, three-, or four-bird pursuits have only related to sexual assaults committed by a paired male on other paired or unattended females. But violations are also frequently indulged in by some lone sexually active unmated males. The ensuing two- or three-bird pursuits are the same as those performed by a paired male while his female is on her nest.

Occasionally a paired or an unpaired male may fly some distance to chase, catch, and rape a strange female. Such incidents involving a paired male are not initiated through an intrusion on his own spacing.

Compared with the total number of incidents of all types of aggressive behaviour only about six per cent have ended in rape (Figure 1). Since the general method of attack is the same as in other high intensity pursuits perhaps *at least* another five per cent should be added to allow for attempted violations where the female successfully evaded the would-be rapist.

It will be seen in Figure 1 that almost all sexual assaults occurred in the main nesting period. The victims were females of almost every class. In one half of the fifty-nine rape attacks the assailant was a male in the company of his own female or a waiting male whose female was known to have been on a nest nearby. In the other half the assailant was a lone male whose precise status was in many cases unknown. Some were single roving sexually active unmated males, but a proportion were, almost certainly, males whose females were on their nests. I believe, therefore, that three-quarters of all violations were carried out by paired males still attending their females. It may well be that much more than ten per cent of all aggressive behaviour constitutes rape and attempted rape attacks, for Johnsgard (1968) considers that the intentions of the male may change from expulsion to rape in the course of the flight.

Observation on pairs has shown how sudden changes in behaviour occur on the part of the male towards his own female. Occasionally, paired males have abruptly pursued, caught and ravished their own females. Alternatively, they have seized and mounted their own females without any pursuit. In neither case was any normal precopulatory display given.

Reactions to rape attacks on females vary and a summary of these is given in Appendix 5. Attacking males normally violated their victims once only. Exceptionally, on May 22, 1964, a frenzied lone male pursued a female thirty times in succession, catching and appearing to rape her on five occasions. Likewise, on July 4, 1965, a lone (waiting) male caught and appeared to ravish a lone female four times, the attacks covering four minutes. Rarely, two males attacked the same female, as for example on June 20, 1961, when two different paired males caught and sexually assaulted the same loner female in about two minutes. Immediately following the raping of a female Tufted Duck both sufferer and attacker usually perform part of, but not the full, post-copulatory ritual.

In many breeding seasons one or two female tufted were seen with bald head patches, especially in the crown. I do not think that the missing head feathers were pulled out during sexual assaults as so commonly happens with unfortunate female Mallard. The completely bare skin on the female tufted was *always* clean and unmarked, quite different from the abraded, and often bloody, scalps of most victimised female Mallard.

In spite of a close watch no pursuits ending in rape were ever observed in Pochard.

Rape attacks by males on other males

Sexual assaults are not exclusively directed at females. On June 29, 1961, a paired male tufted pursued and seized an intruding male by the nape feathers, got on its back, and appeared to be treading exactly as if he was dealing with a female. Three times two or three Red-crested Pochard males, and twice a similar number of Mallard drakes, were seen on top of males of their own species behaving exactly as if their victim was a female.

In the spring of 1983 I saw a full-winged male Ruddy Duck on top of a completely submerged drake tufted and holding the latter's nape with his bill. This behaviour lasted a minute or so and appeared no different from all other rape attacks witnessed over the years.

A male of one species involved with rape parties of another species

Five times single male tufted flew with Mallard drakes to harass females of the latter species, including a mother with small young. However, the tufted were only spectators to, and not participants in, two rape assaults which followed.

One colour-ringed male with a fixation for Chiloé Wigeon in 1969 and 1970 was twice involved with chiloé drakes bent on ravishing a female. When the males all piled on top of the female chiloé the tufted drake abstained and simply ran around the rapists in close attendance.

The motivation behind some interspecific behaviour is not always clear. For example, on May 13, 1969, four male Mallard were struggling to get on top of the female in a typical rape attack when a male tufted left his own mate and rushed to join them. Although the tufted climbed on top of the drakes he may well have been trying to break up the attack on the female Mallard, which eventually got away.

Twice single male Red-crested Pochard were active participants with groups of Mallard drakes engaged in ravishing a female Mallard.

Mallard and Red-crested Pochard rape attacks

Mallard and Red-crested Pochard rape attacks differ from those of tufted in that with the two former species it is commonplace for two or more males to set about a female and for all of the drakes to try and rape her. Male Mallard sometimes maim or kill a female in the frenzy of their assault. Long ago I saw one of several Mallard drakes apparently raping the floating corpse of a female. Then, one April evening in 1975, I was twenty feet from four Mallard drakes all trying to get on top of a female and all tugging at her head feathers. The males were driven off but the female lay motionless. On picking her up I found, to my surprise, that the body was extremely cold, and it appeared that she had been dead for some time. Analogous behaviour concerns several kinds of bird recorded as copulating with dead members of their own species (Armstrong, 1942).

Female Mallard are capable of withstanding extremely rough treatment. One victim was unable to get away from fifteen drakes which piled on top of her for about twenty minutes without a break. Time and time again it was clear she was being raped and I never expected her to survive the ordeal. To my amazement she eventually reappeared from beneath the struggling drakes, broke free for a couple of minutes, after which the ghastly assault began all over again.

The incubation period

The female Tufted Duck spends little time away from her eggs during the incubation period. In St. James's a marked change in behaviour distinguishes many females when they are away from their nests in this part of the breeding cycle. Through hunger they become noticeably bolder, approaching people closely without hesitation (Table 29). Furthermore, they are constantly in a hurry.

Many times females have been seen bustling to water from their nests, then flying to a feeding point and running ashore to join sparrows, pigeons and waterfowl which were being fed by a member of the public. Here, for a minute or two, these females greedily intercepted bread, even fluttering up to snatch pieces from the hand. With bulging crops they then hurried back to water, flying off immediately towards their nest sites. In some summers very few incubating females are hungry enough to come ashore to be fed. This suggests that shortages of natural food for adults occur periodically.

Most adult male Tufted Duck seldom venture so far ashore on the footpaths at any season; a few that do so often display great caution and hesitancy. The apparent hunger of incubating females was not observed in Pochard nor in any other species in the Park. Moreover, exactly the opposite to my observations is recorded by Sowls (1955) for five species of duck he studied under natural conditions in Canada. He formed the impression that food is of secondary importance to females in their off-nest periods and that their activities are unhurried.

Another aspect of the female tufted's behaviour throughout the nesting season is a posture suggesting a cross between threat and fear. When certain, mostly unaccompanied, females are approached, followed, or in a few cases pursued, by one or more displaying males, they respond in a distinctive manner. The head is drawn back onto the shoulders, or to one side of the body, and through a wide open bill a rapid clattering KUK UK KUK note is usually uttered. This pattern is quite different from the normal threat posture with its occasional accompanying call given by females in defence of individual spacing throughout the year.

In fourteen out of the thirty-six instances when this behaviour was observed the status of the female involved was known (*cf.* Table 30). Four cases concerned paired females whose mates were in attendance. Another two were of females with broods and six were of incubating females away from the nest. The two remaining records were of unaccompanied colour-ringed females considered to have been renesting. It is highly probable that most of the remaining twenty-two of unknown status were incubating females in their off-nest capacity. There seems to be some deterrent value in this display. Only on five out of the thirty-six occasions when females adopted the posture were they harried or pursued. Similar behaviour was also noted in Mallard, Pintail and Red-crested Pochard females, but never in the Pochard. This response is Lorenz's *Gesture of Repulsion* which Johnsgard describes in detail and records for the first three of the last four species, plus Bahama Pintail.

Once a female has begun to sit on her clutch the male continues waiting nearby for up to fourteen days. By the end of the second week of incubation most drakes in St. James's have deserted their mates and moved to the vicinity of the western end of Duck Island. For them the pair bond is severed and they may remain bachelors until the coming of another spring.

When females depart from nests to feed the clutch is covered with a mixture of nest material and down. Eggs are rarely concealed by females leaving the site hurriedly through disturbance.

Based on a close check on three nests in St. James's, incubation lasted for twenty-four days in each case. Dementiev and Gladkov (1952) give the incubation period as twenty-three to twenty-five days, while Cramp and Simmons (1977) state twenty-five with a variation of between twenty-three and twenty-eight days.

Nest casualties

Nest casualties in St. James's averaged thirty-five per cent over sixteen years. Analysis of 109 nests of known fate indicated that sixty-three per cent of all losses were due to desertion as against thirty-seven per cent due to destruction (Table 31). Although man was responsible for most desertions and about half of the nests destroyed, the routine activities of Arthur May were but a minor contributory factor. When looking for, or inspecting, tufted nests he always made a point of not disturbing the female if she happened to be on the nest at the time. Unfortunately, raids by boys after eggs, and the authorised work of contractors or other Park staff on and around Duck Island, caused most nest desertions in some years.

Predation was never a major factor in egg losses between 1954 and 1976, the period when I was especially interested in the fate of nests. The large number of left-over eggs at the end of the breeding season was a measure of the safety of unattended nests. Indeed, it was the finding of so many unhatched eggs that prompted my examination of their contents in the 1960s (*cf.* Tables 32 & 33).

Rats (*Rattus norvegicus*) had been practically exterminated by 1956. Although a few were seen subsequently they were never numerous enough to be a particular source of worry. Whenever they were observed prompt action was taken to deal with them. I never heard of these vermin on the scale that occurred in 1950. That year Mr T. Hinton, the Bird Keeper at the time, trapped 100 rats on Duck Island and held them responsible for most of the Tufted Duck's heavy egg-losses that year.

Though Carrion Crows have for long been regarded as the main avian predator of waterfowl eggs in Buckingham Palace Gardens and in the Royal Parks generally, I never saw them on the ground in situations suggesting that they were seeking waterfowl eggs.

In the past fourteen years Magpies have spread to Inner London and were proved breeding for the first time in two Royal Parks in 1971. Since 1973 they have become increasingly familiar birds in St. James's, culminating in single pairs nesting or attempting to do so on the waterfowl breeding islands at opposite ends of the lake from 1977 onwards. By 1984 the population had increased to five pairs, all of which were seen nest building in April and early May. The Magpie is not strictly a newcomer to the Park since Larwood (1872), in one of his interesting anecdotes, refers to it as a nesting species between one and two centuries ago. I regard this predator as a far greater menace than Carrion Crows as it so commonly forages on the ground of the nesting islands.

Filching of an egg from unattended duck nests may not be uncommon. Two nest site searching female Tufted Duck and one Pochard were observed going back to water each with an egg not belonging to them. A male Southern Pochard was also seen returning to water with an almost complete egg-shell in its bill. Both Coots and Moorhens have been known to take and eat waterfowl eggs. In the case of Coots this behaviour was partly responsible for the control measures on this species in St. James's Park referred to by Cramp and Tomlins (1966). Jack Norley informs me *(in litt.)* that in 1960 Arthur May considered that Coots may have been unfairly accused of egg-eating and that Moorhens were probably the real culprits. Throughout the period relating to the examination of ducks' nests, neither species was ever regarded as more than an insignificant predator of eggs.

Three times female Tufted Ducks and twice female Mallard were seen to remove broken or cracked eggs from their own nests and carry them to water. I never fully appreciated the importance of nest maintenance until Arthur May showed me what can happen if a female fails to clean her nest thoroughly soon after egg-breakages. He produced a clutch of Chiloé Wigeon eggs complete with down and some nesting material all glued together in a solid mass. It appeared that several eggs were broken, perhaps by the female when she tried to turn some which were already stuck fast to others or to nest material.

Renesting

The St. James's Tufted Ducks appear to be persistent renesters, though evidence is largely circumstantial. For satisfactory proof, colour-ringed female No. 153 (in her second breeding season) was seen with a crèche of seventeen tiny downies on June 16, 1969. Three days later she had lost her family; then, after but one sighting in the next forty-four days, she appeared with a newly-hatched brood of six on August 3. Colour-ringed female No. 205 (in her third nesting season) was seen leaving a nest with eight newly-hatched young on May 31, 1969. Within a fortnight the brood had vanished, but on June 26 and 28 this female was paired once again. On July 26 she was seen with seven newly-hatched young leaving a nest box only a short distance from her earlier nest site. These two examples appear to be the first recorded instances of females getting two broods to water in one season. However, Sowls' (1955) experiments detailed later in this chapter indicate that his taking all newly-hatched young from a nest presented no barrier to renesting by some females.

In 1970 female No. 205 was sitting on eggs on May 9. Five days later the nest was destroyed, but on July 8 she was seen with a newly-hatched brood of four. The estimated renesting interval in these three cases, that is the gap between the loss of the first young or eggs and the first egg of the repeat clutch, was fifteen, eighteen, and twenty-eight to thirty days respectively. For comparison, Sowls (1955) found that two (both Pintails) out of ten females of several species whose young were removed from the nest at hatching renested after a period of sixteen and eighteen days respectively. Writing of nests which had been lost after the commencement of incubation, Sowls states "all hens waited at least three days before renesting."

Mendall (1958) judged the Ring-necked Duck to be a fairly persistent renester, saying "Based upon indirect evidence, it is estimated that more than fifty per cent of initial nest losses are compensated for by renesting." Mendall's analysis of nest failures in Maine and New Brunswick shows that of 501 ring-neck nests losses were only thirty per cent. We have, therefore, a species of diving duck considered to be a fairly persistent renester in spite of what appears to be a low percentage of nest failures.

First breeding season female tufted are not such persistent renesters as older birds. My observations on the nesting behaviour of colour-ringed birds have shown that only two out of thirty-three first breeding season females were thought to have renested compared with ten out of fifty-six second to fifth breeding season females. Further circumstantial evidence of renesting is provided by the link between nest casualties and late nesting. In the eight years 1954 to 1961 inclusive, when fifty-one per cent of all known nests were casualties, forty per cent of all broods reached water *after* July 24 (Table 34). In the following period of eight years nest losses were cut to thirty-four per cent and the number of broods reaching water after July 24 was, correspondingly, reduced to twenty-four per cent.

A question to be answered: what percentage of all broods result from renesting? If one takes all August hatched broods (Table 35) as the products of repeat attempts, the minimum figure is fourteen per cent. Since some young reaching water as early as July 9 are known to have resulted from a repeat nest, it is believed that between ten and thirty per cent of all broods emanate from repeat clutches.

The amount of renesting varies from year to year according to both the scale of nest failures and losses of broods up to about seven days old. In 1969 the number of nests found on Duck Island was a record seventy-eight, yet the number of pairs that year was only fifty. Even allowing for probable nesting by some loner females there remains a high proportion of nests attributable to repeat layings. Nest losses that year were only twenty-two per cent but losses of small downy ducklings were extremely high (*vide* Table 36).

Renesting does not seem to occur in all Tufted Duck populations. At Hall Place (Breed, 1962 and W. G. Breed *in litt.*) the cumulative total of known broods in the six years 1957 to 1962 was fifty-three. But only one of these broods hatched after July 19, suggesting that little or no renesting occurred. According to Newton and Campbell (1975) this was also the case with the intensively studied nesting population of St. Serf's Island on Loch Leven. Writing of their evidence based upon the recapture of ringed nesting females they state that "if repeat laying occurred in tufted it must have been extremely rare as would be expected from the shortness of its season." These authors show that the peak of the commencement of the laying period was in the last week of May and that only three per cent of 1,436 clutches were started after June 18. Thus, as at Hall Place, relatively few young reached water after July 19. Newton and Campbell also demonstrate that casualties to all tufted nests of known fate in the years 1966 to 1971, inclusive, averaged forty-three per cent. Notwithstanding these moderately high nest failures, practically no renesting appears to have occurred in this species on St. Serf's Island.

The brood season of a population totalling some 170 to 200 pairs in Angus and East Perth, Scotland (Boase, 1954), covered a time-span similar to that of the St. James's tufted, though most ducklings hatched in June. However, this is not indicative of repeat layings on a scale comparable with the St. James's population because Boase clearly states that intact pairs were noted up to June 24, but not after except for one record for July 30. On the St. James's group of waters intact pairs were of frequent occurrence in July and once in August (*cf.* Table 14). Renesting is known in Iceland, for Bengtson is quoted by Cramp and Simmons (1977) as recording that forty-five per cent of fifty-one females renested after the loss of first clutches.

Female tufted not only take a new mate each year but often have a change of male when renesting. Eggs of repeat clutches laid in the same season after a female has been deserted by her mate during incubation are fertilised by a new partner. Fresh pairings for subsequent nesting attempts endure for less than fourteen days. Some couplings appear to be casual, so it is likely that a few loner females seen in an egg-laying condition are renesting females.

It is doubtful if more than occasional renesting occurred within the St. James's Pochard population in two decades. Out of 105 newly-hatched broods up to 1978, none reached water after July 10. Between 1979 and 1983, however, seven broods observed by Peter Oliver hatched out in the period July 7-22. All of these young almost certainly resulted from repeat clutches.

Attachment to natal area

Though a male Tufted Duck exercises his own choice of waters outside the nesting season, it is the female with whom he pairs that selects the breeding ground and leads him to her home range. This, no doubt, is the main reason why, among colour-ringed birds, many more females than males stayed throughout the breeding season. Taking the history of nine males over three to six (average four) breeding seasons they were present in only nineteen per cent of an aggregated thirty-seven seasons. On the other hand twenty females studied over three to five (average four) breeding seasons occurred in seventy-seven per cent of an aggregated seventy-nine seasons. There was a marked trend among the small percentage of males to remain in their natal area during their first spring.

The tendency for females to have a stronger attachment than males for the place where they first reached water was noticeable among colour-ringed young transferred from St. James's to the Serpentine in 1969 before they could fly. Of four known surviving males three returned to the former water in winter or spring but none stayed throughout the breeding season. In contrast all seven surviving females returned to St. James's, where one died and at least two were present there in the breeding season of 1970.

CHAPTER 7
THE BROOD SEASON

Against a pleasant setting of green trees and grassland the well-timed flower beds of St. James's blaze with colour as summer approaches. And when in May the temperature soars to the seventies (F), thousands of human beings converge on the Park. Throughout much of any hot summer's day the lawns and walks around the lake are crowded with people and where footpaths reach to the water's edge visitors enjoy themselves feeding the waterfowl at their very feet. Through their prominence among the eager recipients of food, Tufted Ducks are important contributors to this traditional pleasure.

FAMILY LIFE ON THE LAKE

Duration of hatching season

The hatching season of Tufted Duck in St. James's spans almost fourteen weeks. While the first downies may be expected in the last week of May (earliest recorded May 25, 1976) and the last ones towards the end of August (latest hatching date August 28, 1968) it is throughout July that the majority of newly-hatched broods appear on the lake (Table 35). Over many summer weeks the behaviour and antics of these appealing black balls of fluff delight the public, many of whom may little realise that most ducklings will not survive longer than twenty-one days.

In the Park's much smaller Pochard population the hatching season begins earlier, and is of shorter duration, than that of the Tufted Duck. Freshly-hatched broods reach water between May 10 and July 22, though most are seen in June. They, too, suffer heavy casualties within three weeks of leaving the nest.

The family unit

Tufted ducklings hatch with a complete covering of down, remain in the nest for about twenty-four hours, and are able to feed themselves.

The normal family unit consists of the female and brood; it is rare for the male to accompany them. Only on five instances in thirty years were males seen associating with females and broods. Three times male attendance was brief, but

in two seasons lasted for ten and eleven days respectively. In all but the Shelduck
this behaviour is equally uncommon among British breeding duck. The last-
named species excepted, the only personal observations during many years'
watching on the North Kent marshes were of male Gadwall, Shoveler and
Pochard associating briefly with families on single occasions each. The paucity of
such records is due to most females being deserted by the male during the
incubation period.

Brood sizes: and the vulnerability of newly-hatched young

The sizes of newly-hatched broods, when first observed on water, ranged from
one to eighteen, averaging six or seven over a period of fourteen years (Table
37). After deducting these low figures from an average clutch size of
approximately nine (Table 25) there is a deficiency of three from which must be
subtracted a further one for the average number of unhatched eggs left in nests
after the departure of broods (Table 32). Thus, a final balance of one or two eggs
still needs accounting for.

Some eggs which disappear during incubation are taken by predators, but
evidence also suggests that sitting females remove badly cracked or broken eggs
from their own nests. These, however, are small contributory factors, and it
seems likely that most of the one or two losses are due to newly-hatched downies
dying in the short interval between leaving the nest and the brood first being
observed on water. Although family sizes based on initial sightings average six to
seven ducklings it is almost certain that eight downies leave the nest (Table 37).

Five downies was the average size of 105 Pochard families on reaching water in
St. James's. Broods were rarely over nine and none exceeded eleven ducklings.
This data compares closely with the studies of Hori (1966) in Kent. Over five
seasons he found that the brood sizes of tiny Pochard young aged up to about
three days old averaged five. Ten was the maximum size of a family.

Newly-hatched tufted downies are particularly vulnerable at this tender age
because of inactiveness during at least their first few hours on water. On reaching
the lake the brood keeps in a tight bunch, paddling close to its mother and
looking very much like the compact group it formed in the nest earlier on. At this
stage there is a strong tendency for females with tiny young to hug the shorelines
of the two main nesting islands, a practice which, for the unfortunate ducklings, is
tantamount to running the gauntlet. By these banksides, passing Mallard families,
groups of idling drakes – especially Mallard – a variety of pinioned waterfowl, and
Coots with nests, are a few of the hazards.

I suspect that tufted mothers with newly-hatched young keep close to these
shorelines for two reasons. First, there is the shelter afforded by overhanging

trees and shrubs against predatory gulls. Beneath this protective canopy females dive for food beside their downies, which feed by picking off the water as they cluster during these inert hours. It seems that a mother's underwater activity causes tiny food items to surface for the benefit of the ducklings. Second, there is a female's strong urge to brood her young ashore or to return to the nest for this purpose or to incubate unhatched eggs (Tables 32 & 33).

Return to the nest

Frequently a family arrives on water only to be seen heading back into cover within five minutes. Occasionally a mother needs to return to retrieve ducklings left behind in the nest or along the trail from the nest. Once a female abandoned her brood of eight on water, disappeared into cover and returned with a ninth downy a few minutes later. Another mother twice left her six ducklings on water and returned to the nest. The following day the same family had increased to ten. A third female assembled her downies on water after they had jumped from an elevated nest on a rockery. Then, leaving the brood on two occasions, she returned to what I knew was an empty nest. It may well be that these visits resulted from a strong compulsion to look for stragglers.

Mothers who return to their nests alone usually leave their young in a cluster close to the shoreline. Here the ducklings remain quietly together, or swim a few yards back and forth, awaiting their parent's return. Occasionally a knot of ducklings travels fifty yards along the water's edge and joins another bunch of unattended tufted ducklings. Both broods are friendly to one another, immediately moving about as a single family. Unfortunately such clusters are an easy target for aggressors. For example, on July 5, 1968, a passing female tufted was able to maul, at will, some of a newly-hatched brood of thirteen. As this stranger struck them repeatedly with her bill, the downies remained stationary in a tight group – a good example of 'sitting ducks.'

I never saw Pochard females with freshly-hatched young return to the nest soon after reaching water. If they did so it was infrequent and may be a small contributory factor in this species' slightly lower initial brood size compared with that of the Tufted Duck.

When a female tufted and her newly-hatched ducklings have left the nest it is not unusual for at least one or two eggs to remain. Out of 180 nests containing evidence of successful hatchings there were eighty-eight empty ones. But in the remaining ninety-two, I found 207 left-over eggs and twelve dead downies. Thus, unhatched eggs averaged one per successful nest (Table 32).

Female Tufted Ducks return to sit on their nests soon after taking newly-hatched young to water. The presence of several, or even whole broods, of unaccompanied freshly-hatched downies on the lake, annually, points to the frequency of this practice.

It seems likely that a female's urge to incubate left-over eggs overcomes the drive to stay with the brood on water. While this is temporary in most cases, it can lead to the families being split. Should one or two ducklings follow their mother back to the nest it is unlikely that she would bother about the rest, though such waifs might rejoin her in a day or so should they survive. On June 16, 1968, a female was caught on a nest containing nine eggs, and colour-ringed. Three weeks later she was still incubating three eggs, yet there was ample evidence from shells and membranes in the nest that a number of eggs had hatched successfully.

Over a period of years 154 left-over tufted eggs were collected from nests containing evidence of some successful hatchings and 146 of them were opened for examination of the contents (Table 33). Eight of the seventy-three eggs containing formed chicks were put in the St. James's Park incubator, instead of being opened, and all hatched quickly except for one which took four days. These eight eggs were, of course, taken on the day the females and their newly-hatched ducklings departed from the nest. One cannot rule out disturbance being responsible for some left-over eggs. However, there are other causes. For example, parasitic layings, both by other species of duck and by other tufted after the host has commenced to incubate, occasionally account for females continuing to sit on nests in which hatchings have occurred.

Work on Tufted Ducks in Czechoslovakia (Havlín, 1966) also shows that, in round figures, an average of one left-over egg remained in each successful nest. Of 125 eggs which failed to produce young for various reasons, 113 were found in nests after the departure of broods. Apparently hatching failure of left-over eggs was due to infertility and death of embryos. It is not clear, however, whether seven pipped eggs out of 113 were the only ones containing well-formed young.

Mendall (1958) writes of many instances of Ring-necked Ducks using their nests as brooding sites for two to four days and of a few occasions when eggs hatched out *after* the female had led her brood from the nest.

Loner females with broods

There is strong observational evidence that some loner female Tufted Ducks lay fertile eggs and have broods (*vide* Appendix 4).

Successful breeding by a few of these females may be due to bigamy on the part of males, as has been recorded by Bezzel and Reicholf (*vide* Cramp and Simmons, 1977). Temporary associations between loner females and pairs lend support to this possibility. However, since roving sexually active unmated males also attend unpaired females there is a reason for believing that casual couplings are as likely as bigamous associations in St. James's.

Mr J. C. Rolls (1983), in recording a case of probable bigamy by a male Pochard in 1979, makes no reference to a *close relationship* between the single drake and two females of this species on a Wiltshire lake.

Downy young feeding

While remaining in a tight bunch on water, in the first day or two after leaving the nest, some tufted ducklings begin snatching at insects flying in their immediate vicinity. Within another day or two downies become more agile and soon pursue insects in all directions.

About the same time a few, occasionally all, of the brood commence diving for food. After the first week diving for a meal is commonplace, by which time most ducklings have begun to take bread. When insect food is scarce females conduct their small young alongside the steeper stonework edging the lake. Here whole broods of downies will up-end to feed on or among the algae growing on the vertical facings just below the surface.

With most feeding activities the ducklings stay close to the brood female, whose shielding role is a major contribution to brood survival. Only when feeding on flying insects do the small young stray from their mother's protective mantle. Then it seems as if the ducklings are in a world of their own as, like fast-moving ballet dancers, they weave to and fro, racing across the water to the delight of all who watch them.

Tufted mothers constantly watch over their young. While the ducklings feed on or below the surface, the parent, with neck erect, is ever on the alert. Commonly, broods feed as they travel, the downies moving in a broad fan ahead of their mother, who guides them to suitable feeding grounds. But the mother, too, has to feed, and may for a while dive for food in company with her young. Sometimes, however, she flies off to feed elsewhere, leaving the brood to fend for itself. There is no warning from a departing female. One moment she is guarding her downies as they feed and in the next she is up and away without uttering a sound. One colour-ringed brood female was found feeding, alone, as far away as Long Water in Kensington Gardens. Females which leave their broods to feed some distance away usually return to the spot whence they left their young. Should the ducklings be missing a mother flies up and down the lake calling loudly until she finds them.

When ducklings are over about two weeks old many brood females compete with their young for titbits at the public feeding points. This feeding rivalry also occurs when mothers come ashore with their young to be fed.

On a crowded breeding water like St. James's the most frequent call of a tufted mother is the rolling KURR given while conducting her brood. The rapid PEE PEE PEE of distress is a familiar call of small downies. Both the notes of females and ducklings vary in pitch according to the amount of stress they are under. Other vocal sounds of adults and young are detailed in Appendix 9.

Since young tufted soon recognise food in a visitor's hand, and wait expectantly to be fed, it would not be wholly surprising if at times they react similarly to their parents.

Once a mother surfaced with several thin strands of weed accidentally caught in the base of the bill. Immediately her five young clustered and looked up at her expecting to be fed. With a little hesitancy the mother backed away, then turned from the brood and continued diving.

Soliciting for food sometimes involves strange donors and recipients. Particularly unusual was the sight of a parent Coot satisfying the begging responses of *adult* London Pigeons, an incident serving to highlight the resourcefulness of the latter. One spring evening some visitors were throwing bread to a gathering of birds which included Mallard, a pair of Coots and some pigeons. One of the Coots was particularly busy carrying tiny pieces of bread to its sickly chick resting on the grass on the outskirts of the throng. Not once did the baby Coot respond to the parent's offerings, but three or four cheeky London Pigeons did so. Each time the Coot approached its downy the pigeons were waiting with open mouths and on at least two occasions they were fed by the obliging Coot. However, the Coot's behaviour soon changed and, instead of continuing to feed the pigeons, it chased them away. One of the persons feeding the birds told me that the Coot had fed pigeons several times before my arrival.

Brooding of young
Brooding of very small young occurs at frequent intervals and for this purpose females regularly use the same section of bank. Old Coot nests are favourite resting places and some females occasionally use unoccupied artificial nest sites close to water for brooding purposes. Mothers are no less aggressive on land than on water and brood spacing is just as important as pair spacing was a month or so before. Ashore, brood females normally defend a minimum area of about three feet radius around their ducklings.

When brooding tiny young the female usually stands upright, at the same time lowering the leading edges of her wings to the ground while opening and depressing her tail slightly. Into this 'tent', which has been known to accommodate eighteen, the downies pack from under their mother's tail to her lower breast and between her wings, which are pushed outwards when broods are numerically large.

If approached without being disturbed, some tufted mothers brooding tiny young signal hostility by elevating their scapulars and dorsal feathers. This initial warning, lasting many minutes, is free of threatening gestures with the bill.

I witnessed more elaborate behaviour while photographing a female Carolina brooding newly-hatched young. At six feet range she remained perfectly still with the feathers of her back, rump, marginal upper wing-coverts and scapulars raised. Some lesser upper wing-coverts, upper tail-coverts, and feathers at the sides of the breast were also lifted, while her chest had a puffed appearance. All the time her bill remained closed.

Ducklings just over a week old cluster closely around their mother's body if there are too many of them to use the 'tent'; but from two to three weeks old tend to huddle together, brooding themselves while their watchful mother stations herself beside them or a short distance away. On warm days young tufted aged seven to ten days, or older, may rest side by side strung out in a line along the bank; but a female Mallard was seen brooding six-days-old downies beneath her when the Park temperature was a record ninety-four degrees (F).

Though downies aged about seven days or over tend to cluster when ashore, they adopt a more distinct spacing while idling on water. Then the interval between ducklings varies from about three to twelve inches. By the time young tufted are nearly fully-fledged, they maintain the wider twelve to eighteen inches minimum spacing of adults.

Small lost ducklings, in need of brooding, seek warmth by snuggling up to other waifs or joining other broods. One weak downy, instead of attaching itself to a brood cluster, sought the feathers between a strange brood female's legs. This error of judgment earned continual pecking which might have proved fatal for the duckling had I not ended the attack by flushing both family and newcomer to water. A less distressing case concerned a tiny downy Pochard so much in need of warmth that it came ashore and nestled under the arch of a lady's high-heeled shoe. When this waif's predicament was explained to her, the visitor was eager to help. So with a few tears in her eyes, and the duckling clasped firmly in warm hands, she hurried off to Arthur May's haven on Duck Island.

While brooding young ashore or on old Coot nests tufted females commonly go through the motions of nest building. This behaviour, like that indulged in earlier in the breeding season, consists of pulling small fragments of material to the body or passing the bits over the back and dropping them behind. Sometimes a female indulges in this token nest building when a little distance from the brood or she may walk away from her young, passing scraps of grass or twig over her back while on the move. Much less frequently genuine nest building by brood female Tufted Duck and Pochard was observed.

Instances of downy tufted being carried on their mother's back have been extremely rare, probably because there has not been a necessity for brooding the young on water as sometimes occurs with the Mute Swan. On July 7, 1965, I observed a tiny duckling on its mother's back for a minute or two in St. James's. My only other record is of a little downy which, after several attempts, jumped onto its mother's back in one of the fountain basins in Kensington Gardens on July 29, 1961. At the time this basin was the only one out of four not possessing a floating wood platform for the purposes of resting waterfowl.

Three of the six published accounts of similar behaviour in Tufted Duck refer to the St. James's group of waters in the years 1929 to 1931 inclusive (cf. Bird Life in The Royal Parks reports for 1930 and 1931). The fourth occurrence was at the Sevenoaks Reserve in Kent eleven years ago (Harrison, 1977). Details of this record are accompanied by a fine photograph in which the mother looks weighed down at the stern by her chunky duckling. Considering the youngster's large size both record and picture are unique. The two remaining instances also refer to single ducklings being carried on the backs of females (cf. Brit. Birds 77:318-319).

Reports concerning females of other species of diving ducks giving their young a pickaback on water are by no means common. Kortright (1943) cites an instance of a brood female Goldeneye transporting about a dozen newly-hatched downies on her back for roughly fifty yards. He also mentions some of a Goosander family being carried in the same manner with the rest of the tiny ducklings swimming along behind their mother. Carbonell (1984) draws attention to some published records concerning the back-transport of small downies in three species of swans and eight species of duck, including the waterfowl referred to above.

A parent brooding young on her back when resting ashore may be more frequent, though I have only seen this behaviour twice. The first record is of a female Shelduck sitting on an exposed islet with two downies nestling on her dorsal feathers and partly concealed by her wings. The remaining instance concerns a small downy Mallard which, after falling into the water twice while being brooded with others in the normal manner, leapt onto its mother's back and nestled close to her neck.

Broods leaving the Park
The lot of the little downy Tufted Duck is far from being a bed of roses. Having got their broods to water, some mothers decide that St. James's lake is no place to rear a family. Within a few days of hatching, and almost always before they are ten days old, some broods are led by their parents towards other waters.

Several times in July, in the quiet of the late evening, I stopped mothers with tiny young as they were about to leave the Park. All were escorted back to the lake, but one mother was more determined to depart than the others. Thrice she conducted her downies towards the western end of the Mall and each time I guided them back to water where, to my relief, they finally remained.

During the period 1957 to 1970 alone, at least twenty-six broods totalling 179 downies are known to have been intercepted outside the Park. Many got no further than Horse Guards Parade, the approaches to Downing Street, or the vicinity of Buckingham Palace. A lesser number reached Hyde Park Corner and a minority progressed as far as the Victoria Embankment and the gardens at the southern end of the Houses of Parliament. A female with two downies reported on the Thames, near the Tate Gallery, on June 6, 1963, by Mr. G. H. Gush, may well have come from the Park (*London Bird Report* for 1963).

Although Arthur May was summoned to recover most broods, the London Police were responsible for saving many ducklings. For example, one policeman brought in a brood of four in his helmet; the crew of a patrol car collected a brood of five after their mother had been killed by traffic in Whitehall; and two police motorcyclists rounded up a colour-ringed female and her five young, hailed a lorry for their conveyance, and escorted them back to Duck Island. Yet another policeman caught and brought back a brood of fifteen.

Early one morning a colour-ringed mother of eight was calling her brood back into the Park, presumably after attempting to take them elsewhere. I found her at the foot of the high stone wall at the Palace end of the lake and, on looking up, saw three ducklings jump off a fourteen- to sixteen-foot high ledge. Each one hit the bare, rock-hard, soil with a sickening thud but, to my utter amazement, appeared none the worse as it picked itself up and ran off to water. On the lawns just outside the Park I caught three more ducklings and two others jumped through the stone balustrade to the ground below. In a short while all eight were together with the female.

One police officer who rounded up a brood on the edge of Green Park put three of them in one of the fountain basins of the Queen Victoria Memorial opposite Buckingham Palace. There the little downies led Arthur May a merry dance in his efforts to capture them. On another occasion a citizen put ten downies in one of these basins. This time nine were caught easily because they kept in a tight bunch but the tenth proved particularly elusive.

Fortunately, well over three-quarters of the 179 'migrating' ducklings were apprehended and returned to the Park. At least seventy of them were shepherded back to, or released on, the lake, in some cases to be reunited with their mother.

Once Arthur May was called to collect some ducklings held in the custody of a police officer at the Hyde Park Corner end of Constitution Hill. The female was still in the vicinity while her downies were transferred to a large bicycle saddle bag. As Arthur cycled back to the Park the anxious mother twice flew close to him. She was calling loudly to her young when he reached the waterside to free them.

Most of the ducklings not recovered were almost certainly killed by traffic. Drains and gratings, however, claimed a few victims. Some ducklings which are led by their mother across Horse Guards Parade end up in basements after falling through large iron grilles around the perimeter. On one occasion a female, as well as all of her downies, was recovered from one of these sunken courtyards.

One colour-ringed female was known to have got through from St. James's to the Serpentine but with only one downy out of seven. This family had the misfortune to run in front of a Park's Department lorry inside Hyde Park near the Wellington Museum. Two of the ducklings were killed by the vehicle and four of the five survivors were rounded up and taken to Arthur May. This behaviour is no new development, for on June 18, 1932, the traffic at Hyde Park Corner was held up while a tufted mother and her brood of nine crossed the road (*vide Bird Life in The Royal Parks* report for 1932).

Malcolm Kerr tells me that since he has been Bird Keeper a few straying downies have been brought to him each year, mostly by members of the public. On one of my last July visits to the Park I met two police officers returning two ducklings. These mites were the survivors of a brood rescued from the roadway by the Houses of Parliament. When found they were exhausted but, after a twenty-minutes journey cupped in warm hands, they were lively upon arrival.

No partially-feathered downies were found among those rescued and returned to St. James's.

Conducting tufted young to other feeding grounds sometimes occurs at Finsbury Park. Here the broods are more fortunate in that their journey of about two hundred yards is a downhill one over grassland inside the park to the waters of the New River.

In over two decades no Pochard families were found outside the Park. However, a few downies hatched out in Tufted Duck nests were among broods of the latter rounded up and returned to St. James's.

On land, downies aged over a week run fast and use evasive tactics once a brood breaks convoy and scatters. Ducklings of similar age are proficient at leaping onto the top of six inches high vertical stone embankments. I once saw a tiny Pochard downy spring some nine inches out of the water to seize an overhanging aquatic plant.

When moving from place to place, without feeding, small ducklings often walk or swim in single file behind their mother. It is also common for them to follow in a tight bunch close to their parent's tail as occurs with broods of many species.

Splitting and amalgamation of broods

Losses of one or two ducklings from broods of small young arise from a variety of causes. For example, when tufted and Mallard families meet fights or scuffles break out frequently, leading to the tufted mother becoming separated from her brood or the downies scattering for the first time in their lives. For a few it will be both their first and last dispersal because, when a family reassembles and continues on its way, one or two downies are often missing.

Another source of danger to ducklings, especially those less than a week old, is the splitting of a brood when a family joins other waterfowl competing for offerings at one of the main public feeding points. Apparently hungry mothers, with tiny downies too young to eat bread, are drawn to these gatherings often with disastrous consequences. All too frequently mothers leave these concourses with fewer ducklings than they arrived with. Many downies, particularly the larger ones, rejoin their family later in the day or at night, but some fall prey to ever watchful Herring or Lesser Black-backed Gulls. Cold weather or heavy rain soon weaken the smallest ducklings and many succumb without ever rejoining the rest of the brood.

Fights between two tufted brood females soon after getting their families to water do not always result in a dispersal of the ducklings. Sometimes, say, a mother with eight downies meets another mother with ten. While the females battle with each other the two broods commonly fuse together. When a fracas ends, one mother may sail off with more ducklings than she started with, even with the whole eighteen. Similarly, I have witnessed the combining of two Shelduck broods during fights between parents, but not once in St. James's were Pochard broods seen to unite following scuffles between mothers. In fact no multiple broods of tiny young of the latter species were ever observed in the Park. I did, however, see ten partly feathered young of three distinct sizes accompanied by one female in Holland in 1983.

Small amalgamations of two broods of about three or four downies each are difficult to detect unless the merger is witnessed. But from small beginnings some tufted mothers quickly accumulate up to thirty tiny ducklings.

It must not be assumed that all members of a crèche are acquired solely through parental fights. Some brood females desert their young soon after leading them safely to water. Whatever the cause of being left alone may be, these bumble bee-like waifs are adept at joining other families even on a part-time basis.

There appears to be a kind of love/hate relationship between many foster-mothers and their multiple broods. While tiny tufted readily accept abandoned downies of similar age, their mothers are, as a rule, hostile to newcomers. A female recognises strange ducklings within her brood and attacks them whenever they come close to her. In spite of this, ducklings tolerate parental aggression and an extra-large family may keep intact for several weeks on end. In fact when an intruder attacks any one duckling, it signals to the mother or foster-mother an attack on them all.

Most amalgamations occur when broods are between one and ten days old and the ducklings involved are usually, but not always, the same size. Though large multiple broods are easy to recognise little is known about females regaining their families from crèches. The following example, therefore, demonstrates that a union may not go unchallenged. In 1968 single, extremely late broods hatched out about August 27 and 28 from two nests found on August 21 holding seven and eight eggs respectively. As the latest brood reaching water before these two was on August 6 that year there was no possibility of confusing ducklings whose ages differed by as much as three weeks.

A table of events concerning the two late broods is as follows:—

August 21	Two females sitting on seven and eight eggs respectively.
August 28	One female with five newly-hatched downies.
August 29	One female with thirteen tiny downies. Both nests checked and contained evidence of hatchings. One nest was empty and the other held one unhatched egg.
August 30	One female with seven tiny downies and three tiny downies on their own nearby. A second female was alone not far away but behaving as if she had a brood.
August 31	One female with four tiny downies and one female with three tiny downies.
September 8 to October 2 inclusive	Two females, both with two ducklings each.

Several other mothers are known to have retrieved their broods after losing them through fights.

Females have occasionally been reunited with their ducklings after enforced separations. One pleasant reunion occurred on July 4, 1963. Soon after 0800hrs that day a female without any young was calling excitedly beside the Duck Island boathouse. Somewhat puzzled by her prolonged agitation, I phoned Arthur May later, and learned that he had recovered six downies from Horse Guards Parade an hour or two before my arrival that morning and was keeping them in his office. Returning to the Park ten hours later, I found the same female still calling in the same area, pointing to her knowing the whereabouts of her captive brood. I went to Arthur May's office near the boathouse and told him of the mother's anxiety. Without hesitation he gathered up the three liveliest downies out of the six and we proceeded to the water's edge where the female was still calling. Upon our approach with the cheeping ducklings the mother fluttered to within ten feet of the bank. So this female and her brood were brought together again after a separation lasting at least twelve hours. The remaining three ducklings were retained in captivity.

Nannies, aunties and other fosterers

Nannies were described by me in a paper written some years ago (Gillham, 1958). They are non-breeding or post-breeding female Tufted Ducks which assume the role of mother over small temporarily or permanently lost, or deserted, tufted ducklings. Throughout every brood season in St. James's there are a number of unattached young suitable for adoption. The smallest ones sometimes demonstrate their need for a parent by following nesting females or even adult drakes, few of which respond. Instead, they swim rapidly away ignoring the plaintive calls of the downies. I suspect that most nannies are females which have recently lost either broods or clutches of eggs in the final stages of incubation.

Nannies are not confined solely to one species. For example, a Red-crested Pochard female was observed trying to take over a Pochard brood and a female Mallard adopted three tufted waifs. Yet another female Mallard appropriated a whole tufted brood which the rightful mother recovered some hours later. Similarly, Tufted Duck mothers lost single downies to tufted nannies and got them back within a few hours.

Pochard nannies were not uncommon in St. James's. As with female tufted their activities frequently involved the mothering of single stray downies of their own species. In Sussex, in May 1983, a female with a newly-hatched brood of eleven swam off leaving one of her downies behind. This foundling was immediately followed by an adult drake Pochard which gave the *Sneak* posture to it on several occasions. Eventually, a lone female Pochard came on the scene, drove off the male, and escorted the duckling about the pond.

Two occurrences of a drake acting as a nanny in St. James's were in 1983 and 1984. In the first year I watched a female tufted with a three-weeks-old brood associating closely with a male Chiloé Wigeon. With loud calls he twice chased away a strange brood female tufted which ventured close to his adopted family. Several times, too, the drake chiloé mildly threatened the mother of the brood he was escorting but never menaced the ducklings. During the latter year this same male associated with two different Tufted Duck families in June and September, respectively. His behaviour was solely defence of the female in the first month. Every time one or more of the female's ducklings swam or surfaced near him he gave a loud whistle, causing the young to move away. In September he kept close to the second female who constantly protected her brood. But when the male chiloé was alone with the young he drove away intruders several times.

In its natural habitat, the male Chiloé Wigeon is known to actively assist his mate in rearing and protecting the young (Johnsgard, 1968).

In the *Bird Life in The Royal Parks* report for 1948 there is mention of an Abyssinian Blue-winged Goose protecting a tufted duckling on July 28 and 29 of that year.

In contrast with nannies which assume sole parentage over downies, aunties share brood duties with another female. Because most tufted mothers habitually drive away all intruders from the vicinity of their broods aunties have proved to be rare. Only when two completely passive brood females meet is the stage set for the two mothers and their families to stay together for a while as a single family group. Bezzel and Von Krosigk (Cramp and Simmons, 1977) record the flocking of several females and their young.

The strangest example is of a Pochard auntie observed for some time on June 1, 1975, in St. James's. This involved the prolonged association of a female Pochard and her two small ducklings with a male Tufted Duck paired to a female Pochard. Earlier that day the drake tufted with his female Pochard were on their own as a pair. The close grouping was started by a Herring Gull repeatedly harrying the two downies, resulting in the three adults bunching protectively around the brood as the gull swooped down. After the attack all five moved about the lake together, and in perfect harmony, sometimes being spaced within a foot of one another. At one stage two male Pochard moved in to court the brood female. When the attentions of one of these males caused the mother to paddle quickly away the second female Pochard hurried towards the intruder with neck extended and bill wide open as if defending a brood of her own. Several times the male tufted appeared to be defending all of them by assuming the typical *Crouch* posture as in defence of his female. This unusual behaviour undoubtedly included a combination of at least the following patterns:—

    (a) communal defence of a brood,
    (b) defence of a female by her mate,
    (c) a brood female's unusual passivity leading to a family being joined by an auntie without young of her own.

Other strange partnerships were noted between Barnacle Geese and Mallard throughout ten consecutive breeding seasons from 1962 to 1971. In seven years these involvements concerned one goose annually; in two years two different geese; and in one year three geese were each seen associating with different Mallard. The average duration of relationships lasted seventy days.

Single Barnacle Geese attended female Mallard before the latter became paired to drake Mallard in two years; and in five years individual geese accompanied Mallard pairs. After the female Mallard were deserted by their mates the associations still continued strongly. Every year barnacles were seen protecting a female Mallard and her brood over periods averaging thirty-eight days. From mid-July until mid-February these geese reverted to normal barnacles, only consorting closely with their own kind or as a group with other geese. After 1971 I discontinued looking for these partnerships. That they occurred in the last decade was confirmed by Mr. Harvey Chittey, who saw single barnacles in close attendance on female Mallard with broods in both 1981 and 1982. My attention was drawn to another association in 1984.

Frequently female Tufted Ducks fostered one or two downies of Shelduck, Mallard, Pochard and Red-crested Pochard with their own newly-hatched young. Such instances occurred through females of those four species laying an egg or two, parasitically, in the nests of female tufted. Particularly unusual was a pair of Canada Geese with a newly-hatched brood of downies consisting of four goslings and one Pochard in 1984. They were seen ashore for long periods and the little duckling was accepted by the whole Canada family. This was either a case of parasitic laying by a female Pochard or straightforward adoption.

Notwithstanding plentiful opportunities, unattached downy tufted are not known to have joined families of another duck species permanently. One or two probably do so from time to time but the success of such unions requires a foster-mother who is passive to alien ducklings. Andrew Heaton, warden of Sevenoaks Wildfowl Reserve, tells me (*in litt.*) that, in 1983, a tufted mother of a newly-hatched brood of two disappeared the day after reaching water. Then the downies were on their own for forty-eight hours, after which both were adopted and reared by a female Mallard with her brood of five.

Defence of young

To a tufted mother defence of the family means taking offensive action, for she does not wait idly until her brood is attacked. Instead the female reacts aggressively to most birds which approach, driving away both passers-by and intruders, however innocent. The boundaries of tolerance vary from one female to another. A small proportion of females are bad mothers. They show little interest in their tiny downies and make no effort to protect them. Some are hostile to other waterfowl even up to forty yards from their young. Usually a female defends a *minimum* area of about three feet radius around her brood wherever the family happens to be.

During scuffles tufted mothers seize the flank feathers or a wing of an intruder while alien ducklings may be either pecked repeatedly or caught by the head or neck and shaken.

Besides rail chicks and small ducklings the birds assaulted by tufted mothers include adults of eight species of duck, Woodpigeon, Coot, Moorhen (including one sitting on its nest), Black-headed Gull, and even such giants as pelican, Canada Goose, and Black Swan. Also several times a Cormorant surfacing harmlessly near a family has been chased away, and one brood female deliberately crash-landed on the head of a partially submerged Cormorant. The usual method of expulsion is a threatening gesture with head and neck extended low over the water and bill wide open. But more effective results are achieved when this posture is accompanied by a headlong rush across the surface, causing an intruder to turn and flee.

One of the most persistent attacks on a bird larger than itself occurred in 1966. That year a tufted mother left her ducklings and repeatedly assaulted an unaggressive lone female Shelduck which attempted to escape by diving. Thrice the latter surfaced some distance away, only to be pursued each time by the irate brood female.

Seizure of a duckling by an opponent heightens the defence behaviour of the mother, who may then fly directly at the face of an adversary, crashing into it with body and feet. This type of attack is also used by Pochard and Mallard, and a brood female of the latter species once crashed boldly into the head of a Canada Goose. When one brood female tufted fought a Pochard mother they attacked each other head-on.

That distinguished pioneer of London ornithology, the late A. Holte Macpherson, describes a remarkable instance of this defence behaviour against a human being in the *Bird Life in The Royal Parks* report for 1930. As a boy tried to catch one of four Mallard ducklings their mother flew straight at the youth's face. I witnessed similar aggression by a Mallard when a lady caught one of her downies.

Fights or scuffles between tufted and Mallard brood females were as frequent as those involving two tufted mothers, but under identical circumstances the uniting of broods of different species was not recorded. Observations suggest that a reason for this is the belligerency and dominance of even the tiniest Mallard duckling. When Mallard and tufted families met, the result was often a family attack, with the tiny Mallard setting about the tufted downies. Similar behaviour has been noted with Wigeon. On July 9, 1958, a female Wigeon with five small downies encountered a tufted brood of about equal age. As the two mothers threatened and lunged at one another, the downy Wigeon behaved like little monsters, each attacking a downy tufted with surprising ferocity.

Downy Tufted Duck were not seen threatening birds of other species and rarely drove them away. One of the few pursuits involved a little duckling chasing a much larger Mallard downy. Small young of surface-feeding ducks appear more aggressive than tufted and Pochard ducklings. I once saw a downy Mandarin aged less than seven days rush at and peck an adult female tufted, causing the latter to retreat hastily. Another time one of a brood of three small downy Carolina Ducks thrust its head and neck forward, confronting an approaching London Pigeon with wide open bill.

Mendall (1958) witnessed no hostility between families of Ring-necked Ducks when they intermingled. Neither did he find ring-necks with broods intolerant of families of other species which closely approached them. On the other hand female ring-necks often drove away stray or orphaned ring-necked young from the vicinity of their own broods.

Traditional enemies like Herring and Lesser Black-backed Gulls and Carrion Crows are persistently attacked or driven off whenever they are too close to a family of Tufted Ducks.

On several occasions brood females have been known to go to the aid of ducklings other than their own. For example, a Black Swan was attacked three times by a brood female for seizing a stray downy. When the fracas was over, the tufted mother chased away the downy she had only just rescued. Another instance concerned two brood females rushing at a Herring Gull as it seized a downy not belonging to either of them. A third case was of an attack made by a mother on a Lesser Black-backed Gull as it was about to make off with a duckling belonging to another female. Moreover, several times females *without* any family at all have provided similar protection by driving away predatory gulls.

Tiny ducklings keep close to their mother's flanks when predatory gulls swoop low or just circle overhead. Indeed, almost any sort of commotion or hint of danger is likely to cause small young to cluster around their mother, so putting them within the protective range of her long neck and menacing bill. Mothers rear up on the water with their bills thrusting skywards to ward off attacking gulls. One brood female Mallard rose almost vertically about forty feet to attack a marauding lesser black-back from below. Similarly, another vigilant Mallard left the water to assault a Carrion Crow winging towards her young. When a brood female pursues an adversary the tiny ducklings often stay bunched together but older downies tend to dive or scatter.

Attacks on broods do not always come from the air. A Herring Gull was seen to alight on a bank at a discreet distance from a brood resting ashore and then make a sudden raid by running at great speed to snatch a downy from its mother's side. No doubt as a precaution against this type of surprise attack on land another tufted mother resting ashore has been seen to change position so as to put herself between a lurking gull and her ducklings. Similar behaviour was observed in a female Carolina Duck with one downy under persistent attack on water. As the Herring Gull swooped repeatedly, from different angles, the belligerent mother altered course each time, positioning herself between the predator and her duckling.

Assaults on compact broods of large feathered tufted ducklings were not observed so their reactions to predators are unknown to me. However, on the North Kent marshes I saw Great Black-backed Gulls attacking crèches of almost fully-grown Shelduck young on several occasions. Defence was communal, the fledglings bunching tightly and waving their heads during the gull's onslaught. This protective packing is analogous with that of adult Coots and Eiders in the presence of avian assailants as described by Witherby *et al.* (1948).

Small tufted downies learn which birds are their real enemies. One newly-hatched brood which was seen to leave the nest and drop into the water promptly dived when a Black-headed Gull passed over, while larger ducklings in the vicinity took no notice. The life of a duckling would be impossible in St. James's if it needed to submerge every time a harmless bird flew overhead.

I have known mothers to give warning growls when low-flying Herring Gulls were about 100 yards from their families but remain silent when Black-headed Gulls approached at similar distances.

After ducklings are half-grown mothers tend to be less vocal while in the erect guarding posture. They also become less aggressive to other ducks passing close to their young, especially in the days preceding the abandonment of a brood.

Although a tufted mother's defence mechanism is continually triggered by other birds she reacts differently to man. Trustingly she brings her young to the edge of the shorelines at the public feeding points. In places where grass verges intervene between water and footpaths it is not uncommon for mothers with larger ducklings to come ashore with their young to be fed. At all times, however, the brood female remains alert and sudden movements may send a family scampering back to water. A remarkable example of a brood female's trust in man was that of a tufted mother which allowed a two-year-old child to stroke three of her tiny ducklings over several minutes as they fed at the water's edge.

Females attacking their own young

At times mothers maltreat their own tiny young. On July 17, 1959, three different tufted brood females were seen sharply pecking more than one of their downies, yet their broods were no larger in number than on the two previous days. Likewise, on July 14, 1964, a female was seen pecking one of her brood of six, and on the following day made similar attacks on two out of five. An equally strange case concerned a Pochard mother with a newly-hatched brood of ten. On three consecutive days, July 2, 3 and 4, 1969, this female was seen pecking at a few of the young as they clustered about her. It might, of course, be argued that all of the females in attendance were foster-mothers. But I believe that many of these attacks constitute redirected aggression similar to the behaviour of adult males who often threaten, chase, and sometimes rape their own mates as if they were intruders.

Mendall (1958) writes that on several occasions he saw female Ring-necked Ducks lunge and peck at one of their ducklings for not seeking emergent cover quickly enough when birds of prey were in the vicinity.

The mildest form of hostility towards newly-hatched young is 'nibbling'. On July 4, 1963, a Shelduck was seen following, and running its bill over and gently pecking a tiny tufted downy. The following year a female tufted was seen doing likewise to a diminutive Pochard duckling for short periods on July 5, 8 and 9. As on all three dates the female tufted was parading like a brood female, with neck erect, there seemed a conflict between a desire to attack the duckling and a desire to adopt it. A fifth instance was on June 29, 1973, when a newly-hatched downy tufted followed a pair of adults. The duckling was viciously attacked by a Coot but the tufted female 'nibbled' the waif on and off over a period of ten minutes.

Greeting ceremony of females and young

Female Tufted Ducks with young, sometimes aged less than a week old, commonly perform a greeting ceremony to one another. This occurs when a family is reunited following separations caused through scuffles between brood females, or on the return of a mother who has been feeding alone elsewhere. It also happens after a spell of resting ashore.

On leaving a brooding spot a parent swims a short distance from the bank calling repeatedly to her tardy young. As they join up both female and duckling face each other in an erect posture, then give a gentle chin-lifting display before swimming off together. Downies greet each other, and sometimes other kinds of duck, in the same manner.

This behaviour was also observed when, through a chance meeting, a female associated briefly with two of the brood she had deserted a couple of days before. On a few similar encounters females and their abandoned ducklings continued to perform the gentle chin-lifting ritual to each other.

Driver (1974) records that American Eider ducklings, from the time they leave the nest, give a similar upward nod as a greeting both to other ducklings and to their mother.

Downies crash-diving

From the time that tiny tufted ducklings leave the nest they are able to dive with speed, especially when attacked by predatory gulls. One moment some stray downies are on the surface; then, with almost simultaneous lightning splashes, they vanish below. In all probability the jets of water kicked up by disappearing broods confuse predators as they swoop low. I found this instant diving of frequent occurrence with small young of Shelduck and five kinds of surface-feeding ducks during surprise encounters on pools and along ditches on the North Kent marshes. A week-old Shelduck brood on a small isolated pond so stirred the bottom following split-second dives that I was unable to pin-point downies beneath the muddy waters.

This escape behaviour has been aptly called crash-diving by Driver (1974). He describes it in detail for Old Squaw and American Eider ducklings and considers that all ducks, geese, and swans use this dive when young.

Distraction display

The sole observation of any form of distraction display in St. James's was of an incubating female who briefly thrashed the water with her wings when disturbed from the nest. Similar display was given by a female departing from a nest containing well-set eggs at Liphook in Hampshire.

More elaborate injury-feigning was witnessed on the North Kent marshes when I surprised Shelduck, Mallard, Pintail, Gadwall, Shoveler, Teal, Garganey, and (once only) Pochard, with downy young. The sole example of extravagant behaviour in the Tufted Duck was of a mother with four small ducklings on Eagle Pond, Clapham, London, on August 14, 1968. This female and brood were resting on an exposed concrete drain some six feet from the bank when a dog rushed into the shallows towards them. The family fled to water, all of them pattering over the surface alternated with fast swimming to get away from the animal. Suddenly the female moved at right angles from her fleeing brood and behaved exactly like a wounded duck. Flogging the water with her wings, interspersed with heavy fluttering, she seemed to struggle over the surface, keeping just ahead of the dog and indisputably leading the animal well away from her young.

Not all observations on this distraction display have resulted from close encounters with both the mother and her brood. Once while I was walking beside a North Kent fleet a female Teal appeared out of the blue and began tumbling over the grass at my feet like a crippled bird. I followed her and for a short distance she continued injury-feigning on water before vanishing into the reeds almost as quickly as she came. When I finally located the Teal and her three-weeks-old brood in a wide runnel a quarter-of-a-mile away it was clear that she had left her young and flown some distance to display at my feet. The family had not been disturbed as my movements had been in the opposite direction to the ditch where the brood was eventually found feeding.

Another time a female Mallard behaved similarly, but in this instance I failed to find her brood in spite of a thorough search of all ditches within a radius of three hundred yards.

Desertion of broods by parents and desertion of parents by young

Desertion of a brood during its fledging period is well known among Shelduck and several species of North American and European diving duck. With British Shelduck breeding populations this occurs shortly before the adults' departure for one of several known moult areas where they spend their annual flightless period.

Tufted Duck, too, have a once yearly wing moult. In females this occurs from early July when, for three to four weeks, they are completely flightless until the new flight feathers develop.

With the St. James's tufted many brood desertions are associated with the female's wing moult. Between 1956 and 1964, when some sixty-two per cent of all brood females began their wing moult while still attending young, the duration of a mother's stay with her brood was about three times greater than in the years 1965-1970. In the latter period, it is significant that there was no recorded overlap between wing moult and brood duties among thirty-five colour-ringed mothers (Appendices 6, 7 & 8).

As with Shelduck, on occasions many small tufted ducklings are deserted within ten days of being taken to water. Moreover, whole broods of tiny downies are sometimes seen alone shortly after leaving the nest, so one cannot attribute every family break-up to the onset of a mother's wing moult. On average, females attend their young for about one month or nearly half the usual fledging period.

Some ducklings desert their mothers and odd ones maintain only a loose association with their family, compared with their brothers and sisters. The former behaviour appeared prevalent among tufted downies hatched out in Mallard nests (*cf.* Tables 36 & 38). At least half of those ducklings reared for part of the fledging period by Mallard left their foster-parent when about three weeks old. Since brood female Mallard commonly take their young ashore to feed on lawns and in puddles, it is probable that the developing diving habits of growing tufted lead to the break with the foster-mother. It seems, however, that some mixed families may feed together in the same manner. One year on Mound Pond, Clapham, two young tufted were reared in a Mallard brood. When seven weeks old one of the former was seen up-ending along with the Mallard ducklings. Later, all of the latter and both tufted were seen diving together for food.

Counting the young in broods several times a day highlights fluctuations, especially small ones within families aged one week or less. The following example shows how some tiny ducklings voluntarily leave their parent to become fosterlings.

On July 14 one year I was tracking a mother with seven newly-hatched downies swimming from the Palace end of the lake towards Duck Island. As this family drew level with a newly-hatched brood of four travelling in the opposite direction about four yards from them, two ducklings left the seven. Paddling nimbly to the mother with four they joined her brood which continued on course. Neither female stopped, slowed down, or called, as the families passed one another, so there was no apparent reason for changing parents. It seemed as if the two ducklings were more strongly attracted to the Palace end of the lake than to their mother.

Similarly, some newly-hatched young which cluster on the surface while their mothers dive beside them join other passing ducks or broods. Occasionally these innocents court danger by following Coots. One downy was not deterred from tagging along with a strange female tufted even after having been pecked sharply at least a dozen times.

At Delta, Hochbaum (1944) found that the age at which young Canvasbacks, as well as other young diving ducks, were abandoned depended largely on the date of hatching. Thus a female with a brood hatched early in the season stayed with her young for a longer period than did a female with a late-hatched brood. This pattern is almost certainly the case with tufted, though the average difference in the duration of stay – of about one week – is not obvious in the field. However, the wider the time-span between hatching dates the wider the calculated margin of difference. Taking the first thirteen of eighty-four broods (Appendix 6) hatched in the period June 15 – July 11, the average duration of a mother's brood duties was forty-one days compared with twenty-nine days for the females of the fourteen latest-hatched broods of the same sample which were led to water between August 5 and 22.

Though many tiny lost or deserted ducklings are doomed to die, some do, in fact, rear themselves provided good weather prevails during at least the first fourteen days after leaving the nest. As a general rule the hotter the weather the better the chances of survival for all tiny downies. Week by week the numbers of unattached young increase as larger ducklings, many aged three weeks and over, are deserted by their mothers.

Commonly, these unattended offspring are individualists. Through their dispersal over the whole lake and its shorelines they need careful searching for. After desertion by their mother up to half-a-dozen young aged four to six weeks often continue associating together for a week or two. But the surviving feathered young were never seen in one or two large crèches. However, loose associations are not uncommon when natural food is plentiful in a restricted area. Then as many as thirty feathered tufted ducklings will concentrate in a particular section of the lake for several days.

Following desertion by their mother young Pochard also range over the lake on their own or in loose groups of three or four together.

After the end of August few tufted females are still in attendance on their broods.

THE FLEDGING PERIOD

Development
At a distance tiny tufted ducklings look blackish and in St. James's are most likely to be confused with newly-hatched melanistic downies of Mallard which occur annually. It is not unusual for adult females of the latter species, in normal plumage, to have one or more of these dusky young in their otherwise ordinary broods. Thus it is necessary to inspect ducklings closely instead of assuming that they are tufted downies which have been hatched out in Mallard nests.

Freshly-hatched tufted downies are sooty-brown on the upperparts and yellowish to yellowish white on the chin, throat, and centre of breast. Some have dark heads and cheeks while others have a yellowish face pattern with dark stripes and spots. According to Veselovsky (1951) those without cheek markings are males. In both sexes the iris is brownish-grey. The bill is dark olive with a reddish nail and the white egg-tooth is considered by Veselovsky to disappear within thirty hours of hatching. In approximately a further two weeks the nail alters to a conspicuous creamy-pink bordered by a narrow flesh-red band. Soon afterwards the whole bill end darkens eventually becoming blackish.

At about three weeks old the two different face patterns of downy tufted become more obvious. I have noticed that the face patterns of whole broods of Mallard, Pochard and Rosy-bill ducklings had changed by the time they were aged about three weeks. This may be a reason why some illustrations of tiny ducklings are not portrayed as one sees them in life.

Tufted ducklings remain in down for nearly three weeks, by which time they are paler, less sooty, than earlier on. By about the end of the third week the first feathers appear and fourteen days later ducklings are well-fledged. At thirty days old Veselovsky found that the body is covered with a second growth of down and that the head retains down in the sixth week. In some youngsters down is still visible on the back and rump, as well as on the head, at forty-two days.

By the time ducklings are six weeks old the remaining down looks pale brown. A few wisps still adhere to nape and hind neck feathers, and to the sides of the upper tail-coverts, until the last ten days of fledging.

Coward (1929) writes that as tufted ducklings grow the down becomes browner. Similarly, Hochbaum (1944) noticed a gradual fading of down colour in Canvasback ducklings aged between one and three weeks.

At three to four weeks the eyes of many young tufted change to greenish-grey while those of presumed females have a more brownish tinge.

In the field the bills of both sexes, aged a month or over, look dark slate with a darker wedge-shaped tip. A thin, faint, bluish or whitish line appears behind the nail when young males are between nine and twelve weeks old. This pale area on the bill is seldom noticeable in young females before they are about twenty weeks old.

Feathered ducklings are brown birds like their mother. From about six weeks they are subject to plumage variation due, no doubt, to some of them speeding towards maturity more quickly than others. Taking bare parts, the iris in particular first, all well-fledged ducklings caught and colour-ringed just before they could fly were sexed on eye colour alone. They were held by me at arm's length and, if the yellowish eyes looked dull, they were judged to be females; if the eyes were bright they were noted as males. Based upon all subsequent sightings of colour-ringed birds of proven sex this method of sexing was eighty-two per cent correct.

The duller eyes of young females are caused by noticeable dark smoke-like streaks of pigment clearly visible in the yellowish iris. It follows that errors in sexing by this method are due to a small percentage of young males having dull eyes while in some young females the iris is less streaked, therefore brighter than in the majority.

Young of both sexes aged about six weeks often develop distinctive white feathering at the base of the bill similar to old females, and some also acquire white under tail-coverts. Crests are also perceptible in newly-fledged ducklings but are usually short, thin, and pin-like.

Young males sometimes show plumage characteristics at an early age; for example, a few have small whitish blobs on their flanks from about six weeks old. At eight to ten weeks of age juvenile males often have particularly dark heads and necks, slight crests, bright yellowish eyes and pale brown flanks, while their bulkier body size is obvious. In young females of similar age the head and neck are paler and the eyes noticeably duller compared with many young males. In the field these juveniles of both sexes are often difficult to separate from adult females because of the latter's wide variation in plumage, eye, and bill colour at this season.

Some young males can be recognised without being handled, even when nearly a year old. Out of thirty-four colour-ringed drakes twelve were in full plumage in March at about eight months old. The rest possessed one or more of the following features of immaturity: dark markings on the bill between the base and the black tip; dull yellow-gold eyes; a varying amount of dusky specks or bolder markings on the white flanks; dull body feathering; or some brown juvenile feathers retained in the black and white plumage. Among these remaining twenty-two one half were more retarded than the others. The tapered crest in almost all known males just under a year old was shorter than in older drakes.

Three colour-ringed males with small signs of immaturity in their plumage or bare parts were known to have paired when between nine and eleven months old. Their females were known to have nested.

Flying age

For assessing the age when tufted ducklings fly a close watch was kept on young of the earliest and latest-hatched broods annually. Where hatching dates of these ducklings were spaced at least fourteen days from younger fledglings an estimate of flying age was considered accurate.

Based on these field observations, therefore, I believe that fledging takes between forty-nine and seventy-seven days, with few birds flying well before fifty-six days (Table 39).

Although individuals of the same brood often require differing periods, in general young hatched earlier in the season need a shorter duration than late-hatched birds. For example, one duckling freshly hatched on June 11, 1965, had no primaries at forty-six days, could not become fully airborne at fifty-seven days, but was almost certainly capable of flight at sixty days. In contrast, a duckling of a late-hatched brood had no visible primaries on November 1, 1968, at the age of sixty-five or sixty-six days. This bird could not have flown well much before November 12, thus requiring a seventy-seven days fledging period.

The fledging period of Tufted Duck is recorded by Cramp and Simmons (1977) as forty-five to fifty days, whereas Bauer and Glutz (1969) give a longer span of fifty-nine to sixty-three days.

During the last few days of fledging wing exercising is sometimes observed on land near the water's edge. Individuals will stand almost on tip-toe as they beat the air rapidly with both wings for several minutes on end.

The first sustained flight of young birds is always exciting to watch. Many times I have seen groups of three or more juveniles with necks erect in the centre of the lake drifting slowly from Duck Island towards the Palace end. As they near the bridge all of them give the rapid chin-lifting pre-flight signal for two or three minutes. Suddenly they are up and away, climbing quickly to about forty feet and heading for North Bay. As they sweep right to pass over the Duck Island cottage and South Bay to complete a 'U' turn back towards the bridge there is a need to rise steeply to clear the tops of the tall trees. This turn tests the flying skill of all newly-fledged young who attempt it. On commencing the turn the strongest birds soar to a hundred feet or more, clearing the tree tops with grace and ease. The weakest ones, however, lack the ability to gain height and plummet into North Bay with a mighty splash. In a few days the laggards will be strong on the wing and soon leave for more distant waters. Sometimes within a day or two, and often within a week of making their first sustained flight, most juvenile tufted depart from St. James's. At this time there is no comparable build-up of juveniles in Hyde Park or Kensington Gardens, so it is probable that they fly to reservoirs lying between west and south-west. By the end of October few young of the year are left on St. James's lake.

DUCKLING MORTALITY

Rearing success

During the first twelve years of this study the number of broods reaching water was small enough for families to be closely observed throughout the rearing period. But in subsequent years an increasing number of broods prevented recognition of every family over a long period.

This method, therefore, was replaced by simpler ones throughout fledging.

First was the continued recording of dates on which newly-hatched broods reached water, together with the number of ducklings in each family. Second was the counting, and age assessments, of all attended and unattended young on the lake. Individual family recognition was restricted mainly to those of colour-ringed mothers or of females with easily observed characteristics.

Without watching particular families, the number of large young does not always reflect an accurate measure of brood survival. For example, a female with one or two ducklings aged three to four weeks may have another two young roaming the lake, independently, at the same time. Larger broods of well-grown young are equally suspect. A mother whose six to eight partially feathered young could be thought of as a fortunate low casualty family may have had a crèche of over eighteen downies a month or so before.

The rearing success of the St. James's Tufted Ducks was deduced through frequent counts of young, especially in the two weeks before they made their first flights.

Fledging success varies from year to year. For instance, in the cold and wet summer of 1954 not a single duckling survived, whereas four years later a record minimum average of five young per brood seen took to the wing. Comparison of survival rates for two eight-year periods (Table 34) shows that between 1954 and 1961 approximately four young per brood seen reached the flying stage, in contrast to two young per brood seen between 1962 and 1969. In all probability the greater success in the first period was largely due to three times as many females accompanying their young for longer time-spans than in the latter period. Although, on average, there were an extra fifteen pairs present annually in the second period, the output of flying ducklings only increased by four per year.

Over fourteen years, 1956 to 1969 inclusive (Table 36), fully-fledged young averaged between one and two per pair present in the breeding season and about one third of all young to reach water survived to the flying stage.

As the St. James's tufted population increased, so breeding success declined. Taking all thirty-two breeding seasons, approximately 1,600 young became airborne, averaging fifty-one annually, which works out at one duckling per pair present.

Details given to me by Mr. Andrew Heaton (*in litt.*) show that at the Sevenoaks Wildfowl Reserve breeding success was similar to St. James's. In round figures one duckling per pair present reached maturity in a population averaging seven pairs over thirteen seasons between 1966 and 1983. Unfortunately, information for the period 1974 to 1979 inclusive is not available.

In Finland, Hilden's (1964) figures indicate that over three years an average of a little over one duckling per pair attained the flying stage.

Not all females are successful in hatching a clutch of eggs. Between 1956 and 1969 an estimated sixty-six per cent of all pairs got a brood to water, though the true percentage was lower rather than higher. Since pair and brood counts formed a basis for calculations some allowance must be made for at least occasional loner females having broods, as well as the small number of females getting two broods to water in the same season.

By way of a small comparison seven females of unknown age, caught on their nests, and an eighth caught with tiny young, were colour-ringed (colour-ringed females Nos. 223 to 230 incl.). Six of them had broods soon after ringing while one of the remaining two was killed while still sitting on eggs. In the second season four out of seven of these same colour-ringed females were seen with young, and in the third season only three out of six had broods. Over three seasons sixty-one per cent of these known females got a brood to water. This proportion is not unduly low when compared with figures supplied to me for the Sevenoaks Wildfowl Reserve. There only forty-three per cent of pairs got a brood to water during thirteen breeding seasons.

Fatality in cold and wet weather

Duckling mortality is heaviest in the first three weeks after hatching, most casualties occurring within ten days of leaving the nest. Either directly or indirectly, prolonged cold or wet weather, and especially a combination of both, take the greatest toll. For example, the period July 14-24, 1968, was cool with a lot of rain, and in the seven days up to the 20th some sixty-five downies died. By July 29 of the same year twenty-nine broods had reached water, yet out of a potential of 230 ducklings only fifty-three were still alive.

The following year eighteen hours of rain, commencing on the morning of July 7, accounted for the lives of about forty-five ducklings. Three weeks later there was a further eighteen to twenty-four hours of rain from the night of July 28 during which another twenty-five downies succumbed.

Much of the 1978 brood season was characterised by cold or dull, cool weather with little rain, yet mortality was high. It was estimated that out of a minimum of 100 downies reaching water up to July 7 only fifteen were still alive three weeks later. These relatively dry conditions came to an end in the early hours of July 31 with persistent rain lasting for at least twelve hours. Of a population of just over 100 small ducklings alive between July 28 and 30 there were about seventy still flourishing on August 1.

I do not know how regularly tufted mothers with young aged two or three weeks seek cover in torrential rain. However, during a severe hailstorm one

Male in full plumage in May (note more extensive black bill tip than usual)

Male in post-nuptial moult

Male flightless during post-nuptial moult

Male commencing post-nuptial moult
(note brown neck-ring and dull bill)

Male in post-nuptial moult

Male in eclipse plumage

Female in summer

Female in worn summer plumage (milk chocolate type)

Female flightless during post-nuptial moult

Young male aged 8 to 10 weeks

Young female aged about 7 weeks

Small downy dozing

Female with a prominent crest in winter

A creamy-buff variant female

Female recovering from wing moult
(note 'spotted dog' underparts)

Male 'Lesser Scaup type' hybrid

Hybrid male probably of Tufted Duck × Lesser Scaup parentage

Male 'Scaup type' hybrid of the crested variety

summer, two out of three females with small downies remained on open water. The third parent quickly led her brood of fifteen ashore to the shelter of bushes.

Disease

Disease as a major cause of duckling mortality was only discovered once in thirty years in St. James's Park.

Up to 1968 the lake water was relatively clear in summer. During the next decade, however, it looked a pea-soup colour in most years due to an abundance of microscopic algae. In 1969 the water turned bluish-green and between late June and mid-November an unprecedented number of waterfowl died from disease, some of them from botulism (*vide* Keymer *et al.*, 1972).

As the death toll mounted a rescue operation was necessary if any of the season's tufted ducklings were to be saved. Within a week permission was obtained to catch as many of the surviving young as possible and transfer them to Hyde Park and Kensington Gardens where the clear water was unaffected. Through the efforts of Arthur May and helpers, forty non-flying young were caught between August 22 and 30, thirty-nine of them being released immediately by me on the Serpentine. A single bird was also taken there at a later date. By September 2 only eight surviving tufted young were left in St. James's, most of them fully-fledged birds. At least twenty-one species were affected during the outbreak and deaths of waterfowl totalled over 400, approximately forty per cent of the estimated 1,000-plus ducks and geese in the Park that summer. Tufted made up about sixteen per cent of the total known mortality, the majority being young of the year over three weeks old. Approximately fifty of these large youngsters perished in the period August 6 to September 17.

A much smaller outbreak of botulism and some other disease occurred in St. James's two years later. Only the 1969 epidemic resulted in a temporary setback to the tufted breeding population, the numbers of which were back to normal in the nesting season of 1971 and increasing again by 1972. As previously, the Serpentine, Long Water, and the Round Pond were unaffected.

About seven miles away at the Royal Botanic Gardens at Kew many waterfowl died in mysterious circumstances in the late summer of 1970 (Baker, 1972). The symptoms described suggested that some at least may have died from botulism. Unfortunately, Tufted Ducks suffered heavy losses, their numbers amounting to thirty adults and fifty young out of the 215 waterfowl casualties. As in St. James's there was a much smaller recurrence of the disease in the first eight months of 1971, this time with proven botulism victims. Deaths among Kew's water birds were fewer than in 1970 but ten adult Tufted Ducks were among the twenty-nine known casualties.

In the hot summer of 1983 the Regent's Park duck population was decimated by disease on a scale far greater than occurred in St. James's fourteen years earlier. Tufted Duck casualties were particularly heavy in relation to the numbers present that breeding season. The full details of this epidemic have yet to be made public. Fortunately there were fewer casualties when disease struck waterfowl on the Serpentine and Long Water the following summer.

Drowning

The cold and wet summer of 1954 was outstanding for the unprecedented amount of Blanket weed *(Rhizoclonium hieroglyphicum)* in the lake. Pentelow (1965) records that a little over 100 ducklings, mostly young tufted, died that season through being trapped in this filamentous algae while diving. This supposed cause of so many deaths was, according to my enquiries at the time, based exclusively on the finding of dead ducklings of several species and of unspecified ages among the vegetation after it was raked from the lake. Many of the retrieved corpses must have been in the water for several weeks before weed-clearance led to their removal. In view of this one may question why so many young should have perished *solely* through becoming entangled in plant growth in *the coldest and wettest brood season in thirty-two years*. Furthermore, few tiny tufted ducklings were seen on the lake that summer, pointing to most having succumbed within forty-eight hours of reaching water.

There is no mention of drowning as a cause of this heavy mortality among the St. James's Tufted Ducks in the *Bird Life in The Royal Parks* report for 1953-54. So, in the absence of a first-hand account of the death struggles of at least one or two ducklings, the record cannot be regarded as satisfactory. No casualties of this nature were reported to me in subsequent years.

Accidental deaths

Carelessness on the part of one of the Park's staff could have led to many casualties but for the Bird Keeper's vigilance. Almost every year Arthur May rescued tiny downies, including whole broods at times, which floated over the former Duck Island causeway overflow because the hinged protective wire screen had been left up. Fortunately the ducklings landed at the bottom of a large recessed drain with enough room for them to cluster away from the cascading water until rescued. In six years I knew of thirty-three tufted and two Pochard downies saved out of thirty-seven. Only two little tufted died, either from exposure or drowning.

No duckling over seven to ten days old was ever found in this drain in a period of twenty years, suggesting that the older a downy gets the wiser it becomes.

Apart from already mentioned casualties caused by tufted mothers leading young along some of Westminster's highways, there were a few other accidental deaths. Occasionally small downies were caught up in wire netting, while a Pochard brood also died through failing to leave an unusually deep nest cavity.

It was uncertain whether twelve newly-hatched tufted found dead in nests died from accidents or exposure.

Killers and predators

Predation of tufted ducklings never reached alarming proportions in St. James's throughout this study. Besides man, two species of mammal and ten species of birds make up a list of thirteen killers of young Tufted Ducks. Of these, however, only the Herring Gull can be regarded as the most regular predator over the last two decades.

This Park has for long been regarded as a sanctuary for all land and water birds alike. To the extreme indignation of many regular visitors certain feathered predators enjoy a tolerance which would never be extended to them on many a county nature reserve.

Had the lake been primarily a duck refuge it is unthinkable that Herring Gulls could have been free to nest for so long and that Magpies could establish their headquarters and flaunt themselves on both waterfowl breeding islands. At the present time the continued prosperity of waterfowl and land birds provides no special grounds for requesting urgent punitive measures against avian predators. Nevertheless the present success of wild birds is no cause for complacency. A watch on all predators must continue.

Over the past half-century the Royal Parks Division has, for a variety of carefully considered reasons, applied population controls on several species such as Canada Geese, Mallard, Coot and London Pigeons, but never carried them to the point of extirpation except in the case of the unfortunate introduced cormorants. Sometimes a cob Mute Swan causes problems through venting its territorial 'anger' on the pelicans. Several such incidents necessitated a swan's immediate trapping, temporary pinioning, and removal to another water so that the lives of the pelicans were not put at further risk.

The enemies of young Tufted Ducks are now discussed in detail so that interested observers may know something of their background and numbers when monitoring duckling mortality in the years ahead.

Man was never a grave threat to the young of either Tufted Ducks or other waterfowl in St. James's throughout this study.

The occasional brutal acts against water birds were usually committed when few people were about. Several times young tufted were stoned to death at point blank range while others were caught and taken away from the Park. One particularly callous act was the forcing of a quarter-of-an-inch thick hard rubber washer over the head of a downy tufted. Luckily a business colleague caught the duckling and with scissors borrowed from a visitor cut and removed the torturous band.

Because they are controlled Brown Rats (*Rattus norvegicus*) seldom pose a great danger to young waterfowl in the breeding season. Along with domestic cats they were considered to be the main predators of small ducklings in the late 1940s.

On several occasions I saw rats foraging close to small tufted as they dozed ashore, but never were these rodents seen attacking or seizing downies. It is possible that over-population, leading to food shortages, motivates rats to kill ducklings on any scale. After many years' experience of the small islands of the Medway estuary and the Swale channel, where Black-headed Gulls, Common Terns and these rodents sometimes share the same breeding habitat, I knew of but one season when rats killed many adult and young Common Terns. Rather surprisingly a good proportion of the sea-bird corpses were not even partially eaten, suggesting that aggressiveness rather than hunger induced the carnage.

From time to time stray domestic cats take up residence in the Park and frequent Duck Island. They have been known to prey on ducklings and, of necessity, are soon trapped and handed over to the R.S.P.C.A.

While pelicans are unlikely predators of young waterfowl in a natural environment wild cormorants have occasionally been recorded taking waterfowl, Moorhen, and ducklings of Shelduck (*vide* Cramp and Simmons, 1977). After a lapse of many years the tradition of keeping cormorants in the Park was revived in 1888 but introductions often proved unsuccessful so there has been lack of continuity. Following better luck in 1923 they were thriving by 1936, when there were some thirteen birds and three nests. Soon afterwards the whole population was eliminated by the authorities for eating ducklings (Sims, 1974). Several attempts were again made to keep cormorants after the Second World War, but these efforts, too, met with failure, including a further suppression about the year 1950 (*Bird Life in The Royal Parks* report 1965-1966). Once again they were extirpated for devouring ducklings.

After 1964 reintroduction was successful for approximately seventeen years. Numbers, including one or two wild ones on occasions, varied between four and eight. From 1981 onwards the population dwindled, only one pinioned cormorant surviving by the summer of 1983. This last bird had disappeared by the spring of 1984.

For at least one-and-a-half decades I received no reports of this species preying on ducklings. In July 1981, however, two observers independently noted their misdeeds. Then on August 4 I watched a cormorant swimming towards a female Tufted Duck with four small young. It dived, surfaced near the brood, and swallowed one downy. Within seconds the mother's defence behaviour attracted a second tufted female. This parent left her three partially-feathered ducklings ashore sixty feet away to join in attacking the predator. In less than five minutes the mêlée was over, the victorious cormorant having caught and swallowed all four small ducklings plus one of the brood of three. Sadly, the latter duckling had left the security of its shoreline resting spot to join its plucky mother. Neither the repeated dives of the hunted, nor the constant attacks by the two brood females, deflected the hunter from its goal.

Two days later another downy tufted was caught and swallowed by the same cormorant.

At the beginning of this century the Park authorities of the time appear not to have been averse to the introduction of birds with predatory habits.

In 1903 they welcomed four pelicans which had been banished from Kew Gardens for eating ducklings. This was about the time when the novel idea of having ornamental Herring Gulls came to fruition.

Since those days the former species seems to have broadened its diet from fish to feather on a number of occasions. In 1937 a pelican recently introduced to the Park was seen devouring young Tufted Ducks.

For close on three decades the pelicans had a clean record, so far as personal observations went, until 1981. Although I could not fault pelican behaviour one has to remember that these waterfowl attract constant attention and are, almost certainly, the Park's best-watched birds. In particular, the daily fish-feeding ritual by the Bird Keeper draws pelican admirers to the entrance to Duck Island at the appointed hour. While occasional lapses in the behaviour of other water birds may escape detection the misdemeanours of this species are seldom overlooked by visitors or by their custodian.

To Jack Norley I am grateful for some up-to-date information concerning these birds. First, he informs me (*in litt.*) that according to Arthur May it was not uncommon for a pelican to take ducklings, though this predatory behaviour was never publicised. Second, Jack Norley mentions that in the summer of 1980 the three remaining pelicans were seen attacking and eating ducklings and a London Pigeon. For their sins they were detained in a Duck Island pond enclosure for a short period and were released back to the lake in November of the same year. Within a week of release one of the pelicans was reported to have swallowed a Tufted Duck.

From then until the summer of 1981 two of the pelicans became the lake's best known predators. There were many reports of London Pigeons and ducklings forming a regular part of their diet.

Whereas for over twenty years brood female tufted never showed undue alarm, even when as many as seven pelicans swam near them, they reacted violently from early July of that year. On one occasion nine brood female tufted, with twenty-eight small young in all, fled in panic when the two villainous pelicans appeared at the Palace end feeding point and began hunting them. A week later a mother and her brood had to flee overland when about to be be cornered by the same two unsavoury characters.

Brood females were equally at risk as their ducklings and, through self preservation, none was able to put up more than a half-hearted defence of its young.

Pigeon swallowing incidents were frequent. On July 24 I saw both pelicans with London Pigeons in their pouches. After the prey had been tossed in the pouch many times so that the dead victim's head faced the predator's throat it took nearly half-an-hour to travel from the pouch to the base of the neck, aided by a remarkable continuous rippling effect presumably by the neck muscles. Once a pelican seized a House Sparrow which was fortunate to escape minus a few back feathers as it fed near the water's edge.

Eventually all three pelicans were transferred elsewhere and replaced by others in the spring of 1982. By the summer of 1984 five substitutes had acquired bad reputations. They, too, disgraced themselves by swallowing adult and downy tufted besides pigeons.

On three occasions I saw adult Mallard kill downy tufted and was told of several other instances. These ducks have been known to try and feed off dead birds, including tufted ducklings, and in two of the above-mentioned killings eating attempts followed (Gillham, 1961).

Larger species of duck may account for a number of duckling casualties. For example, in Sussex I watched a pinioned male Goosander seize and kill a week-old tufted downy which swam in front of it, while my son Barry and Mrs. Stephanie Swan observed a brood female Barrow's Goldeneye kill a two- to three-weeks-old tufted downy in Iceland.

Mute Swans and Canada Geese are known to have killed tufted ducklings on a few occasions in St. James's. Aggressive pursuits of these downies by Greylag Geese, Ruddy Shelduck, and several other species, strongly suggest that in these incidents, too, killing might have resulted from capture.

A rare visitor, a female Sparrowhawk, was a resident in and around the Park for close on seven months during 1967. In the breeding season it was seen several times by Arthur May on fence posts of one of his occupied duckling rearing pens on Duck Island where I examined the corpse of this bird shortly after its death in July. Since ducklings with or without a parent are so frequently ashore on the island it is possible that this hawk preyed on them.

I never saw Moorhens harm downies of any water bird, though Coots frequently attacked ducklings viciously. Twice newly-hatched tufted were killed by the latter species.

Jack Norley refers to the Coot's aggressiveness to other ducks and ducklings as one of the reasons why the Department of the Environment controlled Coot numbers for many years.

Herring Gulls must surely rank as the most extraordinary pinioned ornamental water birds kept in the Park this century. In the early 1900s there was a thriving colony of several nesting pairs.

Since 1964 a pair of wild Herring Gulls has nested regularly or attempted to do so. Happily, these birds have preyed neither too heavily nor successfully on ducklings annually. In one or two years, however, they have shown greater predatory capability than in others by taking, over varying periods, almost all of the small unattended tufted downies. This behaviour demonstrates the importance of the protective function of a mother or foster-mother for the survival of small ducklings. Over the past twenty breeding seasons, Herring Gulls have eaten more tufted ducklings than any other predator.

Throughout the 1970s occasional pairs of Herring Gull also frequented tall buildings bordering the Park. Their behaviour throughout the breeding season strongly suggested nesting from time to time. In 1983 and 1984 single pairs each reared two young on different buildings in the vicinity of Horse Guards Parade. A second pair nested unsuccessfully in the same area in the latter year. Unless nests are dealt with speedily it may not be long before these gulls become a nuisance to London property owners as they already are in a number of seaside resorts.

Herring Gulls are opportunists in St. James's and not all of them are predators on young waterfowl. At the end of July, when the breeding pair ceased to be strongly territorial, as many as seven associated together on the lawns adjoining South Bay. It was a relief to find that these powerful gulls preferred competing for food thrown by the public rather than pursuing ducklings. Throughout their stay young Tufted Ducks suffered no abnormal losses.

Two of these predators often attended the Bird Keeper's official pelican and cormorant feeding sessions, where they usually scrounged a meal. Had these gulls not taken advantage of scraps and fish intended for other birds they might have devoted more time to hunting ducklings.

Although a pair of Lesser Black-backed Gulls sometimes remain for part of the breeding season it is the voracious habits of one or two passing migrants between July and September that cause greater concern. Whereas I have not seen Herring Gulls seizing ducklings much over two to three weeks old in the Park, lesser black-backs often kill considerably larger tufted youngsters. Luckily, not all lesser black-backs have a palate for ducklings.

Carrion Crows were near the bottom of the list of predators reported to me for taking tufted downies. For about two decades only one pair nested in the Park, often unsuccessfully. Recently, in spite of territorial battles, two pairs have managed to tolerate each other. Despite close observation of crows on the ground, on the infrequent occasions that they were seen near attended and unattended young, none was ever seen to seize ducklings.

Magpies are a far greater menace than the previous species. In the past decade I have seen them kill Starlings, Blackbirds and downy tufted. In 1979 I watched a pair worrying a female tufted with tiny young resting ashore. As the brood female's attention was divided between the two, one of these villains was able to seize and eat two of her downies without difficulty. The Magpie's habit of foraging on the ground on both islands during the breeding season points to this species becoming a serious predator of ducklings. If population control measures can be applied to Coots, which many observers regard as acceptable risks, there is a much stronger case for trapping and deporting at least the Duck Island Magpies.

The fish in the lake today are mainly introduced stock and their descendants. I know of no reports of fish preying on ducklings; and it is significant that, for many decades, official policy was to exclude predatory Pike (*Esox lucius*).

Life expectancy

For a minority of ducklings the gloomy prospects they face as small downies recede as they take to the wing.

From calculations based more on live birds than on dead ones the average minimum life span of 132 colour-ringed tufted was approximately two-and-a-half years. Taking first the 115 young of the year caught and released in the period September 1962 to September 1969, the average age works out at twenty-five months. The second group of seventeen hand-reared young, released on attaining flight between 1965 and 1969, averaged thirty-three months of life.

Thirteen birds found dead are not representative of all which died because none was over three-and-a-quarter years old whereas thirty-one were still alive at ages ranging from three-and-three-quarters to ten-and-a-half years old. Though dead colour-ringed birds ceased to be reported to me after early August, 1971, a watch for live ones continued for another eight years.

Ten per cent of the 132 were never seen again after release. It is unlikely that all died soon after ringing because this group must have included those with the strongest pioneering drive. Indeed, one of the 115 was not observed on the St. James's group of waters in the first six-and-a-half years following banding, thus confirming the existence of a pioneering element among Park-reared tufted.

Recent marking with British Trust for Ornithology numbered rings, carried out by Stephen and Tim Christmas, and Roy Sanderson, throws further light on the life expectancy of this species (*cf.* Chapter 4). The minimum age of forty-four dead and fifty-five live birds averages thirty-seven months. The oldest bird was a female trapped on her nest in St. James's on July 3, 1983, after having been ringed at Abberton, Essex, on April 29, 1972.

Live birds constituted sixty-four per cent of the 231 sightings, re-traps, and recoveries discussed above. There can be little doubt that Tufted Ducks frequenting the St. James's group of waters live for an average of approximately three years.

Cramp and Simmons (1977) mention a life expectancy of one point seven years on the authority of Boyd. They also refer to a British Trust for Ornithology record of fourteen-and-a-half years for the oldest ringed tufted.

The longevity of these ducks inhabiting Inner London must at least be partly due to the capital's mainly mild winters these past two decades, to a plentiful food supply, and to a safe refuge.

CHAPTER 8
THE POST-BREEDING SEASON

Early in June, about the time of the Trooping of the Colour ceremony on Horse Guards Parade, the life of the Tufted Duck undergoes a major change. Along the shorelines of the islands friction begins to wane as males desert their incubating mates, forsake their individual waiting spots and assemble once again off the western end of Duck Island. Here, on open water, they linger for several weeks, moving regularly to the public feeding points or resting ashore in small groups in the vicinity. For drakes the beginning of summer heralds not only a transformation of plumage but a period of migration as well.

Plumage and flightless period of adult drakes

The onset of the post-breeding moult of a few males starts in the nesting season, coinciding with the time when the earlier nesting females commence to lay. By the middle of May the bills of some drakes are already duller as the white area on the distal half of the bill either disappears or diminishes to a narrow palish line behind the nail. Similar changes in bill colour, in this month, have been recorded for the male Ring-necked Duck (Mendall, 1958). During the third week irregularly-shaped dusky spots and patches appear on the normally 'well-laundered' white side panels of a few drakes and by the end of May one also sees a bird with a brownish ring at the base of its neck.

Throughout June an increasing number of males acquire, in varying degrees, darkening side panels, duller plumage, and duskier bills. For these tufted, the post-breeding moult is in full swing and most soon migrate to another water for their once yearly flightless period. With the completion of this wing moult drakes assume a new plumage called the eclipse. Many males are in the eclipse for less than two months, after which they start the pre-nuptial moult into breeding plumage. For the majority, however, full nuptial dress is not attained until the middle of December. Thus drakes spend about four out of the six months between early June and early December in transition from one plumage to another. Pochard drakes are in eclipse plumage for a shorter period than male tufted.

Usually the earliest moulting tufted drakes shed their flight feathers in the first week of July and the latest ones by the third week of September, but some seventy-seven per cent begin their flightless period between mid-July and mid-August (Table 40, Figure 3). Throughout this study only one male was observed in a flightless condition in June (see footnote to Table 40). However, in other European regions some adult males commence their wing moult in the latter half of June (*cf.* Cramp and Simmons, 1977). Among the smaller and earlier nesting population of Pochard in St. James's I observed twenty-three flightless adult males in June, from the 18th onwards. The peak of the flightless period of male Tufted Duck is in the middle two weeks of August, fourteen days later than in the case of drake Pochard (Figure 4).

Drake Tufted Duck discard their flight feathers simultaneously and lose their tail feathers at the same time or a few days afterwards. But they are seldom in the tidy eclipse plumage when this moult process begins. Commonly, newly-flightless males are dull, ragged, almost 'moth-eaten' looking birds, some of which closely resemble females. Hochbaum (1944) found that in several species of North American diving duck the tail was shed first, followed simultaneously by all the flight feathers, the latter occurring when most or all of the eclipse was assumed. Among drake tufted on the St. James's group of waters there is a wide variation in plumage at the time of the wing moult. Some males completely lose the crest while others retain, temporarily, an almost complete tuft or just two or three long head-plumes. The head and upperparts are, in varying degrees, browner than earlier on. The side panels become patchy, turning considerably darker than in the subsequent eclipse. Plumage, generally, is duller, lacking much of the purple gloss and green sheen, especially on the head. Some birds develop a distinctive brownish neck-ring close to the body and white on the under tail-coverts. Slatey-black markings spread over the upper mandible and the white area behind the nail either disappears or is greatly reduced.

A few males have their side panels so heavily splashed with black or blackish-brown that at a distance on water they appear uniformly sooty. In July some of the latest paired males are in this dark plumage while others still have predominantly white flanks and much of their breeding dress. Only twice were single moulting drakes seen with female type patches of dull whitish feathering either side of the base of the bill. This feature, however, is much more common among young males when between about six and thirteen weeks old. In spite of a few males retaining some white on the flanks when flightless, none was seen in its smart black and white plumage during the wing moult. On the other hand several newly-flightless adult male Pochard were observed in practically all of their pre-moult splendour. Hochbaum writes of a prolonged and gradual post-breeding moult for some diving ducks but mentions exceptions like an eight-year-old

FIG. 3   TIME-SPAN OF THE COMMENCEMENT OF THE FLIGHTLESS PERIOD OF ADULT TUFTED DUCK ON THE ST JAMES'S GROUP OF WATERS (EXCLUDING BUCKINGHAM PALACE LAKE)

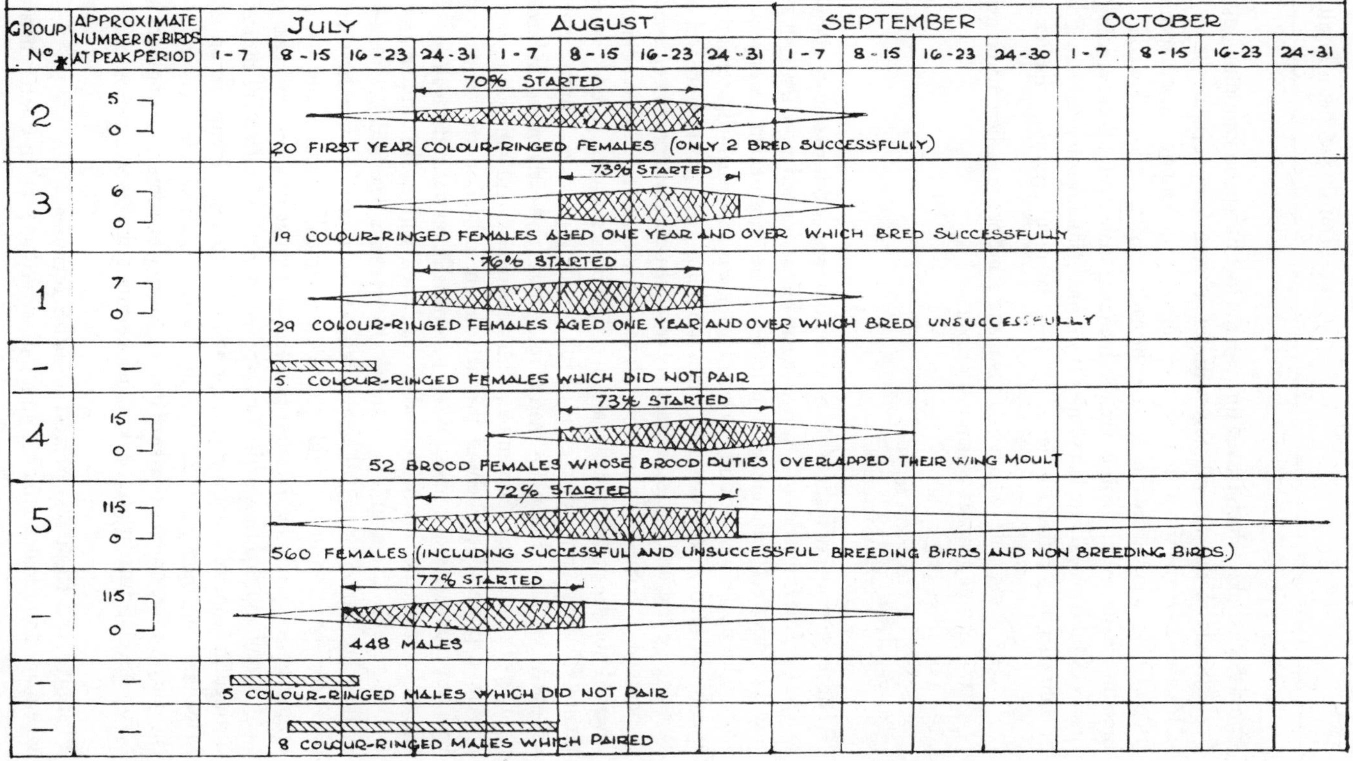

* REFER TO TABLE 41

Canvasback drake, which passed through the flightless period, moulting directly from the old to the new plumage without an intervening eclipse.

He also gives the moult sequence of some North American duck species as follows. First to moult are the mates of the earliest paired males followed by non-breeding males. After them come the breeding males, then non-breeding and unsuccessful females. The last to moult are successful breeding females. For the St. James's group tufted I believe that a similar moult sequence applies:—

(1) Some males which fail to pair and some of the earliest mated drakes.
(2) Some females which fail to pair.
(3) Breeding males.
(4) Unsuccessful females.
(5) Successful females.

The replacement of flight feathers takes from twenty-one to twenty-eight days and by the time the male is full-winged again he has donned most, if not all, of his neat but drab eclipse plumage. No longer is he 'moth-eaten' in appearance. Instead his upperparts are dull black and his side panels usually lighter and more evenly coloured grey-brown than when moulting. The crest is short and often bushy at the end, and males generally are of more uniform appearance, especially in September. Some birds have no tuft at all while others possess rudimentary ones. Although a proportion of males in eclipse possess short tapered crests none retains the long limp tuft typical of full breeding plumage. Throughout the eclipse drakes have duller bills than in mid-winter and early spring. Indeed, the sighting of a bird, late in September, with a cleaner bill and with white markings appearing prominently behind the nail, is an indication that transition to breeding plumage is in progress. While superficially, on water, the male in eclipse resembles a female, his lighter sides, combined with darker upperparts, are usually reliable distinguishing features. However, a few males, with evenly marked but darker brownish side panels, are so much like females that at a distance separation in the field is extremely difficult. Occasionally a male in eclipse causes a sex identification problem at a range of about ten feet.

Moulting and flightless male Ring-necked Ducks and tufted are difficult to distinguish from one another except at close quarters. Identification is not helped through the former shedding their semi-crested head feathers and losing the narrow white line at the base of the bill. Moreover, some male ring-necks and Scaup develop pale brown neck-rings like tufted drakes when moulting.

Plumage and flightless period of adult females

Like many adult males, females often look ragged and 'moth-eaten' when they discard their flight feathers. Unlike drakes, few have a distinctive crest to moult, for most shed this adornment by the onset of the laying season. As the wing moult approaches females, too, are in differing stages of plumage which fall broadly into two types – light and dark-brown birds. The less common light-coloured birds are characterised by their paler warm brown upperparts liberally marked all over with distinctive light edges to the feathers, giving a scaly or barred appearance. The contrast between these two kinds of plumage is as distinct as the difference in tone between milk and plain chocolate.

Both types commonly develop small round or lozenge-shaped white or whitish patches either side of the base of the upper mandible or a continuous frontal patch of varying size sometimes encircling the base of the bill. Writers who emphasise that female tufted never have a blaze comparable with that of a female Scaup usually omit to state that the period when many female Tufted Duck develop this white on the face overlaps the time when female Scaup have smaller and less distinctive 'masks'. According to Dementiev and Gladkov (1952) female Scaup in transition may lose both the white on the forehead and on the chin. I have seen old female Scaup, as late as the end of January, with a much smaller white face patch than a female tufted in the vicinity.

The duration of the flightless period in females is three to four weeks, the same as for males; and, similarly, the wing feathers are moulted simultaneously, often together with or just before the tail. From June onwards the bills of adult females become almost wholly dark as the small slate-blue area behind the nail fades to an obscure line. With the approach of, or during, the flightless period some females develop white on the under tail-coverts.

The time-span of the wing moult in adult females begins in the second week of July, about a week later than in adult males, but because of nesting and brood duties extends over a much longer period. The latter start their flightless period within the space of about ten weeks compared with fifteen weeks for females (Table 40, Figures 3 & 4). Post-breeding females mingle with drakes, sometimes two or three of them keeping company. Once two females associated closely with a brood female. From their persistent manoeuvring around this mother, together with her reciprocal behaviour, and the strangers' complete lack of interest in the young, it seemed that all three females were intent on forming a group of adults.

The commencement of the wing moult of most females who attend broods for several weeks is not only delayed but is compressed into a shorter time-span (Figure 3). Taking August 7 as the date after which most mothers begin their flightless period, only about ten per cent of brood females are flightless before this deadline compared with thirty-five to forty-five per cent of known unsuccessful females (Table 41). Tufted mothers whose wing moult overlaps

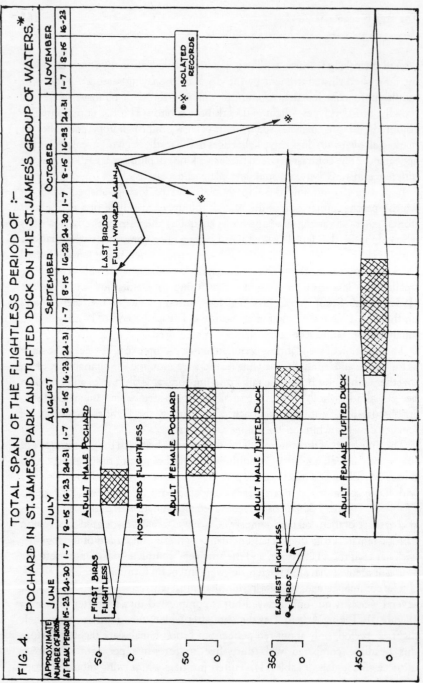

FIG. 4.   TOTAL SPAN OF THE FLIGHTLESS PERIOD OF :—
POCHARD IN ST. JAMES'S PARK AND TUFTED DUCK ON THE ST. JAMES'S GROUP OF WATERS.*

* EXCLUDING BUCKINGHAM PALACE LAKE

their brood duties stay with their young for between one and twenty-five days after dropping their flight feathers. The average extent of this overlap is about thirteen days, the duration being the same both for females of broods hatched early and those of broods hatched late in the breeding season (Appendices 6 & 8).

Despite a handicap, many flightless mothers protect their young, though defensive action is limited to the vicinity of the family. Likewise, an occasional Mallard parent in wing moult will defend her brood.

The prolonged peak period of flightless female tufted is between August 19 and September 19, while most female Pochard are flightless between July 23 and August 15 (Figure 4). As the latest female tufted are not fully airborne again until the third week of November the wing moult of this sex is spread over close on five months (Figure 4). The last of all flightless females observed was an unpinioned Scaup x Tufted Duck hybrid. She was still in worn summer plumage when shedding her flight feathers on November 9 and was unable to fly before December 5.

In mid-summer and early autumn female Tufted Ducks may be seen with underparts heavily blotched with brown often resembling the pattern of a spotted dog. Out of 1,700 field sketches of breast and belly patterns of females throughout the year, all seventy-five depicting blotchy underparts relate to the period June – October inclusive. Seventy of the latter are split almost equally between August and September. Since these blotchy-bellied birds tend to replace those seen with the darkest evenly marked underparts between May and July they are assumed to be females in transition from summer to winter plumage.

However, the late Drs. J. M. and J. G. Harrison (1960 A & B; 1961) record that a female caught and ringed on August 13, 1959, had a predominantly white belly. Three weeks later this same female was found to have much more dark brown flecking on her underparts. In their third paper these authors also have a photograph of a variant first winter female with a closely barred lower breast and belly reminiscent of some adult females in summer. None of my first winter colour-ringed females was ever seen with so much barring below. Clearly there is a need for more observations on females of known ages to establish the normal patterns of their underparts throughout the year.

In September, with the completion of the wing moult, females look neat in their new plumage. For the first time since late April many have good stand-off crests which are broad at the base, thick, but not as long as those of the short-crested first year males in spring. A few females at this time have a clean white 'mask', sometimes comparable with that of the female Scaup, and prominent white under tail-coverts, besides a striking crest. Others possess only one or two of these three features.

Moult movements of adult drakes and their moult areas on the St. James's group of waters

In the last week of May and the beginning of June drakes from other breeding areas move into the Park, where they remain for less than a month. Because numbers vary from year to year this passage is sometimes masked by the departure of a similar quantity of the St. James's population. Based on the last sightings of colour-ringed males it would seem that the majority of drakes present in the Park in the nesting season depart in June (Table 43).

Throughout July the male population dwindles rapidly, culminating in only a handful of birds remaining at the end of the month or in the first few days of August. For example, in 1975 there were 143 on June 4; 104 on June 20; fifty-five on July 4; and six on July 25. In 1981, through an influx on May 28 or 29, there were 123 drakes on the latter date; 118 on June 23; 103 on July 1; seventeen on July 28; and six on August 4.

Much diurnal movement at this time of year is to or from the direction of Hyde Park. After the middle of June, when courting parties have disbanded, those seen leaving or arriving in St. James's are usually loners or two or three birds together.

Corresponding with the fall in numbers in St. James's Park (*cf.* Table 43) there is a build-up on the two other largest lakes of the group. From early July onwards there are more on the Serpentine and Long Water than can be accounted for by the few nesting pairs, while the Round Pond becomes an even more favoured area until the third week of that month. Between 1961 and 1969, on average about eighty-eight per cent of all flightless adult males recorded were to be found on these two water areas (Table 42).

One must not assume that the majority of the St. James's Park breeding season population moult on the St. James's group of waters. In four of the nine years between 1961 and 1969 this was not the case since the aggregate of flightless drakes on the three moulting waters was much lower than the male nesting season population of St. James's Park. Even the few drakes which remain to moult in the Park are not necessarily the residue of breeding season birds. For example, one of them, colour-ringed male No. 88, spent his first breeding season and first wing moult in the Park but in the next four years was present only from mid-summer until spring. Nevertheless, each year this male returned to St. James's to moult and his approximate arrival and flightless period dates are as follows:—

Year	Arrival date on St. James's Lake	Date of commencement of flightless period on St. James's lake
1964	July 5	August 10
1965	August 6	August 11
1966	August 6	August 11
1967	July 24	July 29

Another colour-ringed male (No. 97) spent his first breeding season in St. James's Park and his first flightless period on the Serpentine and Long Water. For the next four years he was absent from the Park in the breeding season but in three of those years was seen in a flightless state on the Serpentine and Long Water.

Moult movements of adult females and their moult areas on the St. James's group of waters

Among several species of diving duck many females are known to moult on or near their breeding grounds. I have come across flightless female tufted on several small breeding waters, including the tiny Eagle Pond on Clapham Common near London. Unsuccessful breeding females who have reached the end of their reproductive cycle join the moult gatherings of drakes. In 1961 and 1963 counts showed a marked influx of females to the St. James's group moult areas from the end of July.

Although relatively more females than males remain in St. James's Park to complete their wing moult the majority depart, the first to go being females not seen with broods (Table 43). Coinciding with this fall in numbers increases occur, more particularly on the Serpentine and Long Water than on the Round Pond. Out of a total of 458 flightless females recorded on the three main lakes of the St. James's group of waters between 1961 and 1969 one-third completed their wing moult in St. James's Park and two-thirds on the other two water areas. Taking both sexes together, sixty-one per cent of adults favoured the extensive continuous stretch of the Serpentine and Long Water (Table 42).

Colour-ringing indicates that only a proportion of adults which nest in St. James's moult their flight feathers on the St. James's group of waters. Another trend is that a percentage of adults reared in St. James's Park, but which are not present in subsequent breeding seasons, come to these moult areas for their flightless period. On both counts a higher percentage of females than males moult on the St. James's group of waters.

Behaviour of moulting adults

Considering the large number of people in boats using the greater part of the

Serpentine and, until a decade ago, Long Water flightless tufted have come to terms with man's activities during their annual period of maximum vulnerability. They show no marked fear of people or craft. Not once did I see them display alarm like wilder birds, which make frequent dives, then surface with only the eyes and top of the head above water.

Moulting birds are not averse to dozing in the open well away from the shore but have equally strong preferences for idling on water close to, or under, the trees overhanging the south bank of Long Water and sitting ashore beneath trees on the island on the north side of the Serpentine. Both resting areas are conveniently close to the main points where the public come regularly to feed the waterfowl. This crucial factor enabled me to feed moulting birds close in to check their legs for colour ring combinations. Since the Round Pond is devoid of cover tufted have no shelter there throughout the flightless period.

Flightless Tufted Duck do not form into a compact flock but tend to disperse over the favoured parts of the moulting lakes. On open water they are noticeably well spaced and when ashore maintain a minimum average individual distance of about three feet.

Other moulting waters in: the London Area, the Home Counties, and Holland

The departure of drakes from Finsbury Park follows a pattern comparable with St. James's. Based on limited counts made in five out of ten recent years the average number recorded there between June 4 and July 6 was forty-one, falling to an average of four between July 30 and August 17. Parallel movements have been noted among several small populations, both in the Home Counties and further afield. This annual migration of males must be widespread, for large moulting concentrations are known to occur within twenty miles of London. It is only since the middle sixties, however, that they have received regular attention and publicity. For many years interest was centred chiefly on winter numbers, yet nearly fifty years ago Glegg (1935) recorded 100 on Staines Reservoir on July 19, 1930, with a rapid increase to 600 or 700 by the end of September. He also observed similar assemblies in 1931. On August 8, 1936, I found 200, along with a comparable number of Pochard, on the same reservoir.

The Birds of the London Area has little to say about post-breeding gatherings except for a passing reference that "the increase in numbers after the breeding season may be apparent as early as July." Looking through *London Bird Reports* from 1946 onwards, one is able to build up an interesting picture of moulting Tufted Duck mainly on ten large reservoirs or groups of reservoirs close to the capital. In the *London Bird Report* for 1968 it is stated that Queen Elizabeth II and

Walton reservoirs "are still popular for moulting flocks", but in subsequent reports there is no clear indication that other reservoirs were used annually by moulting birds. From some of the published figures it is obvious that numbers fluctuate markedly from one year to another, suggesting that the highest aggregations at the peak of the male's wing moult period may be linked with an abundance or otherwise of food. However, as mentioned in an earlier chapter, summer sailing is considered to have reduced the numbers of tufted on one moulting water.

It seems that moulting flocks of Tufted Duck totalling from about 1,000 in the late 1950s to 4,000 in the middle 1970s have occurred regularly on these reservoirs for at least the past twenty-five years. Even the lower figure is equivalent to a sizeable proportion of the whole British breeding season population at that time. Whether one takes the Tufted Duck breeding community of Britain as totalling 1,500 to 2,000 pairs by about 1970 (Yarker and Atkinson-Willes, 1971) or 4,000 to 5,000 pairs by 1975 (Sharrock *et al.*, 1976) the importance of these moulting waters can be seen in perspective. The London reservoirs may draw together a substantial proportion of Britain's male Tufted Duck for their wing moult but numbers are possibly augmented by a huge influx from overseas.

Uncertainty concerning the numbers of Tufted Duck using the principal waters in the London Area has been settled in the last few years. Writing in the *London Bird Report*, Oliver (1980) tells how organised counts in 1979 resulted in 5,300 being found chiefly on London reservoirs on July 28 and 29, and 6,600 on August 18 and 19. Sample counts by sexes show that seventy-nine to eighty-five per cent of all tufted were males. These figures need to be viewed against an estimated British breeding population of about 45,000 birds in September 1980 (Tuite and Owen 1984).

Much smaller moulting concentrations, comparable with those on the St. James's group of waters, are also known to occur in the London Area. In *London Bird Reports* there are references to moulting lakes near Sevenoaks, Rainham and Rickmansworth.

In Holland, Van der Wal and Zomerdijk (1979) found a huge population of moulting Tufted Duck on the Ijsselmeer numbering 22,500 in 1976 and 35,000 in 1977. Evidence indicates that the Netherlands hold the highest moulting concentration in Western Europe. For the United Kingdom these authors mention Abberton Reservoir in Essex as a regular moulting area with a population fluctuating between 2,000 and 3,000 Tufted Duck. On the Ijsselmeer moulting birds are said to keep an individual distance of 0.5 metres apart and are considered to maintain a wider spacing than in winter. This is particularly true of

2,300 moulting birds seen by Peter Oliver and myself at Walton, Queen Mary, and Staines reservoirs on August 19, 1979. The average individual spacing, however, was over a metre and on all the reservoirs we visited Tufted Duck were extremely well dispersed.

Taylor *et al.* (1981) state that between 1972 and 1976 over 300 drakes occurred in Kent in August, so in all probability well above 9,000 tufted complete their annual wing moult in South-East England alone. It is to be hoped that counts in the London area may stimulate investigations on a national scale so that the numbers and sex ratios of moulting tufted in the British Isles between late July and the end of September may be better understood.

CHAPTER 9

FOOD AND FEEDING HABITS

Feeding

All the year round many of the St. James's Park tufted seek natural and artificial food by day and during at least part of the night. On a calm evening, in a mild December, I have seen nearly three-quarters of the population receiving large quantities of foodstuffs from the public in the first two hours of darkness. In daytime there are always some birds resting and some diving in addition to those around the feeding points.

On one mid-winter visit to the Park at dawn over ninety-five per cent of some 300 birds present were dozing on water mostly within ten feet of the island shorelines. Three hours afterwards numbers remained unchanged and at least half still slept. Twelve days later this pattern had altered. Forty-five minutes following daybreak only one-quarter were dozing; and within a further seventy-five minutes those resting had decreased to ten per cent. On this particular occasion passing commuters threw enough bread into North Bay to attract nearly fifty tufted from the vicinity of Duck Island. Few of these tufted engaged in diving for natural food.

Nocturnal feeding occurs on the Thames around the period of low water. Since the winter of 1981-82 my friend, Mr. George Andrews, has seen small numbers of Tufted Ducks feeding at night beside the Victoria Embankment near Cleopatra's Needle. On three nights, January 17-19, 1984, he counted over seventy-five, with a maximum of two groups totalling 130 on the last date.

About three weeks later, three hours before low tide, I visited the same area after dark and was in time to find thirty birds arriving. Most drifted with the current from further up-stream, then swam quickly inshore. A few more flew in from the same direction. Thirty minutes later the gathering had increased to fifty, most of them diving close to the embankment below my viewing point where the water was shallowest. Between 1981 and 1984 neither of us saw any birds at similar stages of the tide in daylight hours. In a letter concerning the largest assemblies George Andrews commented, "there is a two-outfall drain and I could smell washing-up water. The ducks were diving and swimming around so something good was on the menu!" In all probability this discharge into the river is equally beneficial to the animals upon which the Tufted Ducks feed in this part of the river.

Some of these birds may come from the Park for, in the last two winters, I have occasionally seen six or fewer depart from St. James's at dusk heading for Westminster Bridge, barely 600 yards away. As the state of the night tide determines the arrival of tufted on the river others possibly leave, and return to, St. James's well before first light.

Throughout its Western Palearctic range this species seems best-known for feeding in daylight, though some birds are considered to feed nocturnally, even on dark nights (*cf.* Bauer and Glutz, 1969; Cramp and Simmons, 1977). While more investigations are needed to determine the rhythm of feeding activity there are pointers to seasonal differences. In his Czechoslovakian study areas Folk (1971) found that Tufted Ducks fed by day and rested at night between April and October in the years 1967 to 1970. Pedroli (1982) records that large wintering populations on three Swiss lakes fed constantly at night between 1975 and 1979. Apparently resting was the main diurnal activity.

Apart from fish, referred to later in this chapter, most natural food is consumed under water. Some small, as well as larger, compact-looking items, however, are brought up from below and swallowed by a bird upon surfacing. At Staines Reservoir I sometimes saw unusually large prey, resembling clusters of three or more mussels, brought to the surface where bits were broken off and devoured. Folk (1971) relates how tufted often emerged from shorter than usual dives with food which they ate above water.

Coot nests, situated short distances from the Park shorelines, are regular places around which tufted dive for food. For about six weeks up to early June, 1962, the immediate vicinity of one nest continually attracted many feeding birds including, on some dates, Pochard and a number of Mallard.

Competition for food

Adult and young Tufted Ducks have to compete with others for scraps from the public. Few people are selective when feeding water birds so food tends to be distributed at random. Adult tufted, being smaller and more agile than the commoner duck species, intercept a fair share of the offerings, many diving with a morsel and surfacing clear of a throng to prevent it being stolen. Individuals, as well as ducks of other species, frequently have their food snatched away, often by tufted, Mallard, Coot, and Black-headed Gulls. Many of the last-named birds are particularly skilful at intercepting food in the air before it reaches the water.

A male *Preens-dorsally* to his mate, a female Scaup

Male soliciting a female

A pair about to copulate

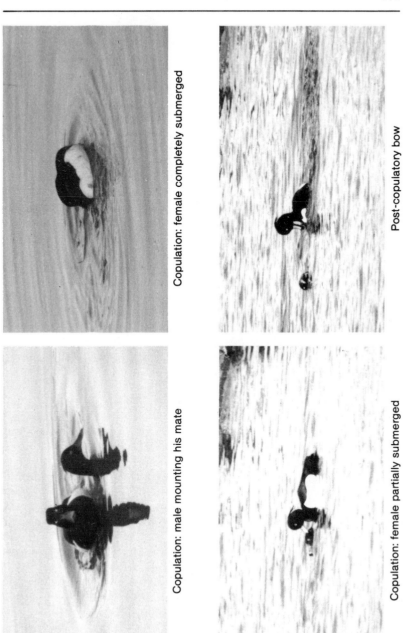

Copulation: male mounting his mate

Copulation: female completely submerged

Copulation: female partially submerged

Post-copulatory bow

The boundaries of tolerance: two pairs approach one another

Paired male chasing a pair

A paired male chases away an intruding male

A paired male chases away an intruding male Pochard

Female taking-off following an underwater pursuit

Paired male threatening own female

A male leads his mate ashore to search for a nest site; another paired male waits in the water for his female who is also ashore looking for a nest site

A type of duck nest site in use on Duck Island in the 1980s

Male on guard while his mate dives for food

Other birds using Tufted Duck to obtain food

Sometimes these gulls switch from their successful traditional piracy to harassing tufted diving for natural food. One January day in the Park six of them made repeated short flights from water to alight by the heads of the ducks whenever they surfaced. As the tufted swallowed any prey underwater the flights were pointless. The ducks were neither nervous nor frightened and it was obvious that the black-heads expected their victims to bob up with food in their bills. In Surrey a dozen of these gulls followed some courting Tufted Ducks waiting for them to stir up the water through diving or alighting after short flights.

However, I have seen Black-headed Gulls using tufted far more effectively to obtain food. On a Sussex reservoir a small party trailed a group of these wildfowl which were swimming fast in one direction with occasional diving. The gulls flew astern then, one or two at a time, swooped low causing a tufted to dive. Immediately after they alighted just to the rear of a swirl left by a vanishing bird and fed busily in its wake.

Equally cheeky was a female Shelduck which dabbled continuously almost beneath a male Tufted Duck's tail for nearly a hundred yards. Though the drake changed course he was unable to evade an unwanted companion. Eventually he ended the association by making a long underwater swim.

The attraction of shallow waters

On the St. James's group of waters most tufted dive to depths of less than five feet in daytime. According to Homes and his co-authors (1964), Tufted Duck wintering in the London Area have a preference for shallower reservoirs like those of Barn Elms, about ten feet deep, and four basins at Walthamstow, which are twelve feet in depth. On a few occasions half the entire winter population of this species within twenty miles of St. Paul's has been recorded at Barn Elms, only five or six miles south-west of the Park.

Some organisms in the lake

Unfortunately, published information on the lake's flora and fauna is scanty. In a valuable paper Pentelow (1965) recalls that when the lake was emptied in 1953, Mr. W. G. Teagle collected specimens of the Wandering Snail (*Limnaea peregra*) and the Water-louse (*Asellus aquaticus*), and the following year frequently reported water beetles but was unable to identify the species. During the course of the former's survey no macroscopic animals, except a few Blood Worms (larvae of the midge *Chironomus*), were found in the mud. Pentelow also mentions attempts at various times since 1955 to introduce bottom-living animals to feed on, thereby aiding the decomposition of, dead leaves and other organic matter building up in the lake. The introduction of freshwater mussels was considered but thought inadvisable for several reasons.

The filamentous alga Blanket weed, that became such a nuisance in 1954 before being raked from the lake and dumped in great quantities on one end of Duck Island, is reported by Pentelow as having been drastically reduced by 1958. Since then he records the occurrence of vast quantities of microscopic algae in the water. One profusion of this growth, in the autumn of 1961, was investigated by Mr. B. A. Whitton who found that the dominant organism was a blue-green alga known as *Oscillatoria limnetica*. Another particularly heavy bloom, which Keymer and his associates (1972) found to be almost entirely of *Oscillatoria agardhii*, occurred in 1969, the year of a botulism outbreak. At one time it was thought that algal poisoning may have been responsible for the numerous water bird deaths that year. This possibility was investigated by Keymer and his fellow scientists who found that though *O. agardhii* was toxic to mice this could not be related to toxicity for waterfowl. Another kind of alga proved troublesome in 1982. Within three months of the lake being refilled following a thorough cleaning, one-sixth of the water surface was a patchwork of weed.

Pentelow considers that St. James's lake is capable of producing abundant crops of various living organisms. The presence of copious amounts of bird excreta, leaves from bordering trees, and foodstuffs thrown in by the public, helps create a particularly fertile water.

On occasions fish have caused problems for the Park authorities. Department of the Environment records show that Roach were introduced in 1947 from which time on they proliferated. Though thousands died at the end of May 1960, and in the third week of June 1961, many of all sizes were still present in 1963. Rainbow Trout were put in the lake in 1961 in the hope that they would eat the small fry of Perch and Roach. Unfortunately they did not survive the heavy fish mortality the same year. The next introduction was a thousand Elvers in 1962, followed by large Rainbow Trout and Goldfish in 1964. The two last-named species came from the Jewel Tower moat.

Because the fatality among fish was due partly to deoxygenation and partly to a high concentration of carbon-dioxide remedial measures were taken. For several years, including and after 1961, whenever there was a sudden drop in the dissolved oxygen in the water mobile pumps at both ends of the lake each directed a jet of water high into the air from which it fell back as fine spray. In due course this temporary equipment was replaced by the now familiar attractive fountains operated by remote control.

After the cleansing of part of the lake in 1964 fish have never regained their abundance of the previous decade. In the winter of 1981-82 the whole lake was emptied and thoroughly cleaned in one main operation instead of the usual one-third at a time. This made restocking necessary. The office of the Bailiff of the Royal Parks informs me that in excess of 7,000 fish were put in the lake in October 1982. The main species were: Crucian Carp, Carp (including Mirror Carp), Gudgeon, and a small number of Roach. In 1984 myriads of fish fry were observed by Malcolm Kerr. Such was the abundance of various-sized fish that three pairs of Little Grebe and two pairs of Great Crested bred, most of them successfully. One pair of the former made six nesting attempts and both adults were seen on many occasions catching their prey beside each nest.

Some foods consumed in the British Isles and abroad

We know little of the animal and plant life beneath the surface or of the natural food which Tufted Ducks obtain by diving in St. James's lake. It is necessary, therefore, to examine some of the published data on this waterfowl's diet under normal conditions elsewhere.

In this country the food of Tufted Duck had not been well studied until Olney's (1963) analysis of the contents of ninety-five stomachs of birds collected by the Wildfowlers' Association of Great Britain and Ireland. All but one of these birds were obtained inland, fifty-seven of them being taken over Colnbrook Gravel Pit within about twenty miles of the Park. Apart from three of the fifty-seven whose stomachs were empty, detailed examination showed that just on ninety per cent of the volume of food taken by the remainder was animal. These birds had fed primarily on molluscs, mainly on the Zebra-mussel (*Dreissena polymorpha*). Olney's analysis of the stomach contents of a further twenty Tufted Duck shot in Northern Ireland, where the Zebra-mussel did not occur, revealed a more varied diet which he considers was probably because no one food item was present in such relative abundance. Of the total volume of food taken by the Irish birds seeds amounted to just on thirty per cent. Apparently the main diet of Danish and Russian birds, discussed in the same paper, also consisted of molluscs. Other foods found in stomachs included various insect larvae, crustaceans, and leaves, stems, and roots of aquatic plants. After outlining the spread of the Zebra-mussel in Britain, Olney concludes that this source of food is at least one of the factors which has aided the spread of the Tufted Duck.

According to Pedroli (1982) an invasion of Lake Neuchâtel by Zebra-mussels in 1967 led to a great increase in wintering Tufted Ducks on this Swiss water.

While tufted are welcome visitors to ponds and reservoirs Zebra-mussels are far from popular. Fitter (1945) highlights the major problem caused by this animal. He tells us that in 1912, when ninety tons of Zebra-mussels were removed from a quarter-mile stretch of unfiltered water-main at Hampton, in Middlesex, it was found that their numbers had reduced the diameter of the pipe from three feet to nine inches. He also states that the Zebra-mussel probably came to this country from the Volga on Russian timber. Apparently it was first recorded here in 1824 when large numbers were found attached to shells and timber in London's Commercial Docks. Another invader providing a food source for Tufted Ducks is Jenkins' Spire Shell (*Potamopyrgus jenkinsi*) which, in all probability, came from Australasia (Whitton, 1979).

Folk (1971) found vegetable food prevailing over animal in fifty-eight stomachs and four crops of Tufted Ducks shot between March and October in Czechoslovakia. He also mentions two other widely separated European localities where vegetable matter predominated in the stomachs of this species in autumn and winter.

A food study conducted at Loch Leven in Kinross, Scotland, is recorded by Laughlin (1974). He found that Chironomid larvae formed sixty per cent of the Tufted Duck's diet between 1966 and 1970. Other preferred foods were caddis larvae and molluscs (mainly *Valvata* spp.). This was shown by an examination of 159 gut contents of birds obtained on this loch which holds the largest breeding population of tufted on mainland Britain.

Some foods consumed in the Park

Most sightings of small numbers of Tufted Duck catching and eating fish were in May 1960 and June 1961 when particularly heavy fish mortality occurred. Fish-catching was also observed during a sharp reduction in the water level in the 1964 lake-cleaning operations.

In the first two years dead, moribund, and live fish were brought to the surface, nibbled at the head and then swallowed. All were less than four inches long. A few Pochard in 1960, and four Mallard in 1964, also dived and brought up fish, both species nibbling the heads of their prey before swallowing them. On May 28, 1960, six adult and one downy Mallard, and single Gadwall and Chiloé Wigeon retrieved what were thought to be dead or dying fish by immersing only their heads and necks without up-ending or diving.

On January 6, 1964, a dense concentration of roughly 2,000 Black-headed Gulls was attracted to one small corner of the dammed section of the lake by an immense shoal of tiny fish. At least a hundred of these gulls at a time dived excitedly and, between them, caught about 1,000 live fish, approximately two inches long, in ten minutes. On the fringe of the gulls six Tufted Duck were diving and surfacing with live fish of similar size but not every one was nibbled at the head as the catch had to be swallowed quickly or be stolen by the screaming mass of piratical gulls.

Crushing of food on the surface before swallowing was known to an earlier generation of observers. Bent (1923), on the authority of Millais, records that a fish, frog, or large piece of vegetable matter, was dealt with by tufted in this manner.

Between mid-May and mid-June, 1967, individual Tufted Duck and Pochard were seen on a dozen occasions each feeding off dead fish between four and eight inches long. Most fish were floating on the surface and only three times were they brought up by diving. Both species, including a one-month-old Pochard, shook and pulled at the dead fish to break off small pieces which they devoured. In August, 1957, three well-feathered tufted ducklings were seen feeding off dead fish of similar size.

A few Tufted Duck and Pochard consume some of the grain provided regularly for the ornamental waterfowl. Among other foods, a female was seen to swallow a two-thirds grown embryo and pieces of shell from one of her own eggs on July 3, 1957. Altogether, ten cases of egg-shell eating involving Mallard (once), Tufted Duck (seven times) and Pochard (twice), were recorded. Two four-weeks-old tufted ducklings were seen eating leaves of the White Poplar (*Populus alba*) plucked from low branches overhanging the water on August 19, 1957. Feathers were eaten by two adults and one juvenile in 1959.

Tufted Ducks will eat vegetables and fruits of the kind we ourselves consume. From a few personal experiments conducted only in September certain tendencies were noted which require more quantitative backing. Size of food pieces may be important. However, favoured items of acceptable size were ignored if they sank immediately, for most birds never dived to retrieve them. Though both adults and feathered young took bits of shredded Watercress, Mustard and Cress, and Garden Lettuce in their bill, these vegetables were discarded without even tiny pieces being eaten. Most of one brood of five, aged about five weeks, continually ate flattened halves of green grapes and small squashy pieces of diced cucumber thrown to them. While many adults and young ignored sliced 'circles' of cucumber, a smaller number appeared equally disinterested in the broken grapes and diced cucumber favoured by others. An overwhelming majority of Tufted Ducks, however, had a strong preference for crushed tomato provided the small pieces did not consist solely of the outer skin. A similar pattern of likes and dislikes was noted when small pieces of other vegetables and fruits were thrown to them. Only one or two birds ate cooked Marrow, though cooked Potato was taken by a total of at least half-a-dozen adults and young, as were pieces of Victoria Plum, Peach and Strawberry. On the whole partly fledged young appeared much more receptive to these foods than adults. A shortage of natural food in the lake may have caused ducklings to take anything palatable because, being unable to fly, they were tied to their environment for several more weeks. On the other hand lack of experience may have been responsible for their eating these foods.

One winter's day a gentleman arrived at the Cake House feeding point with two large boxes of eatables, including sandwiches, cakes, and spaghetti. As he fed delicious chocolate éclairs to a pair of seemingly enthusiastic Mute Swans, and sandwiches to tufted and other ducks, he threw in a large handful of spaghetti which sank and was ignored by all. After five minutes, however, a small number of Tufted Ducks retrieved this cord-like pasta from the bottom, eating it on the surface as if it was a familiar food. I asked the donor if he gave this to them regularly. He informed me that he did so but the tufted sought other offerings first. Apparently they regarded the spaghetti, which lay untouched by other water birds, as a second choice to be dealt with later.

Tufted ducklings are resourceful. At Finsbury Park, where broods commonly invade the fenced-off corner of the lake reserved for anglers, twenty-three downies, about two weeks old, were seen diving continually around floats and feeding on ground bait as soon as it was thrown in. Not surprisingly, the fishermen were greatly displeased by these intrusions.

SOME METHODS OF OBTAINING FOOD

Unobvious foot-paddling associated with diving

On June 22, 1974, I watched a nesting female at a distance of twenty feet foot-paddling many times while diving repeatedly in water about two feet deep. On surfacing in between dives over the same spot, she held her wings close to the body with crossed tips slightly elevated. In an otherwise normal swimming posture the feet moved rapidly but *inconspicuously* up and down. There was no rearing up at an angle to the surface nor was there any side-to-side wobbling of the body. Since the foot movements were difficult to detect this method of stirring water to obtain food may be commoner than a single record suggests.

Besides diving for food Tufted Ducks, like dabbling ducks, feed in a variety of ways while swimming on the surface. The use of a particular method may be influenced by water levels, an abundance of food at various depths, or by both.

Feeding with head and neck below the surface

There are four positions in which Tufted Ducks procure nourishment with only the head and neck below the surface. These are:— (1) from a normal swimming posture; (2) from a forward body tilt with the underparts at about thirty degrees to the surface; (3) from a forward tip-up with the underside at seventy to eighty degrees to the surface; (4) typical up-ending in which the body is carried at ninety degrees to the surface.

The first pattern is fairly common in St. James's when birds feed at the edge of the shorelines or in the shallows following a dramatic fall in the water level during lake cleaning operations. When the latter occurred as many as six to twelve birds at a time have been seen feeding with heads and necks beneath the surface. Small downies not infrequently feed in an identical manner.

The second and third practices have not been observed in the Park. The fourth method, complete up-ending, proved to be rare among adult tufted in St. James's in so far as I saw it performed only once in three decades. However, up-ending is common in several species of surface-feeding ducks, and Shelduck, and causes great amusement among Park visitors. Over shallow water, by the Cake House feeding point, a duck in this comical feeding posture readily attracts attention. Head and neck are immersed so that the rest of the body is vertical to the surface. The tail is depressed at an angle and the feet paddle continuously to maintain balance.

As referred to in an earlier chapter downies less than about two weeks old resort to up-ending at times. This feeding behaviour is more clumsy than in adults and is accompanied by rapid foot movements.

Although I have observed adult Tufted Ducks up-ending only on half-a-dozen dates outside London, this behaviour is considerably commoner among adult Pochard.

The second method, a thirty degree body tilt with tail depressed, was frequently observed on shallow inland ponds in Sussex. Tufted Ducks fed this way for many minutes at a time while stationary. Moreover, some slowly swam distances of about fifty yards, feeding as they moved and maintaining this oblique posture all the time.

The third type of behaviour was seen only on November 16, 1975, when twelve tufted flew onto a tidal lagoon on a North Kent marsh. Every bird fed by making continual brief forward tips so that the underside of the body was seventy to eighty degrees to the surface. Unlike the other three methods this stern-up posture was maintained for only a few seconds.

Sometimes Tufted Ducks vary their mode of feeding when together. For example, in one pair the female continually up-ended in contrast to her mate, who immersed only his head and neck from the normal swimming pose. On a single date a male was seen partially submerging by plunging at an angle to obtain food. Another time a female fed with only her wings and mantle above the surface.

Dabbling and Skimming

Dabbling, with the head and neck drawn towards the body like surface-feeding ducks, is fairly common feeding behaviour on water. Adults and ducklings of both tufted and Pochard use this method.

Skimming for food involves a duck or duckling lying prone with head and neck flat on the surface. Alternatively, the head and neck are extended low with chin and throat just clear of the water. Either way the distal two-thirds of the bill is immersed for long periods and moved from side-to-side. Several times single Tufted Duck and Pochard swam prone with the whole of the upper mandible just touching the surface but not moved laterally. This feeding method was identical to that of Shovelers which, on one occasion, were feeding on the same pond.

In St. James's, adult, feathered and downy young Tufted Duck and Pochard commonly fed by skimming in years when there was an abundance of microscopic algae in the lake. Other waterfowl, including Shelduck, Gadwall, Mallard, and Red-crested Pochard, congregated with these two species to feed in exactly the same manner in the middle of the lake.

For example, on July 29, 1969, shortly before the heavy water-bird casualties occurred, about 250 ducks of eight species were all feeding in one dense pack, mainly by skimming. Among them were twenty-two young and five adult tufted. In 1972 many ducks were again seen feeding by skimming and tufted, mostly young birds, were prominent among them. On July 28 there were two concentrations roughly equal in size, totalling 110 ducks in all, of which thirty-seven were tufted. A few weeks later, on August 18, a group of seventy-one ducks of five species, including six Ruddy Shelduck, were feeding in close company in the same fashion besides dabbling. Almost half were Tufted Ducks comprising five adult females and thirty young of the year. Though Keymer and his associates found evidence of a blue-green alga in the crops of several dead ducks in 1969 there is nothing to suggest that the large concentrations of waterfowl referred to above were feeding even partly on this or similar organisms. Over the years I saw far more ducklings than adult tufted feeding by skimming.

Picking from the surface

This method of taking tiny food items from the surface occurred mainly when flying insects were present in large but well-dispersed numbers and hit, or alighted on, the water over a wide area. One of these infrequent occasions was on August 26, 1964, and, as with some other feeding methods, adult tufted were not alone in taking advantage of an abundant food supply. In all, sixteen species of waterfowl, including Barnacle Goose, Shelduck, Mandarin, Wigeon, Garganey, Coot, Moorhen, and six-weeks-old Tufted Ducks fed similarly. The many birds were well scattered and swam leisurely about picking the insects off the surface. On another date a few tufted were observed picking what appeared to be fine breadcrumbs off the water in the same manner.

Snapping at, and catching, flying insects
The antics of the nimble and energetic small downy tufted as they chase after, and snap at, flying insects, are often a source of wonder or entertainment for some of the public on a hot summer's day. But even when insects are abundant they seldom prove attractive to almost fully-grown ducklings or adults unless they can be caught with ease. On only a few occasions, therefore, were the two last-named seen to snap at and catch insects which flew close to their heads.

Obvious foot-paddling not associated with diving
On five occasions three different females with small young were seen foot-paddling in water about a foot deep. This behaviour appeared to dislodge food for the brood even though on one occasion the ducklings were several yards from their mother. Vigorous alternate foot movements were accompanied by a conspicuous side-to-side wobbling of the body. One female gave soft TUK TUK notes as she stirred the water. Similar foot-paddling was observed by a non-breeding female in water of comparable depth. This bird, however, reared up while treading water.

The observations of Boyle (1968) and Simmons (1968) indicate that foot-paddling associated with diving is a characteristic behaviour pattern of Pochard. The latter observer noted a slight side-to-side rocking of the body as birds rose up and trod water at an angle of forty-five degrees, moving their feet alternately. Eiders at Seafield, near Edinburgh, on the Firth of Forth, were found by Player (1971) to sit fairly upright in shallow water and push aside dead mussel shells with their feet to get at food. Pinioned Eiders in St. James's sometimes foot-paddle in an identical posture at the edge of the shorelines. Once one of a Greylag pair with a small gosling repeatedly foot-paddled then fed by up-ending. This behaviour was of no benefit to the downy, which was not feeding.

Grazing
In St. James's Park Tufted Ducks rarely seek natural food ashore. Some well-grown ducklings reared by Arthur May out of water in turfed enclosures ate grass, as did many surface-feeding and other ducks with which they were confined. On different occasions two hand-reared and colour-ringed females, both with

experience of these pens, were seen grazing two years after their release. An adult male feeding similarly was also considered to have been a hand-reared bird.

Two other hand-reared and pinioned old drakes, both paired to the same female Chiloé Wigeon, were disinterested in grass. When the chiloé led her partners ashore she was the only one to graze. The two male tufted continually picked up tiny pieces of debris but always discarded them.

Though many Park-bred and immigrant Tufted Ducks commonly rest on grassy verges, none was ever seen grazing apart from the hand-reared birds referred to.

CHAPTER 10
FUTURE PROSPECTS

Tufted Ducks breeding in the British Isles have a secure future because of their wide distribution and diversity of breeding habitat. In the London Area continued prosperity on the present scale depends on the maintenance of suitable conditions in considerably fewer types of physical environment than exist in Britain as a whole. For example, widespread infilling of gravel-pits and drastic changes in usage of waters in parks or on commons are two measures likely to dent their present status. With the forecast of more leisure for working people pressure will mount for an increasing number of lakes and reservoirs to be used for water sports.

However, if changes to breeding waters occur gradually then there is reason for believing that the present Tufted Duck population of the London Area will remain at its current level for some years. Without any changes these diving ducks should continue to increase.

The steady growth and stability of the St. James's community throughout this study might have been a different story if boating, an established tradition from 1847 to 1914, had not been discontinued after the First World War. Over the last three decades pairs of Tufted Ducks in St. James's have, on average, increased by about six per cent per annum, reaching six potential breeding pairs to the acre of water in 1984. Together with surplus adults the whole breeding season population of this species has exceeded fifteen birds to the acre of water since 1980. In relation to the Park's other waterfowl tufted have constituted between one-fifth and one-quarter of all pinioned and free-flying ducks, geese and swans in the decade up to the summer of 1984.

Such a high concentration of breeding Tufted Ducks is unlikely to have been maintained if any revolutionary changes had affected this man-made waterfowl environment. Throughout the Park's long history major alterations have come gradually and this tradition has proved beneficial for these diving ducks. Certain measures, suited to the convenience of the public besides the well-being of water birds, have also had an effect; none more so than the regular cleaning out of the lake which has been completed outside the breeding season.

Equally fortunate was an absence of any drastic tidying-up on Duck Island, particularly at a time when natural ground vegetation had declined and nest boxes were few in number. The removal of disused stores like old wooden doors, corrugated iron sheeting, stone slabs and miscellaneous items such as a derelict boat and a water tank would have reduced the number of nest sites for Tufted Ducks. Similarly, over-zealous smartening-up in and around the boathouse, the aviaries, one rockery and one old shed would have limited the number of favoured nesting areas. For example, inside the small shed alone there were five nests of this species in 1969.

The long-term provision of strongly constructed and well-maintained artificial nest sites is essential on this island until ground vegetation is as plentiful as it was before the early 1950s. Adequate nesting facilities are vital to safeguard the future prosperity of Tufted Ducks in St. James's Park. It is a measure of the adaptability of this species that, on this small lake which has been described as "one of the most public sheets of water in the world", the population has gone from strength to strength.

To Tufted Ducks breeding conditions in St. James's must seem ideal. In contrast many breeding areas, which to us may appear suitable, fall short of the requirements of this species. Among populations which have made little headway over the past forty to eighty-four years are those of Dulwich, Kelsey and Battersea parks. Between them they could only muster twenty-seven potential nesting pairs in 1984, a total representing a little over doubling-up of the figures of two decades ago.

The principal lakes in the last two parks have had mammoth silt problems dealt with since the late 1970s. Within the next five years we shall be able to gauge the extent of the Tufted Duck's response to cleaner waters. With the completion of Kelsey's draining and dredging operations the breeding water was given an additional islet, a rare, though commendable, bonus for suburban waterfowl these days.

Decreases in communities at some sites and more rapid expansion at others suggest that birds are ready to exploit those areas more suitable to them. Two old established haunts with fifty pairs between them in the 1970s suffered a decline to fourteen pairs in 1984. Three others with a total of half-a-dozen pairs in the 1960s had increased six-fold by 1984. Although all of Inner London's eight breeding waters have not been closely monitored throughout the past quarter-of-a-century their combined populations appear to have doubled from roughly sixty pairs in the early 1960s to about 125 pairs in 1984. The Tufted Duck's success is best appreciated by the fact that, in the breeding season, as many pairs now occur in Inner London's forty square miles as were found in the London Area's ca.1,200 square miles twenty-five years ago.

In London parks the Mallard has been the favoured species for many years. In wet weather groups become a nuisance through feeding in puddles beside grass borders and destroying parts of lovingly-tended verges. They also damage lawns by feeding in hollows when the turf is waterlogged. Because Tufted Ducks do not contribute to this damage, park authorities should try encouraging more of them to breed by providing suitable artificial nest sites on islands which have little cover. A handful of duck nest boxes that I have observed on islands in bygone days were sited too conspicuously, were too flimsy in construction, and lacked maintenance in subsequent years.

Duck Island in St. James's is an ideal location for a long-term study of different types of sturdy artificial nest sites for tufted. It would be useful for other park authorities to know whether one particular model was more acceptable to this, or indeed other, species in areas where ground cover is negligible. The artificial nest sites constructed by Malcolm Kerr, as shown in one of the photographs, are worthy of trying out on islands, especially those which are predominantly large tree-covered earth mounds. These can be buried so that they resemble a burrow or placed on a levelled area and camouflaged with debris as mentioned in Chapter 6.

While Tufted Ducks have been consolidating their westward expansion, by a coincidence, on the other side of the Atlantic, Ring-necked Ducks have been trail-blazing in North America. In *Waterfowl Tomorrow* (Linduska, 1964) Mendall and Nelson tell us that "The Ring-necked Duck is an example of pioneering on a major scale." After leap-frogging from breeding grounds in Western Ontario and the Lake States into Maine and New Brunswick they then moved westward to fill the gap. Though at present tufted and ring-necks are no more than accidental visitors to each other's homeland, one may wonder whether any future pioneering drives will overcome the barrier of seas and oceans.

Among ducks which have come to terms with civilization, Mendall and Nelson specifically mention only Mallard and Blue-winged Teal as nesting on waters in parks in the heart of large North American cities. The Ring-necked Duck, therefore, has some way to go to equal the adaptability of its Eurasian cousin, the Tufted Duck.

Čestmir Folk (1971) on the behaviour of Tufted Ducks when studying their feeding habits in Czechoslovakia:—

"I observed that the Tufted Duck gets used to the presence of man very quickly, particularly if offered some food. It gradually loses its shyness and even seeks the presence of man. For this reason I had to use shelter during my investigations to avoid attracting rather than disturbing the Tufted Duck under my observations."

TABLE 1

BREEDING SEASON POPULATION OF TUFTED DUCK IN ST. JAMES'S PARK BETWEEN 1954 AND 1984 INCLUSIVE

Period	Maximum number of breeding pairs in one season	Average number of breeding pairs for period	Average number of surplus males for period*	Average number of surplus females for period
1954 to 1961 inclusive	32	21	9	4
1962 to 1969 inclusive	50	36	29	10
1970 to 1977 inclusive	60	48	39	6
1978 to 1984 inclusive	68	61	43	9

* Figures for surplus males based, primarily, on counts made between May 15 and June 15. Any obviously large numbers, considered to have been birds on passage to moult areas, have been excluded. Unusually high numbers occurred on passage in the first half of June in 1975 and 1977.

TABLE 2

26 APPROXIMATE RETURN DATES TO THE ST. JAMES'S GROUP OF WATERS (EXCLUDING BUCKINGHAM PALACE LAKE) OF COLOUR-RINGED MALE TUFTED DUCK WHICH WERE NOT PRESENT IN ST. JAMES'S PARK IN THE BREEDING SEASON AND WHICH COMPLETED THEIR WING MOULT ELSEWHERE

August	September				October				November				December			
24-31	1-7	8-15	16-23	24-30	1-7	8-15	16-23	24-31	1-7	8-15	16-23	24-30	1-7	8-15	16-23	24-31
3	2	3	2	1	2	–	2	1	1	3	2	–	–	1	1	–

January				February				March			
1-7	8-15	16-23	24-31	1-7	8-15	16-23	24-28	1-7	8-15	16-23	24-31
–	1	–	–	–	–	–	–	–	1	–	–

TABLE 3

15 APPROXIMATE RETURN DATES TO THE ST. JAMES'S GROUP OF WATERS (EXCLUDING BUCKINGHAM PALACE LAKE) OF COLOUR-RINGED FEMALE TUFTED DUCK WHICH WERE **NOT** PRESENT IN ST. JAMES'S PARK IN THE BREEDING SEASON

July		*August*				*September*				*October*			
16-23	24-31	1-7	8-15	16-23	24-31	1-7	8-15	16-23	24-30	1-7	8-15	16-23	24-31
1	2	1	–	1	1	–	4	1	–	–	–	–	–

November				*December*				*January*	
1-7	8-15	16-23	24-30	1-7	8-15	16-23	24-31	1-7	8-15
–	2	–	–	–	–	–	1	–	1

Eight return dates of females to complete their wing moult on these waters were between July 1 and September 23. Seven return dates of females after completing their wing moult elsewhere were between September 8 and January 15.

TABLE 4

50 APPROXIMATE DEPARTURE DATES FROM THE ST. JAMES'S GROUP OF WATERS (EXCLUDING BUCKINGHAM PALACE LAKE) OF COLOUR-RINGED MALE TUFTED DUCK WHICH WERE **NOT** PRESENT IN ST. JAMES'S PARK IN THE BREEDING SEASON

January				February				March				April			
1-7	8-15	16-23	24-31	1-7	8-15	16-23	24-28	1-7	8-15	16-23	24-31	1-7	8-15	16-23	24-30
—	—	1	—	1	1	3	4	3	2	6	6	6	4	3	6

May			
1-7	8-15	16-23	24-31
3	—	1	—

TABLE 5

30 APPROXIMATE DEPARTURE DATES FROM THE ST. JAMES'S GROUP OF WATERS (EXCLUDING BUCKINGHAM PALACE LAKE) OF COLOUR-RINGED FEMALE TUFTED DUCK WHICH WERE **NOT** PRESENT IN ST. JAMES'S PARK IN THE BREEDING SEASON

January				February				March				April				May			
1-7	8-15	16-23	24-31	1-7	8-15	16-23	24-28	1-7	8-15	16-23	24-31	1-7	8-15	16-23	24-30	1-7	8-15	16-23	24-31
1	–	–	–	–	–	–	–	2	1	3	4	–	–	4	4	4	5	2	–

TABLE 6

APPROXIMATE SEX RATIOS OF TUFTED DUCK ON THE ST. JAMES'S GROUP OF WATERS
(EXCLUDING BUCKINGHAM PALACE LAKE) BASED ON COUNTS IN PERIOD NOVEMBER
TO FEBRUARY INCLUSIVE

Period	*Horse Guards end population*	*St. James's Park lake*		*Long Water and Serpentine*	*Round Pond*
		Bridge population	*Palace end population*		
Nov. 1966 to Feb. 1967	1 male to 2.75 females	Sexes equal	1 male to 2.00 females	2.50 males to 1 female	3.00 males to 1 female
Nov. 1967 to Feb. 1968	1 male to 3.00 females	Sexes equal	1 male to 2.50 females	3.00 males to 1 female	3.00 males to 1 female
Nov. 1968 to Feb. 1969	1 male to 2.25 females	1.25 males to 1 female	1 male to 3.00 females	2.50 males to 1 female	4.50 males to 1 female
Nov. 1969 to Feb. 1970	1 male to 1.75 females	1.50 males to 1 female	1 male to 2.50 females	3.50 males to 1 female	4.00 males to 1 female (Nov. 22 to Dec. 13) After Dec. 13 pond drained.*

* Cleaning out operation.

TABLE 7

COMPOSITION OF 162 CLOSE-KNIT PRE-NUPTIAL COURTING PARTIES OF TUFTED DUCK IN ST. JAMES'S PARK IN PERIOD 1959 TO 1970 INCLUSIVE

These courting parties, consisting of up to 14 males and 1 female in a group, were observed between January 20 and June 17. An analysis of the number of males with one female in the various groups is as follows:—

Number of males with one female in a group	Number of courting parties of each grouping seen
2	5
3	31
4	28
5	21
6	32
7	18
8	10
9	2
10	7
11	4
12	2
13	1
14	1
	162

89% of all courting parties contained 2 to 8 males with 1 female

Note: Since the completion of this summary a courting party of 20 males and 1 female was recorded on April 30, 1975.

TABLE 8

TIMETABLE OF PAIRING OF TUFTED DUCK IN ST. JAMES'S PARK IN PERIOD 1960 TO 1970 INCLUSIVE

Month or period	Average percentage paired. Both sexes together.	Average percentage paired. Colour-ringed birds only. Both sexes together. 1963 to 1970 only.	Average percentage paired. Females only.	Average percentage paired. Colour-ringed females only. 1963 to 1970 only.	Maximum percentage paired in a particular year. Both sexes together.
January	Under 1	Nil	—	Nil	Under 1
February	Under 5	Under 1*	—	Nil	Under 5
March 1-15	5	9	4	Under 1	10
March 16-31	9	9	6	10	65
April 1-15	32	24	32	32	74
April 16-30	47	33	46	36	84
May 1-15	56	43	57	47	92
May 16-31	60	—	—	—	—
June 1-15	63	—	—	—	—

* Date of earliest colour-ringed bird to be paired February 16.

TABLE 9

PERCENTAGES OF FEMALES PAIRED IN SOME SMALL TUFTED DUCK POPULATIONS

Year	Place	Date of count	Count of pairs & unpaired birds	Percentage of females paired
1967	Dulwich, S.E.21	March 19	4 pairs, 2 males	100
1968	Dulwich	March 24	2 pairs, 6 males, 4 females	33
1968	Kelsey Park London Borough of Bromley	April 15	5 pairs, 5 males, 1 female	83
1969	Sevenoaks, Kent	April 5	5 pairs	100
1969	Dulwich	April 5	2 pairs	100
1969	Wimbledon, S.W.19	April 6	5 pairs, 2 males	100
1969	Kelsey Park	April 6	6 pairs, 1 male, 4 females	60
1969	Godalming, Surrey	April 7	5 pairs, 1 female	83

TABLE 10

COPULATION, ATTEMPTED COPULATION AND SOLICITING (WITHOUT EVENTUAL COPULATION) BY TUFTED DUCK IN PERIOD APRIL 13, 1954 to JUNE 6, 1970

PAIRED BIRDS ONLY

ANALYSIS OF 229 COPULATIONS, 44 ATTEMPTED COPULATIONS, AND 261 INSTANCES OF SOLICITING

	February				March				April			
	1-7	8-15	16-23	24-28	1-7	8-15	16-23	24-31	1-7	8-15	16-23	24-30
Copulation	—	—	—	—	1	1	4	8	16	14	15	23
Attempted copulation	—	—	—	1	—	3	2	3	8	3	4	2
Total	—	—	—	1	1	4	6	11	24	17	19	25
Soliciting only by males of pairs	4	2	4	3	3	10	11	46	21	53	26	10

	May				June				July			
	1-7	8-15	16-23	24-31	1-7	8-15	16-23	24-30	1-7	8-15	16-23	24-31
Copulation	13	18	12	25	25	23	7	9	9	5	1	—
Attempted copulation	2	4	3	1	—	3	1	2	1	1	—	—
Total	15	22	15	26	25	26	8	11	10	6	1	—
Soliciting only by males of pairs	15	12	8	5	4	7	4	4	3	4	2	—

(continued)

Table 10 (continued)

UNPAIRED BIRDS ONLY

ANALYSIS OF 63 COPULATIONS, 8 ATTEMPTED COPULATIONS, AND 36 INSTANCES OF SOLICITING

	February				March				April			
	1-7	8-15	16-23	24-28	1-7	8-15	16-23	24-31	1-7	8-15	16-23	24-30
Copulation	—	—	—	—	—	1	3	6	9	7	14	6
Attempted copulation	—	—	—	—	1	—	—	1	2	3	—	1
Total	—	—	—	—	1	1	3	7	11	10	14	7
Soliciting by unpaired males	—	—	1	—	2	—	10	4	2	3	5	2

	May				June				July			
	1-7	8-15	16-23	24-31	1-7	8-15	16-23	24-30	1-7	8-15	16-23	24-31
Copulation	4	7	3	2	1	—	—	—	—	—	—	—
Attempted copulation	—	—	—	—	—	—	—	—	—	—	—	—
Total	4	7	3	2	1	—	—	—	—	—	—	—
Soliciting by unpaired males	1	1	—	2	3	—	—	—	—	—	—	—

Notes: Those birds which stayed together after copulation, attempted copulation, or soliciting were considered to have been fixed or temporary pairs.

Those birds which split and went their separate ways after copulation, attempted copulation, or soliciting were deemed to be unpaired birds.

TABLE 11

ANALYSIS OF PRECOPULATORY DISPLAY BY PAIRED AND UNPAIRED TUFTED DUCK IN PERIOD APRIL 12, 1961 TO JULY 20, 1967

BASED ON 150 INSTANCES OF COPULATION (105 INSTANCES BY PAIRED BIRDS AND 45 INSTANCES BY UNPAIRED BIRDS)

	Dorsal and/or Behind the Wing Preening			Neck-stretch posture (either with bill held horizontally or with bill depressed about 45° by male)			Female only displaying before copulation	Other displays introduced before copulation	No display either by male or female before copulation
	By male only	By female only	By male and female together	By male only	By female only	By male and female together			
By paired birds	29	—	1	23	1	72	1 (Neck-stretch posture)	—	7
By unpaired birds	21	1	2	17	—	27	—	1 (A male gave the Headthrow twice)	1
Total instances of display	50	1	3	40	1	99	1	1	8

Note: For definition of paired and unpaired birds see Table 10.

TABLE 12

ANALYSIS OF POST-COPULATORY DISPLAY AND BEHAVIOUR OF PAIRED AND UNPAIRED TUFTED DUCK IN PERIOD APRIL 12, 1961 TO JULY 20, 1967

BASED ON 188 INSTANCES OF COPULATION (137 INSTANCES BY PAIRED BIRDS AND 51 INSTANCES BY UNPAIRED BIRDS)

	Bow (= Bill Down) posture			Rigid Swim away from female	Bathe			Wing Flap		
	By male only	By female only	By male and female together	By male	By male only	By female only	By male and female together	By male only	By female only	By male and female together
By paired birds	4	1	111	54	1	53	8	1	67	1
By unpaired birds	1	1	46	32	—	12	1	3	28	—
Total instances of display and behaviour	5	2	157	86	1	65	9	4	95	1

Note: For definition of paired and unpaired birds see Table 10.

TABLE 13

SOME APPARENT REASONS FOR THE SHORTENING OR ABSENCE OF THE USUAL SEQUENCE OF POST-COPULATORY DISPLAY AND BEHAVIOUR OF TUFTED DUCK

Reasons	*Number of instances*
Because of disturbance by Mallard (twice) and other tufted (three times) immediately following copulation	5
Because copulation resembled rape	3
Because male did not mount female in the correct position	2
Because copulation was prolonged	1
Because copulation occurred several times in quick succession	1
Because male Pochard copulated with the female tufted immediately after the male tufted had finished	1
Because an unpaired male copulated with two unpaired females in quick succession	1
Because erratic diving or swimming immediately followed copulation	3
Because female started diving for food immediately after copulation	2
Because immediately after copulation a male left his mate and swam 12 yards to drive away another pair	1
Because pre-nuptial display immediately followed copulation	4
Because a male performed ritualised drinking immediately after copulation	1

25

TABLE 14

LATEST DATES ON WHICH TUFTED DUCK WERE OBSERVED IN PAIRS IN ST. JAMES'S PARK

Year	Latest dates for pairs
1954	August 9
1955	July 16-21
1956	July 21
1957	July 21
1958	July 22
1959	July 15
1960	July 17
1961	July 23
1962	July 19
1963	July 23
1964	July 18-19
1965	July 16
1966	July 26
1967	July 25
1968	July 30-31
1969	July 19-20
1970	July 23

Note: Between 1971 and 1984, inclusive, no pairs were seen in August.

TABLE 15

15 APPROXIMATE RETURN DATES TO ST. JAMES'S PARK LAKE OF COLOUR-RINGED MALE TUFTED DUCK WHICH HAD BEEN PRESENT IN THE BREEDING SEASON BUT WHICH LEFT TO COMPLETE THEIR WING MOULT ELSEWHERE

Oct	November				December				January			
24-31	1-7	8-15	16-23	24-30	1-7	8-15	16-23	24-31	1-7	8-15	16-23	24-31
1	—	—	2	—	—	—	3	—	1	1	—	2

February				March	
1-7	8-15	16-23	24-28	1-7	8-15
1	—	—	2	1	1

TABLE 16

38 APPROXIMATE RETURN DATES TO ST. JAMES'S PARK LAKE OF COLOUR-RINGED FEMALE TUFTED DUCK WHICH HAD BEEN PRESENT IN THE BREEDING SEASON BUT WHICH LEFT TO COMPLETE THEIR WING MOULT ELSEWHERE (16 WERE SEEN IN A FLIGHTLESS CONDITION ON THE SERPENTINE AND LONG WATER)

August				September			
8-15	16-23	24-31		1-7	8-15	16-23	24-30
2	1	—		—	—	1	2

October				November			
1-7	8-15	16-23	24-31	1-7	8-15	16-23	24-30
3	2	3	3	1	2	—	—

December				January			
1-7	8-15	16-23	24-31	1-7	8-15	16-23	24-31
—	—	1	4	3	—	—	1

February				March			
1-7	8-15	16-23	24-28	1-7	8-15	16-23	24-31
—	—	1	—	1	1	3	—

April				May		
1-7	8-15	16-23	24-30	1-7	8-15	16-23
—	1	—	1	—	1	1

TABLE 17

BREEDING SEASON ATTACKS ON VARIOUS SPECIES OF DUCK AND HYBRIDS BY PAIRED, OR LONE, MALE TUFTED DUCKS IN ST. JAMES'S PARK

	Number of individual attacks on males, females and young				
	On males	*On females*	*On feathered young*	*On downy young*	*Totals*
ATTACKS ON DIVING DUCKS					
‡On Pochard	50	38	—	5	
†On Southern Pochard	1	1	—	—	
‡On Red-crested Pochard	25	9	—	1	
On Rosy-billed Pochard	2	3	—	—	
On Red-crested Pochard × Rosy-billed Pochard hybrid	2	—	—	—	
On 'Scaup type' *Aythya* hybrid	2	—	—	—	
	82	51	Nil	6	139
ATTACKS ON SURFACE-FEEDING DUCKS					
On Mallard	76	11	13	4	
On Gadwall	2	2	—	—	
†On Pintail	1	—	—	—	
†On Bahama Pintail	1	—	—	—	
†On Mandarin	1	2	—	—	
†On Carolina	—	1	—	—	
†On Wigeon	1	2	—	—	
	82	18	13	4	117
TOTALS	164	69	13	10	256

†Pinioned birds
‡A few were pinioned birds

TABLE 18

NUPTIAL BEHAVIOUR OF TUFTED DUCK

ANALYSIS OF 164 RECORDS OF NUPTIAL BEHAVIOUR ON LAND AND WATER, AND IN FLIGHT

	March	April				May				June				July			
	24-31	1-7	8-15	16-23	24-30	1-7	8-15	16-23	24-31	1-7	8-15	16-23	24-30	1-7	8-15	16-23	24-31
Behaviour on land and water					2	2	9	7	13	9	12	10	9	4	3	2	
Behaviour in flight	1				6	1	7	10	15	7	8	4	6	11	6		
TOTAL RECORDS	1	—	—	—	8	3	16	17	28	16	20	14	15	15	9	2	—

TABLE 19

MALE TUFTED DUCK GUARDING HIS MATE WHILE SHE ENGAGES IN FEEDING

ANALYSIS OF 307 RECORDS

Year	March	April				May				June				July			
	24-31	1-7	8-15	16-23	24-30	1-7	8-15	16-23	24-31	1-7	8-15	16-23	24-30	1-7	8-15	16-23	24-31
1961		1	1	1	1	1	4	7	7	9	9	6	4	5	2	1	
1962		1		2			3	3	6	8	9	7	4	4	2	1	
1963					1		2	1	1	7	7			2	2	2	
1964					2	1	1	6	6	2	9	5			1		
1965				1			1	2	8	5	12	3	3		2		
1966			1				1	3	3	5	12			4			
1967								2	8	10	8			1			
1968	1		1		1	1		4	4	8	7					1	
1969					1				8		6					1	1
TOTALS	1	2	3	4	6	3	12	28	51	54	79	21	11	16	9	6	1

TABLE 20

BEHAVIOUR PRECEDING COPULATION BY PAIRED TUFTED DUCK IN PERIOD MARCH 27 TO JULY 13

Behaviour	Number of records	Percentage of total number of records
Copulation occurring after a spell resting ashore or after female dived for food while her mate was on guard	16	40.0
Copulation occurring after a spell of nest site searching or in between spells of nest site searching	17	42.5
Copulation occurring after defence of the female or after a pair had been evicted by a male who was defending his female	5	12.5
Copulation occurring after a female had left her nest and rejoined her mate at his waiting spot	2	5.0
	40	100.0

TABLE 21

NEST SITE SEARCHING ACTIVITY OF TUFTED DUCK IN ST. JAMES'S PARK

ANALYSIS OF MOVEMENTS ASHORE

Action by one partner or by both of the pair	Number of records	Percentage frequency of the behaviour
ONE ONLY OF THE PAIR GOING ASHORE TO COVER		17
(a) Female ashore while her mate waited on the water nearby	95	
(b) Male ashore while his mate waited on the water nearby	9	
BOTH OF THE PAIR GOING ASHORE TO COVER		83
(c) Both of the pair ashore in cover when first seen	204	
(d) Female ashore first leading her mate into cover	192	
(e) Male ashore first leading his mate into cover	105	
	605	

TABLE 22

NEST SITES OF TUFTED DUCK AND POCHARD IN ST. JAMES'S PARK (MAINLY ON DUCK ISLAND) BETWEEN 1954 AND 1970 INCLUSIVE

Nest locations	Number of nests shared between tufted and other species of duck	Number of nests	
		Tufted Duck	Pochard
ARTIFICIAL NEST SITES			
In nest boxes and similar man-made sites: *e.g.* wooden boxes; larger wooden chicken type coops or shelters; wire frame structures covered with rush, straw, plastic sheeting, or canvas; small plastic pail with part of side cut away; Dutch nest baskets for duck; log or stick piles grouped to form shelters; short sections of drain pipe dug into ground as Shelduck nest sites	16	305	59
In or behind various objects not originally intended as duck nest sites. After initial use duck were allowed to continue using most of them in subsequent years: *e.g.* under a wheelbarrow upside down; in a basket on its side; on ground behind wooden doors, corrugated iron sheeting, or stone slabs resting at an angle against sheds or buildings; inside a large galvanised water tank on its side; in loose straw inside sheds; in locker of boat on its side	7	34	29
NATURAL NEST SITES			
Sheltered nests on ground: *e.g.* in vegetation, under bushes and shrubs; in hollows in rockeries or in vegetation on rockeries; in holes in logs or tree bases; on bare ground screened by low walls; or at sides of sheds	2	76	12
Completely open nests: On leaf debris heaps or on spoil banks	—	4	1
In nests of other species of waterfowl after vacation by original owner (but not since 1961): In old Coot, Moorhen, and Mallard nests	—	6	1
(In occupied nest of another species of waterfowl. Tufted Duck only: With Moorhen – 1).			
	25	425	102

NOTES
1. Nests shared by Pochard with species other than tufted are not given.
2. Of the 25 nests shared by tufted with another species of duck, 15 were with Mallard and 2 with Pochard.
3. Purpose made artificial nest sites were seldom situated less than roughly six feet apart but there was no standard distance between them. Some were spaced at greater intervals than others.
4. Does not include 6 nests of known fate taken into account in Table 31 because exact details of the nest sites were not given to me.
5. One section of drain pipe, longer than others, qualified as an underground nest site. See section on **Nesting cover and artificial nest sites** in Chapter 6 for more recent sites of this nature.

TABLE 23

MALE AND FEMALE TUFTED DUCK SIMULATING NEST BUILDING IN A SPOT COMPLETELY UNSUITABLE FOR A NEST

ANALYSIS OF 66 RECORDS

	Adult Males			
	April	*May*	*June*	*July*
Lone males	10	1	4	5
Paired males	4	2	7	2
	14	3	11	7

	Adult Females			
	April	*May*	*June*	*July*
Lone females	1	1	4	9
Paired females	1	7	6	2
	2	8	10	11

SPAN OF RECORDS

Adult males – April 2 to July 29
Adult females – April 10 to July 31

Note: Brood females are *excluded* from this summary.

TABLE 24

NUMBER OF TUFTED DUCK NESTS FOUND ON DUCK ISLAND, NORTH BAY ISLETS, PALACE END ISLAND, AND IN MAINLAND EDGE COVER, BETWEEN 1954 AND 1970 INCLUSIVE

Period	*Nests found in natural sites*	*Nests found in artificial sites*	*Percentage of nests in artificial sites*
1954 to 1961 inclusive	37	6	14
1962 to 1970 inclusive	51	356	87
In seventeen years	88	362	80

TABLE 25

TUFTED DUCK CLUTCH SIZES IN ST. JAMES'S PARK BETWEEN 1954 AND 1968 INCLUSIVE

Number of eggs in a clutch	4	5	6	7	8	9	10	11	12	13	14	15	16
Number of clutches of above-mentioned sizes	3	4	1	9	15	22	9	14	7	3	2	2	1

Average size of 92 clutches = 9.3

TABLE 26

COMMUNAL CALLING WARNING BEHAVIOUR OF ADULT FEMALE TUFTED DUCK IN THE NESTING SEASON

ANALYSIS OF 31 RECORDS

Year	April				May				June			
	1-7	8-15	16-23	24-30	1-7	8-15	16-23	24-31	1-7	8-15	16-23	24-30
1961						2	1			1	1	
1962			1			1	1					
1963							1			2	1	1
1964								1	3	1		
1965				1	1		1					
1966				1	2		2	1			1	
1967					1		1					
1968									1			
	—	—	1	2	4	3	7	2	4	4	3	1

Note: Since completion of this Table communal calling was recorded on April 4, 1976.

TABLE 27

BREEDING AGE OF FEMALE TUFTED DUCK

Colour-ringed female's number	Age when female began laying	Date of first egg
114	11½ months	June 15
165	11 months and one week	May 30
205	10½ months	May 22
218	10½ months	June 1

Note: A duckling colour-ringed, wing-clipped and released in 1970 (outside the colour-ringing period covered by this book) was seen with a newly-hatched brood on July 21, 1971. This female was then approximately twelve months old and her first egg would have been laid about June 20, 1971.

TABLE 28

LONER FEMALE TUFTED DUCK SEEN ASHORE IN AN EGG-LAYING CONDITION (i.e. DROOPY AT THE REAR END)

ANALYSIS OF 76 RECORDS

Year	May 16-23	May 24-31	June 1-7	June 8-15	June 16-23	June 24-30	July 1-7	July 8-15	July 16-23	July 24-31	August 1-7	August 8-15
1958				2		1						
1959											1	
1961			1	4	2		7	1				
1962				1			1	2				
1963			1	2	1	1	2					
1964		2	1	7	2		5	3				
1965	1			2	2	3	1					
1966				5	2	1						
1967	1		1	1								
1968	1				1							
1969			1	2	1							
	2	1	4	10	23	12	15	8	—	—	1	—

Note: No males were seen in attendance on these females on any occasion.

TABLE 29

APPARENTLY HUNGRY FEMALE TUFTED DUCK COMING ASHORE TO BE FED IN THE BREEDING SEASON

ANALYSIS OF 87 RECORDS

Year	June				July				August			
	1-7	8-15	16-23	24-30	1-7	8-15	16-23	24-31	1-7	8-15	16-23	24-31
1957						1						
1958				1								
1959				4	3							
1960						7	1					
1961		2										
1962			3			5	6					
1963			3		3	5						
1964			3	1	2	5						
1965				2	4					1	1	
1966		4		2		3	2	1				
1967	1					1						
1968		2			2	2	1	2				
1969					1							
	—	3	15	10	15	29	10	3	—	1	1	—

TABLE 30

GESTURE OF REPULSION BEHAVIOUR BY FEMALE TUFTED DUCK

ANALYSIS OF 36 RECORDS

May	June				July		
24-31	1-7	8-15	16-23	24-30	1-7	8-15	16-23
1	5	3	9	9	4	3	2

A paired female in an egg-laying condition

Hungry (incubating) female begging for food

A rape attack on a female Red-crested Pochard by two males of the same species and a male hybrid probably of Red-crested Pochard × Mallard parentage

Female brooding young

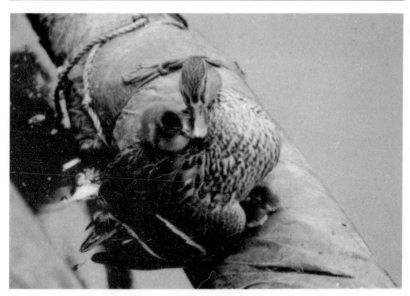

Female Mallard brooding a duckling on her back

An amalgamated brood of 23 downies

Female and brood being escorted from Buckingham Palace forecourt

The brood referred to in the previous photograph *en route* to St. James's Park

Male and his mate, a female Pochard, associating closely with
a female Pochard and her brood

Male and his mate, a female Pochard, associating closely with
a female Pochard and her brood

The female Pochard, paired to a male tufted, threatens a lone male Pochard whose behaviour causes the brood female Pochard to flee

A downy aged about three weeks (note streaked head);
this duckling is being reared by a Mallard

Brood female threatening a Moorhen

TABLE 31

SUCCESS OF TUFTED DUCK NESTS IN ST. JAMES'S PARK

NESTS WITH SUCCESSFUL AND UNSUCCESSFUL HATCHINGS

Period	Nests of known fate		Percentage of casualties to nests of known fate
	Number with successful hatchings	Number deserted, destroyed, etc.	
1954-1961 inclusive	15	16	51
1962-1969 inclusive	190	96	34
Totals 1954-1969 inclusive	205	112*	35

*With 3 nests it was undecided whether desertion occurred before destruction. These are excluded from below.

CAUSES OF NEST FAILURES

Period	Destroyed nests					Deserted nests	Nests lost through death of female	Total nests
	Clutches taken for incubators	Clutches taken by raiding boys	Destroyed By predators	By other causes	Clutches buried when nests taken over by another species			
1954 to 1961 inclusive	5	1	4	—	1	5	—	16
1962 to 1969 inclusive	4	8	10	3	3	64	1	93
Totals 1954 to 1969 inclusive	9	9	17	4	4	69	1	109

In the sixteen years, 63% of all failed nests were deserted and 37% destroyed.

TABLE 32

EGGS LEFT IN TUFTED DUCK NESTS AFTER DEPARTURE OF THOSE YOUNG WHICH HATCHED

Number of nests examined for left-over eggs and dead young	Nests which did not contain any left-over eggs or dead young	Number of left-over eggs found in remaining nests	Number of dead downies found in nests
180	88	207	12

The number of left-over eggs and dead young averaged 1.2 per nest for 180 nests examined.

TABLE 33

EXAMINATION OF CONTENTS OF 146 LEFT-OVER TUFTED DUCK EGGS TAKEN FROM NESTS AFTER THE DEPARTURE OF THE FEMALE AND THOSE OF THE BROOD WHICH HATCHED

Eggs without formed chicks (presumed infertile or partially incubated)	Rotten eggs (contents mostly a blackish evil-smelling liquid)	Eggs containing formed chicks (47% of 154)	
		Eggs opened	Eggs put in incubator and hatched
38	43	65	8

TABLE 34

SOME COMPARISONS CONCERNING TUFTED DUCK BIOLOGY OVER TWO CONSECUTIVE EIGHT-YEAR PERIODS IN ST. JAMES'S PARK

Period	Average number of pairs annually	Availability of artificial nest sites	Percentage of casualties to known nests	Percentage of pairs getting a brood to water	Percentage of broods reaching water after July 24	Percentage of females attending their broods for longer duration during fledging period	Percentage of young reared	Total number of broods reaching water	Estimated total number of young to reach the flying stage
1954 to 1961 incl.	21	Scarce	51	53	40	38	60	92	357
1962 to 1969 incl.	36	Numerous	34	71	24	12	30	206	390

TABLE 35

HATCHING DATE ANALYSIS OF 287 TUFTED DUCK BROODS IN FOURTEEN YEARS IN ST. JAMES'S PARK

Hatching Period	1956	1957	1958	1959	1960	1961	1962	1963	1964	1965	1966	1967	1968	1969	Total Broods
May 31 - June 6														2	2
June 7-14										1			1	4	6
June 15-22									1	2			3	2	8
June 23-30	1		1	1	1	1	1	2	1	3	4	2	1	6	25
July 1-8		1	1	1	1		1	2	4	2	4	6	12	10	45
July 9-16	6	3	6	6	4	2	3	1	2	1		5	8	8	55
July 17-24	2	6	3	5	4	2	4	5	4	7	8	4	2	6	62
July 25-31		3	2	2	2	3	4	4	2	4		7	5	6	44
August 1-8		2	2	2	1		2	2	1	4	5	2	1	3	27
August 9-16		3						1		1	2	3			10
August 17-22						1									1
August 23-29													2		2
	9	18	15	17	13	9	15	17	15	25	23	29	35	47	287

Broods hatched in May   = 1   Hatched May 31st
Broods hatched in June   = 40   = 14%
Broods hatched in July   = 206   = 72%
Broods hatched in August = 40   = 14%   Latest broods hatched August 28th
                                   287

From 1970 onwards there have been three earlier broods than the one given above, viz May 28, 1975; May 25, 1976; and May 27, 1977. Span of hatching period, therefore, is almost 14 weeks.

TABLE 36

REARING SUCCESS OF TUFTED DUCK IN FOURTEEN YEARS IN ST. JAMES'S PARK

Year	Estimated total number of pairs present on lake in the breeding season	Total number of young to reach water	Total number of broods seen	Total number of young reared by tufted	Young reared by other species			
					By female Mallard	By female Wigeon	By female Chiloé Wigeon	By female Pochard
	(a)	(b)	(c)	(d)	(e)	(f)	(g)	(h)
1956	14	45	9	25	2			
1957	18	107	18	50	5			
1958	22	106	15	82	6			
1959	27	130	17	81	2			
1960	30	110	13	46				
1961	32	71	9	35	1			
1962	30	113	15	37				
1963	22	113	17	49				2
1964	28	108	15	59	4			
1965	33	174	25	83	4			
1966	38	150	23	36	2			
1967	44	169	29	60	2	1	1	
1968	45	244	35	25				
1969	50	321	47	41				
	433	1961	287	709	28	1	1	2

(Continued)

Table 36 (continued)

Year	Young hand-reared by the Bird Keeper (i)	Total number of young reared (j)	Percentage of young reared annually (k)	Number of young per brood reared annually (l)
1956		25	55	2.8
1957		52	48	2.8
1958		87	82	5.4
1959		87	67	4.7
1960		48	43	3.5
1961		35	49	3.9
1962		38	33	2.5
1963		49	43	2.9
1964		65	60	3.9
1965	1	88	50	3.3
1966	7	45	30	1.5
1967	1	65	38	2.0
1968	4	29	11	0.7
1969	4	45*	14	0.8
	17	758		

Percentage of tufted ducklings reared in 14 years = 38 based on Columns (b) & (j) or, 33 based on 8 young per brood to reach water.
Number of young per brood seen to reach the flying stage = 2.5 based on Columns (c) & (d).
Number of young per pair present during the breeding season to reach the flying stage = 1.6 based on Columns (a) & (d).

Notes: Columns (d) to (h) inclusive = reared for part of the fledging period.
Column (i) includes some waifs brought in from the lake. These hand-reared birds were later released on the lake.

*includes most of the 40 caught and transferred to the Serpentine during the outbreak of disease that year.

TABLE 37

ANALYSIS OF TUFTED DUCK BROOD SIZES WHEN NEWLY-HATCHED BROODS WERE FIRST SEEN ON WATER IN FOURTEEN YEARS IN ST. JAMES'S PARK

Year	\ Number of ducklings in broods																		Total number of broods in a year
	1	2	3	4	5	6	7	8	9	10	11	12	13	14	15	16	17	18	
1956	2		1	1		2	1	1	1										9
1957		1		4	7	1		3		2									18
1958		1	2	3	3	1	1	1			2		1						15
1959			1	3	2	3	1		4	1		1	1						17
1960	1	1	1		1	2		2	1	1		1		1			1		13
1961				1	2	2		1	1	1	1								9
1962			1	1	6	2	1	2				1		1					15
1963		1	3		2	2	2	4	2		1								17
1964		2	1		2	3	2	2	1			1	1						15
1965	1	2	3	1	4	2	4	2	2	1	1		1		1				25
1966		2	2	2	4	2	3	4	2		2								23
1967	1	1	4	4	5	6*	2*	4			1		1						29
1968		3	2	3	2	3	5	9	2	4	1		1						35
1969		2	2	2	7	10	13†	5	2	1	2	1							47
	5	16	22	25	42	45	36	39	20	12	10	6	5	2	1		1		287

*A brood of 19 treated as 2 broods of 6 each and 1 brood of 7.
†Two broods totalling 21 each are treated as 6 broods of 7 each.

Average size of 287 broods totalling 1855 young when first seen on water = 6.5.

TABLE 38

NUMBERS OF NEWLY-HATCHED TUFTED DUCKLINGS REACHING WATER ANNUALLY IN TUFTED BROODS AND IN BROODS OF OTHER SPECIES IN ST. JAMES'S PARK

Year	Total young to reach water annually	Tufted young in tufted broods	Newly-hatched tufted ducklings alone on lake	Tufted ducklings in other species' broods						Escapes from captivity to lake
				With female Mallard	With female Pochard	With female Red-crested Pochard	With female Garganey	With female Wigeon	With female Chiloé Wigeon	
	(a)	(b)	(c)	(d)	(e)	(f)	(g)	(h)	(i)	(j)
1956	45	45								
1957	107	103		4						
1958	106	91	4	6	3					2
1959	130	121	1	7		1				
1960	110	102	6	2						
1961	71	64	4	3						
1962	113	111	1	1						
1963	113	108		5						
1964	108	99	2	5	2					
1965	174	161		9			4			
1966	150	143		7						
1967	169	160		6				2	1	
1968	244	241		1				2		
1969	321	306		6	2			7		
	1961	1855	18	62	7	1	4	11	1	2

Notes: Column (c) – Ducklings which were either lost or deserted on reaching water.
Column (j) – Hand-reared ducklings which escaped from the Bird Keeper's pens.

TABLE 39

FLEDGING PERIOD OF YOUNG TUFTED DUCK

42 to 49 days Some birds make short fluttering flights of a few yards at 42 days and flights of up to about fifty yards just clear of the surface at 49 days.

49 to 63 days Most birds capable of sustained flight between 56 and 63 days old.

63 to 77 days Some birds are backward in development and are only capable of flight when between 63 and 77 days old.

TOTAL SPAN OF FLYING PERIOD

First young birds fly about July 16 and the last birds by about November 12, giving a total span of about 17 weeks.

TABLE 40
DATES ON WHICH ADULT TUFTED DUCK WERE FIRST SEEN TO BE FLIGHTLESS ON THE ST. JAMES'S GROUP OF WATERS (EXCLUDING BUCKINGHAM PALACE LAKE) BETWEEN 1953 AND 1969 INCLUSIVE

MALES

Date	Number of birds commencing flightless period on or within the 7 days preceding dates given	Estimated number commencing flightless period in month	Approx. percentage commencing flightless period in month
June	Nil	Nil	Nil
July 6	3		
July 9	1		
July 16	18		
July 23	43		
July 30	128	200	44.6
August 6	103		
August 13	73		
August 20	60		
August 27	15	246	55.0
September 3	3		
September 10	—		
September 17	1		
September 24	—	2	0.4
October 1	—		
October 8	—		
October 15	—		
October 22	—		
October 29	—		
	448	448	

(Continued)

Table 40 (*continued*)

FEMALES

Date	Number of birds commencing flightless period on or within the 7 days preceding dates given	Estimated number commencing flightless period in month	Approx. percentage commencing flightless period in month
June	Nil	Nil	Nil
July 6	—		
July 9	2		
July 16	8		
July 23	16		
July 30	37	73	13.0
August 6	70		
August 13	83		
August 20	115		
August 27	79	392	70.0
September 3	87		
September 10	43		
September 17	8		
September 24	6	89	16.0
October 1	2		
October 8	2		
October 15	1		
October 22	—		
October 29	1	6	1.0
	560	560	

Notes:

(a) Allowances have been made for, *e.g.* some birds seen flightless in the first week of August having dropped their flight feathers at the end of July.

(b) Since the above summary was completed one male was seen to be newly-flightless on June 17, 1976. A second male, newly-flightless on October 1, 1974, would not have been full-winged again before October 25-28. Also, of two females newly-flightless on October 28, 1975, one would not have been full-winged again before November 21-24.

(c) The grand total of 1,008 males and females is made up of the St. James's Park birds between 1953 and 1969 inclusive (331) plus Serpentine, Long Water and Round Pond birds between 1961 and 1969 inclusive (677) as given in Table 42.

TABLE 41

COMMENCEMENT OF THE FLIGHTLESS PERIOD OF ADULT FEMALE TUFTED DUCK

Groups of females studied between 1953 and 1970 incl. (see Figure 3)	*Percentages of females starting flightless period in each month*				*Approximate percentage of females starting their flightless period by August 7*
	July	*August*	*September*	*October*	
GROUP 1 29 colour-ringed females aged one year and over which were considered to have bred unsuccessfully between 1963 and 1970 inclusive	21	69	10	—	45
GROUP 2 20 first year colour-ringed females considered to have paired up and attempted breeding between 1963 and 1970 inclusive. Two bred successfully but eighteen were unsuccessful	20	65	15	—	35
GROUP 3 19 colour-ringed females aged one year and over which bred successfully between 1963 and 1970 inclusive	5	80	15	—	10
GROUP 4 52 brood females whose flightless period overlapped with their brood duties between 1956 and 1964 inclusive	—	85	15	—	10
GROUP 5 560 females which completed their wing moult on the St. James's group of waters between 1953 and 1969 inclusive. This group included successful and unsuccessful breeding, and non-breeding, females	13	70	16	1	24

TABLE 42

DISTRIBUTION OF FLIGHTLESS ADULT TUFTED DUCK ON THE ST. JAMES'S GROUP OF WATERS (EXCLUDING BUCKINGHAM PALACE LAKE*) IN THE YEARS 1953 TO 1969 INCLUSIVE

Year	ST. JAMES'S PARK LAKE		SERPENTINE AND LONG WATER		THE ROUND POND	
	Males	Females	Males	Females	Males	Females
1953	—	4	No investigation 1953 to 1958 inclusive		No investigation 1953 to 1960 inclusive	
1954	1	2				
1955	—	6				
1956	2	12				
1957	5	12				
1958	5	20				
1959	5	21	(18)**	(10)**		
1960	8	25	(20)**	(5)**		
1961	8	20	45	34	21	7
1962	9	35	33	27	18	4
1963	7	25	23	20	11	9
1964	6	15	23	19	16	12
1965	4	18	24	28	8	3
1966	3	11	25	30	10	4
1967	3	9	29	35	9	3
1968	5	11	50	36	1	1
1969	5	9	25	33	1	—
Totals 1953 to 1969 incl.	76	255	—	—	—	—
Totals 1961 to 1969 incl.	50 (11.9)†	153 (33.4)†	277 (65.6)†	262 (57.2)†	95 (22.5)†	43 (9.4)†

* No positive information for Buckingham Palace lake but the reported presence of one or two birds in some years suggested that, occasionally, one or two completed the wing moult there.

** Odd counts only. They are not included in any totals but serve to show that the water area has been used as a moult area since at least 1959. The presence of 50 birds on July 17 and regular flocks assembling in August, 1952 (*cf. Bird Life in The Royal Parks* report for 1952), suggests a probability of some moulting Tufted Duck there that summer.

† Figures in brackets after each total for the period 1961 to 1969 inclusive are the percentages of the total number of flightless males or females using that particular water area.

TABLE 43

APPROXIMATE DEPARTURE DATES FROM ST. JAMES'S PARK LAKE OF COLOUR-RINGED
ADULT TUFTED DUCK WHICH WERE PRESENT IN THE BREEDING SEASON BUT WHICH
LEFT TO COMPLETE THEIR FLIGHTLESS PERIOD ELSEWHERE

19 DEPARTURE DATES OF MALES

	May				*June*				*July*				*August*			
	1-7	8-15	16-23	24-31	1-7	8-15	16-23	24-30	1-7	8-15	16-23	24-31	1-7	8-15	16-23	24-31
	–	–	1	–	3	3	5	4	–	2	–	–	1	–	–	–

16 DEPARTURE DATES OF FEMALES SEEN WITH BROODS

	May				*June*				*July*				*August*			
	1-7	8-15	16-23	24-31	1-7	8-15	16-23	24-30	1-7	8-15	16-23	24-31	1-7	8-15	16-23	24-31
	–	–	–	–	–	–	–	1	–	1	–	7	4	1	2	–

38 DEPARTURE DATES OF FEMALES NOT SEEN WITH BROODS

	May				*June*				*July*				*August*			
	1-7	8-15	16-23	24-31	1-7	8-15	16-23	24-30	1-7	8-15	16-23	24-31	1-7	8-15	16-23	24-31
	–	–	–	–	2	5	3	3	4	3	7	5	4	1	1	–

APPENDIX 1

EXAMPLES OF PAIRING DATA OF
4 COLOUR-RINGED TUFTED DUCK

Colour-ringed male or female number	Age by breeding seasons	Dates and number of days seen alone therefore considered not to be paired	Dates and number of days seen paired	Dates seen in a close-knit courting party	Other breeding season behaviour observed	Days gap between being seen unpaired and fixed pairing
88 male	First season	March 13 to April 18, alone on 9 dates	(a) April 24 & 25			
		April 26 alone	(b) April 30 to May 2 paired to a female different from (a)			
		May 3 to 23 alone on 5 dates			May 24 with another male flew in with a pair	
				In a courting party on May 28		
		May 30 alone	(c) Paired from June 4 to July 19 on 11 dates to same female but to a different female from those in (a) and (b) above			Four

(Continued)

Appendix 1 *(continued)*

Colour-ringed male or female number	Age by breeding seasons	Dates and number of days seen alone therefore considered not to be paired	Dates and number of days seen paired	Dates seen in a close-knit courting party	Other breeding season behaviour observed	Days gap between being seen unpaired and fixed pairing
88 male	Sixth season	January 3 to April 13 alone on 19 dates				
					With two other males tagged onto a pair on April 17	
		April 20 and May 3 alone	Paired on 4 dates May 6 to June 7			Two
96 male	Second season	February 4 to April 13 alone on 19 dates	(a) Paired on April 25 & 26			
		April 27 and May 8 alone	(b) Paired on May 10			
		May 11 to 20 alone on 5 dates	(c) Paired on 14 dates May 24 to July 12			Three

(Continued)

Appendix 1 (continued)

Colour-ringed male or female number	Age by breeding seasons	Dates and number of days seen alone therefore considered not to be paired	Dates and number of days seen paired	Dates seen in a close-knit courting party	Other breeding season behaviour observed	Days gap between being seen unpaired and fixed pairing
110 female	First season	January 3 to May 14 alone on 8 dates	Paired on 12 dates from May 17 to June 17 to same male			Two
	Second season	January 15 to March 14 alone on 12 dates	Paired on 23 dates March 22 to June 20 to same male			Seven
	Third season	January 20 to March 19 alone on 8 dates	Paired on 14 dates March 23 to May 27 to same male Note: different males each year			Three

(Continued)

Appendix 1 (continued)

Colour-ringed male or female number	Age by breeding seasons	Dates and number of days seen alone therefore considered not to be paired	Dates and number of days seen paired	Dates seen in a close-knit courting party	Other breeding season behaviour observed	Days gap between being seen unpaired and fixed pairing
118 female	First season	February 12 to March 26 alone on 10 dates	(a) March 27 to April 10 paired on 4 dates			
		April 12 to 20 alone on 5 dates	(b) Paired on April 26			
		April 28 alone		May 14 and 24 seen in a courting party		
			(c) Paired on 6 dates June 2 to 29			Eight
	Second season	January 28 to April 22 alone on 19 dates	(a) April 25 paired			
		April 28 to May 19 alone on 4 dates	(b) Paired 9 dates May 22 to June 20			Two

APPENDIX 2
WATER AREA PREFERENCES OF COLOUR-RINGED FEMALE TUFTED DUCKS WITHIN THEIR HOME RANGES

Identification number of colour-ringed female	Approximate age of female in years (e.g. 1st, 2nd year, etc.)	Period during which a female was seen mainly in a particular part of the lake before and after pairing NOTES: § These females, not seen after April 30, and not subsequently proved to have nested, may have moved elsewhere, except for one which was found dead. * These females were paired when first seen. † This female had eggs when first seen. ‡ This female was a non-breeding bird which did not pair.	Favoured sections of the lake based on sightings: (a) Palace end island (b) Whole lake (c) Horse Guards end of lake (d) Bridge to Horse Guards end of lake (e) Bridge to Palace end Island
98	1	April 11, 1965 – July 18, 1965	Bdge to H.G.
	2	March 12, 1966 – July 16, 1966	Bdge to P.Isle
	3	March 13, 1967 – July 3, 1967	Bdge to P.Isle
	4	March 27, 1968 – July 1, 1968	P.Isle
	5	September 30, 1968 – June 7, 1969	Bdge to P.Isle
100	1	April 8, 1965 – June 2, 1965	P.Isle
102	1	March 27, 1966 – July 14, 1966	Bdge to P.Isle
110	1	February 26, 1966 – July 8, 1966	Bdge to P.Isle
	2	December 18, 1966 – July 19, 1967	Bdge to P.Isle
	3	December 16, 1967 – July 11, 1968	Bdge to P.Isle
	4	§ January 5, 1969 – April 23, 1969	Bdge to P.Isle
	5	§ October 4, 1969 – March 25, 1970	Bdge to P.Isle
115	1	‡ January 3, 1966 – July 19, 1966	Bdge to H.G.
	2	‡ September 24, 1966 – July 29, 1967	Bdge to H.G.
	3	‡ November 9, 1967 – June 14, 1968	Bdge to H.G.
	4	‡ August 16, 1968 – June 6, 1969	Bdge to H.G.
	5	‡ August 12, 1969 – June 23, 1970	Bdge to H.G.
118	1	February 12, 1966 – June 29, 1966	H.G.
	2	January 28, 1967 – June 20, 1967	H.G.
	3	§ December 30, 1967 – April 25, 1968 (found dead)	H.G.
119	1	February 12, 1966 – June 18, 1966	H.G.
125	1	* May 23, 1966 – June 28, 1966	Whole lake
	2	* May 10, 1967 – June 27, 1967	Bdge to H.G.
	3	April 9, 1968 – July 18, 1968	Bdge to H.G.
	4	* April 29, 1969 – June 20, 1969	Bdge to H.G.
	5	April 7, 1970 – June 23, 1970	Bdge to H.G.
126	1	Not seen	
	2	* April 22, 1967 – June 9, 1967	P.Isle
	3	February 17, 1968 – June 18, 1968	Whole lake
	4	April 26, 1969 – June 18, 1969	H.G.
	5	April 4, 1970 – June 24, 1970	H.G.

(Continued)

Appendix 2 *(continued)*

Identification number of colour-ringed female	Approximate age of female in years (e.g. 1st, 2nd year, etc.)	Period during which a female was seen mainly in a particular part of the lake before and after pairing NOTES: § These females, not seen after April 30, and not subsequently proved to have nested, may have moved elsewhere, except for one which was found dead. * These females were paired when first seen. † This female had eggs when first seen. ‡ This female was a non-breeding bird which did not pair.	Favoured sections of the lake based on sightings: (a) Palace end island (b) Whole lake (c) Horse Guards end of lake (d) Bridge to Horse Guards end of lake (e) Bridge to Palace end Island
127	1	* April 27, 1966 – June 29, 1966	P.Isle
	2	* May 19, 1967 – June 18, 1967	Whole lake
	3	† June 22, 1968 – July 13, 1968	H.G.
	4	March 19, 1969 – June 12, 1969	Whole lake
131	1	January 29, 1966 – May 7, 1966	Bdge to H.G.
132	1	March 9, 1966 – May 16, 1966	H.G.
135	1	February 4, 1966 – May 8, 1966	H.G.
	2	December 31, 1966 – May 2, 1967	H.G.
	3	Not seen	
	4	* April 10, 1969 – May 9, 1969	H.G.
	5	§ January 13, 1970 – April 30, 1970	H.G.
136	1	February 1, 1966 – July 5, 1966	H.G.
	2	November 4, 1966 – July 31, 1967	Bdge to H.G.
	3	September 22, 1967 – June 29, 1968	Bdge to H.G.
	4	October 2, 1968 – July 2, 1969	Bdge to H.G.
	5	January 3, 1970 – June 26, 1970	Bdge to H.G.
	6	February 13, 1971 – June 29, 1971	Bdge to H.G.
138	1	April 12, 1966 – June 1, 1966	P.Isle
	2	January 14, 1967 – May 3, 1967	Bdge to P.Isle
139	1	March 2, 1966 – June 1, 1966	Whole lake
	2	April 8, 1967 – May 3, 1967	Whole lake
142	1	February 12, 1966 – June 29, 1966	P.Isle
	2	November 11, 1966 – June 27, 1967	P.Isle
	3	October 30, 1967 – April 17, 1968 (Seen with a brood on July 11)	P.Isle
	4	October 5, 1968 – July 4, 1969	P.Isle
148	1	December 10, 1966 – May 10, 1967	Bdge to P.Isle
149	1	November 11, 1966 – July 6, 1967	Bdge to P.Isle
	2	§ September 22, 1967 – March 2, 1968	Bdge to P.Isle
152	1	January 3, 1968 – July 5, 1968	P.Isle
	2	January 9, 1969 – July 12, 1969	P.Isle
	3	January 3, 1970 – May 13, 1970	P.Isle
153	1	December 30, 1967 – June 15, 1968	H.G.
	2	March 7, 1969 – May 19, 1969	H.G.
156	1	§ December 14, 1967 – April 16, 1968	H.G.

(Continued)

Appendix 2 *(continued)*

Identi-fication number of colour-ringed female	Approxi-mate age of female in years (e.g. 1st, 2nd year, etc.)	Period during which a female was seen mainly in a particular part of the lake before and after pairing NOTES: § These females, not seen after April 30, and not subsequently proved to have nested, may have moved elsewhere, except for one which was found dead. * These females were paired when first seen. † This female had eggs when first seen. ‡ This female was a non-breeding bird which did not pair.	Favoured sections of the lake based on sightings: (a) Palace end island (b) Whole lake (c) Horse Guards end of lake (d) Bridge to Horse Guards end of lake (e) Bridge to Palace end Island
159	1	March 14, 1968 – June 15, 1968	Bdge to H.G.
	2	January 12, 1969 – May 31, 1969	Bdge to H.G.
	3	January 24, 1970 – July 4, 1970	H.G.
165	1	* April 19, 1968 – June 15, 1968	H.G.
	2	January 5, 1969 – July 4, 1969	Bdge to H.G.
	3	March 7, 1970 – June 18, 1970	H.G.
177	1	* April 26, 1968 – June 29, 1968	Bdge to H.G.
	2	March 13, 1969 – June 26, 1969	Bdge to H.G.
184	1	January 7, 1970 – June 18, 1970	H.G.
191	1	§ November 22, 1969 – March 21, 1970	Bdge to P.Isle

Females caught on their nests and colour-ringed. Their exact age was unknown so their second breeding season is given as +1 (one female, caught with newly-hatched young, is included)

223	+1	February 28, 1968 – July 2, 1968	Whole lake
	+2	December 16, 1968 – June 24, 1969	Whole lake
	+3	January 13, 1970 – May 22, 1970	Whole lake
224	+1	* April 19, 1968 – June 13, 1968	H.G.
	+2	* April 16, 1969 – July 3, 1969	H.G.
225	+1	January 6, 1968 – July 2, 1968	H.G.
	+2	§ January 21, 1969 – April 23, 1969	H.G.
227	+1	January 9, 1969 – July 7, 1969	P.Isle
	+2	January 3, 1970 – June 6, 1970	P.Isle
228	+1	January 6, 1969 – June 2, 1969	P.Isle
229	+1	* April 28, 1969 – May 1, 1969	H.G.
	+2	April 17, 1970 – June 20, 1970	H.G.
230 Caught with brood	+1	* April 26, 1969 – May 17, 1969	Bdge to H.G.
	+2	April 17, 1970 – May 8, 1970	H.G.

APPENDIX 3

HOMOSEXUAL BEHAVIOUR OF FEMALE TUFTED DUCK

Date   *Detail of observations*

June 6, 1958   One male and two females observed close together. Both females were in the **Neck-stretch** posture. Then the loner female tried to mount the paired female which was receptive. This occurred four or five times but the submissive female did not lie prone. The paired male made a weak thrust at the loner female and then tried to copulate with his own female but was unsuccessful. Then the pair swam off together.

May 22, 1963   One male and two females seen together. The male approached 'A' female in **Neck-stretch** posture and making dorsal preening movements. He then approached 'B' female, also in the **Neck-stretch** posture. Then 'B' female, also in the **Neck-stretch** posture, tried to mount 'A' female. This was followed by copulation between the male and 'B' female.

June 22, 1963   One male and two females watched in close association. Both females were in the **Neck-stretch** posture when one mounted the other like a copulating pair. This lasted for at least a minute with the male remaining passive about a foot away. Another pair came close and the male chased them off. Afterwards the trio remained close to one another.

July 3, 1963   A loner female swam up to a pair and gave the **Neck-stretch** and chin lift posture. The pair had just returned from a search for a nest site and subsequent events were as follows. 'C' paired male threatened loner female 'D' and pursued her ashore into cover. He returned to his own female and gave the **Neck-stretch** and chin lift posture. 'C' paired female also assumed the **Neck-stretch** posture and her mate tried to mount her. 'C' paired female gave another **Neck-stretch** then left him, and went ashore nest site searching. Later 'C' pair were together and both birds assumed the **Neck-stretch** posture when a loner female 'E' swam to them in the same posture and giving the chin lift as well. 'C' paired female then mounted loner female 'E' for about a minute during which time 'C' paired male chased off a lone male which approached the trio.

June 24, 1967   A pair and a loner female observed in close company. Both females assumed the **Neck-stretch** posture, then one female mounted the other at the same time grasping the submissive female's nape feathers and going through the motions of copulation. While this was going on the paired male took no action. Later, the loner female swam off and joined another pair closely.

NOTE: All females referred to above matched others of this sex on the lake. There were no significant differences in plumage or bare parts suggesting that any of those behaving like males were actually males in a female type plumage.

APPENDIX 4
EVIDENCE OF NESTING BY LONER FEMALE TUFTED DUCK

1959 AN UNMARKED FEMALE

Date	Sightings
July 27	Female seen alone nest site searching in North Bay on small islets.
July 28	– ditto –
July 29	– ditto –
July 30	– ditto –
August 4	Same female, still alone, vigorously nest building on one of the islets.
August 5	Arthur May visited the nest at my request and found it to contain 3 eggs.
August 9	Arthur May visited nest but the eggs were gone.

No tufted pairs were observed after July 15 and no males were present in North Bay.

1963 FEMALE WITH A DISTINCTIVE ALUMINIUM RING ON HER RIGHT LEG AND DISTINCTIVE UNDERPARTS

Date	Sightings
May 20	Female seen alone at Palace end island.
May 21	– ditto –
May 22	– ditto –
May 24	– ditto –
June 12	– ditto –
June 18	– ditto –
June 25	Female seen with a brood of 8 newly-hatched ducklings in same area.
June 26	Female with 4 young in same area.
June 27	Female without any young in same area.
July 12	Female seen with a male in attendance. She went ashore nest site searching in same area.
July 18	Female seen alone near the bridge.
August 3	Seen alone (still full-winged).
August 10	Seen alone (still full-winged).

1964 COLOUR-RINGED FEMALE NO. 217

Date	Sightings
June 7	Female seen with a male in close attendance in North Bay.
June 13	Female seen alone in North Bay.
June 16	– ditto –
June 17	– ditto –
June 18	– ditto –
June 23	– ditto –
June 27	Female seen with a male spaced one yard from her in same area.
July 1	Female seen alone in North Bay.
July 3	– ditto – (she is now very droopy at rear end).
July 6	– ditto –
July 11	Female seen alone in same area.

(Continued)

Appendix 4 *(continued)*

1970   COLOUR-RINGED FEMALE NO. 202

Date	*Sightings*
May 1	Female seen alone.
May 6	– ditto –
May 8	– ditto –
May 13	– ditto –
May 22	– ditto – (she is now very droopy at rear end).
June 12	Female seen alone.
June 19	– ditto –
June 26	– ditto –
July 26	– ditto –
August 7	Female seen with one newly-hatched duckling.
September 4	Female seen alone. Now flightless.

1970   COLOUR-RINGED FEMALE NO. 205

Date	*Sightings*
May 14	Female seen alone.
May 15	– ditto –
May 16	– ditto –
May 22	– ditto –
May 30	– ditto –
June 5	– ditto –
June 9	– ditto –
June 27	– ditto –
July 8	Female seen with a brood of 4 newly-hatched ducklings.

This female was sitting on 4 eggs on April 28. The nest was destroyed between May 10 and May 13, so the above constitutes repeat nesting.

A Herring Gull swooping down to seize one of a variant (white) Mallard's six downies

A light-faced downy

A dark-faced downy

Dark- and light-faced downies

Duckling with a white 'mask'

Brood female with her one duckling aged almost six weeks

Duckling with white
under tail-coverts

Duckling aged nearly 8 weeks
exercising its wings

A juvenile male at the beginning of March aged 7 to 9 months

Male Ring-necked Duck commencing post-nuptial moult

Male flightless during post-nuptial moult

A juvenile male at the end of October aged 3 to 5 months

Male in post-nuptial moult (July)

Male Ring-necked Duck in post-nuptial moult (July)

Male Scaup in post-nuptial moult (July)

Flightless female with white 'mask' (August)

Flightless female with a white 'mask' (August)

Female with a white 'mask' and white under the tail (December)

Female Scaup with a smaller than usual white 'mask' (January)

APPENDIX 5
SUMMARY OF 19 RECORDS OF THE REACTIONS, MAINLY BY MALE TUFTED, TO RAPE ATTACKS BY OTHER MALE TUFTED

Paired male remaining passive and taking no defensive action while his mate was being raped by another male —

> 7 records: May 25 and 26, 1956; May 21 and June 18, 1960; June 10, 1961; May 26, 1964; and June 25, 1966.

Rapist driving off a paired male and attacking the paired male's mate —

> 4 records: May 27, 1958; June 18, 1960; June 2, 1964; and June 19, 1967.

Paired male leaving his own mate and driving off a rapist which was attacking another female —

> 4 records: June 12, 1961; May 31, 1963; July 4, 1965 (two records).
> On one date the paired male was, in turn, driven away by the rapist and a second paired male then attacked the rapist. This time the rape attack was broken off.

Lone male driving off a rapist which was attacking a loner female —

> 1 record: On June 21, 1967, a lone male was raping a loner (egg-laying) female. A second lone male drove off the rapist which, however, recaught and raped the female.

Rape attack attracting curiosity —

> 1 record: On May 26, 1964, a lone male and a paired male (accompanied by his mate) took no action but watched a male raping a female.

Rapist driven off and replaced by his attacker —

> 1 record: On May 5, 1959, a lone male was driven off a female's back by another lone male which, in turn, raped the female.

Behaviour of a female to a rape attack by her mate on another female —

> 1 record: On June 11, 1959, a paired male caught and raped another paired female. The rapist's own mate swam to them, gave the **Neck-stretch** posture, climbed onto her mate's back as he continued to rape the strange female.

APPENDIX 6

TIME-SPAN OF A TUFTED BROOD FEMALE'S STAY WITH HER YOUNG DURING THE DUCKLINGS' FLEDGING PERIOD, TOGETHER WITH AVAILABLE DETAILS OF A BROOD FEMALE'S WING MOULT

BASED ON 84 RECOGNISED FEMALES AND BROODS BETWEEN 1956 AND 1964
THESE FEMALES WERE NOT COLOUR-RINGED

EARLY-NESTING FEMALES
Those females getting broods to water between June 15 and July 28

Brood female number	Date when brood first reached water	Date when brood female first became flightless	Age in days of young when mother became flightless	Age in days of young when deserted by mother		Notes
1	June 15	?	?	34	)	
2	June 28	August 1	35	42	)	Sample of
3	June 30	August 4	36	44	)	13 broods.
4	,,	August 1	33	46	)	Average age
5	July 2	?	?	52	)	of young on
6	July 3	?	?	42	)	desertion, of
7	July 7	?	?	35	)	broods
8	,,	?	?	32	)	reaching
9	July 10	?	?	43	)	water
10	,,	?	?	43	)	between
11	,,	August 18	40	40	)	June 15 and
12	July 11	August 6	27	46	)	July 11 = 41
13	,,	?	?	40	)	days
14	July 12	August 21	40	48		
15	July 14	August 6	24	40		
16	,,	August 10	27	36		
17	July 16	?	?	26		
18	,,	?	?	22		
19	July 17	August 18	33	49		NOTE:
20	July 18	August 7	21	37		49% of
21	,,	?	?	38		brood
22	,,	August 24	38	45		females
23	,,	?	?	40		stayed with
24	July 19	?	?	6		their young
25	,,	August 15	28	38		for 40 days
26	,,	August 19	32	44		or over
27	July 19/20	August 15	27-28	41		
28	July 20	?	?	30		
29	July 21	August 10	21	42		
30	,,	August 21	32	41		

(Continued)

Appendix 6 *(continued)*

EARLY-NESTING FEMALES *(continued)*

Brood female number	Date when brood first reached water	Date when brood female first became flightless	Age in days of young when mother became flightless	Age in days of young when deserted by mother	Notes
31	July 22	August 12	22	39	
32	,,	August 28	38	45	
33	,,	August 21	30	40	
34	July 23	?	?	16	
35	,,	August 18	27	41	
36	July 24	August 31	39	39	
37	,,	?	?	32	
38	July 25	August 13	20	39	
39	,,	?	?	23	
40	,,	?	?	31	
41	,,	?	?	25	
42	July 26	August 10	16	35	
43	,,	August 13	19	39	
44	,,	?	?	26	
45	July 27	?	?	35	
46	,,	August 30	34	35	
47	July 28	August 20	24	42	
47 broods and brood females	Sample of 47 broods reaching water between June 15 and July 28 incl.	Sample of 26 brood females. 90% of brood females flightless between August 1 and 24	Sample of 26 broods. Average age of young when brood female flightless = 29 days	Sample of 47 broods. Average age of young when deserted by parent = 37 days	

LATE-NESTING FEMALES

Those females getting broods to water between July 29 and August 22

48	July 29	August 25	28	40	
49	,,	?	?	16	
50	,,	?	?	13	
51	,,	August 27	30	38	NOTE:
52	,,	September 3	36	38	21% of brood
53	July 30	August 12	14	33	females stayed
54	,,	August 23	25	38	with their young
55	,,	?	?	25	for 40 days or
56	,,	?	?	27	over
57	,,	August 24	26	40	
58	,,	August 23	25	34	
59	,,	August 30	32	44	
60	,,	?	?	14	

(Continued)

Appendix 6 (continued)

LATE-NESTING FEMALES (continued)

Brood female number	Date when brood first reached water	Date when brood female first became flightless	Age in days of young when mother became flightless	Age in days of young when deserted by mother		Notes
61	August 1	August 28	28	40		
62	,,	September 1	32	41		
63	August 2	August 26	25	39		
64	,,	August 22	21	33		
65	,,	?	?	19		
66	August 3	?	?	35		
67	,,	August 29	27	42		
68	,,	August 27	25	34		
69	August 4	August 22	20	36		
70	,,	August 22	20	39		
71	August 5	September 12	39	39	)	
72	,,	?	?	13	)	Sample of
73	,,	?	?	40	)	14 broods.
74	August 6	?	?	12	)	Average age
75	August 8	August 29	22	46	)	of young on
76	,,	August 30	23	37	)	desertion, of
77	August 9	August 28	20	31	)	broods
78	August 10	August 27	17	19	)	reaching
79	August 12	September 2	22	32	)	water
80	August 14	September 3	21	29	)	between
81	,,	September 8	26	36	)	August 5
82	August 15	September 3	20	39	)	and 22
83	,,	?	?	8	)	= 29 days
84	August 22	September 7	17	24	)	
37 broods and brood females	Sample of 37 broods reaching water between July 29 and August 22 incl.	Sample of 26 brood females. 96% of brood females flightless between August 22 and September 12	Sample of 26 broods. Average age of young when brood female flightless = 25 days	Sample of 37 broods. Average age of young when deserted by parent = 31 days		

APPENDIX 7

DURATION OF A TUFTED BROOD FEMALE'S STAY WITH HER YOUNG DURING THE DUCKLINGS' FLEDGING PERIOD

BASED ON 35 COLOUR-RINGED FEMALES SEEN WITH BROODS BETWEEN 1965 AND 1970

Colour-ringed female's number	Date brood first seen on water	Total days female seen with brood	Days gap between female last being seen with brood and being seen alone	Female's age by seasons
(a)	(b)	(c)	(d)	(e)
205	May 31 (First brood)	7	6	3
205	June 9	12	None	2
153	June 16 (First brood)	1	2	2
205	June 22	4	3	1
152	June 24	1	*	3
229	June 27	10	*	Unknown
223	June 30	44	*	Unknown
98	July 1	8	7	4
112	July 2	36	*	3
218	July 2	26	7	1
227	July 2	49	*	Unknown
224	July 3	1	*	Unknown
165	July 3	23	*	1
136	July 4	5	2	5
136	July 7	42	2	3
205	July 8	10	8	4
223	July 9	1	*	Unknown
223	July 11	1	2	Unknown
142	July 11	2	*	3
127	July 12	2	*	3
114	July 12	2	*	1
225	July 20	1	6	Unknown
118	July 21	21	*	2
110	July 23	5	2	3
126	July 23	11	*	5
125	July 25	1	*	4
126	July 26	20	5	4
152	July 26	1	6	2
205	July 26 (Second brood)	1	4	3

(Continued)

R

Appendix 7 (continued)

Colour-ringed female's number	Date brood first seen on water	Total days female seen with brood	Days gap between female last being seen with brood and being seen alone	Female's age by seasons
(a)	(b)	(c)	(d)	(e)
230	July 26	1	1	Unknown
159	July 28	1	*	3
230	July 28	9	*	Unknown
229	August 1	19	3	Unknown
153	August 3 (Second brood)	2	*	2
202	August 7	1	*	4

NOTES:

(i) Col. (b) — The two females who got two broods each to water in the same season either deserted their first brood or the young died while under their care.

(ii) Col. (d) — * = females not seen alone within 8 days after last being seen with their brood.

(iii) Col. (e) — Females of *unknown* age were those caught on the nest and colour-ringed.

(iv) None of these females became flightless while attending their young.

APPENDIX 8

OVERLAP BETWEEN A BROOD FEMALE TUFTED DUCK'S WING MOULT AND HER BROOD DUTIES

BASED ON A SAMPLE OF 52 BROODS BETWEEN 1956 AND 1964
AS DETAILED IN APPENDIX 6

IN RESPECT OF BROODS REACHING WATER BETWEEN: June 15 and July 28 incl.		*IN RESPECT OF BROODS REACHING WATER BETWEEN:* July 29 and August 22 incl.	
Brood female number	*Days overlap*	*Brood female number*	*Days overlap*
2	8	48	13
3	9	51	9
4	14	52	3
11	1	53	20
12	20	54	14
14	9	57	15
15	17	58	10
16	10	59	13
19	17	61	13
20	17	62	10
22	8	63	15
25	11	64	13
26	13	67	16
27	14-15	68	10
29	22	69	17
30	10	70	20
31	18	71	1
32	8	75	25
33	11	76	15
35	15	77	12
36	1	78	3
38	20	79	11
42	20	80	9
43	21	81	11
46	2	82	20
47	19	84	8

Average duration of overlap for 26 females = *ca* 13 days (Variation 1-22 days)

Average duration of overlap for 26 females = *ca* 13 days (Variation 1-25 days)

APPENDIX 9
VOICE OF THE TUFTED DUCK

Although 20 calls are listed below, they are likely to amount to only 12 main ones (Nos. 1 to 12 inclusive. Three of the latter are given by adult males, seven by adult females and two by downy young.

ADULT MALE

1. WHA WA WHEW

This triple call is the commoner of the two display notes (Nos. 1 and 2) given by males of close-knit courting parties. A body shake (or wing-and-tail-flick) accompanies this wavering whistle. The first note is the loudest. I have heard it between October 3 and July 12 and it is common from late December onwards. This call is sometimes given by males waiting to be fed by the public and by presumed courting males in flight.

2. WHEE-OU

This is a mellow double whistle. It is heard during courtship, accompanies the **Head-throw** posture and is given (though I have no personal record) following copulation. A slight body shake may accompany this call which I have recorded from October 22 onwards until July 15. This note is commonly given by males on water in the presence of other drakes in situations not involving courting parties. On one occasion an isolated male, dozing on a water devoid of other tufted, gave this double note to me on being disturbed. Also heard from drakes in flight.

3. WEE WEE WEE

This faint call repeated several times through a quivering or rapidly opened and closed bill has only been heard from males when adopting the **Crouch** posture in defence of the female. I have been unable to detect this call at distances beyond three or four feet.

ADULT FEMALE

4. KURR

Variations of this common call are given by females on land, on water, and in flight. As a rolling growl it is the usual note of a female when conducting her brood. As a shorter less rolling but oft repeated note it is the communal alarm call. A softer and more gentle version has been heard during nuptial flights. On water a slight body shake accompanies this call.

5. TAK
6. TARR

These two soft notes, the second a trifle longer and sharper than the first, are frequently heard during courtship and may occur as a double TAK-TARR.

7. TUK TOOK TUK

This rather pleasant double or triple note, lacking the harshness of other calls of the female, has been heard during courtship and from females waiting to be fed by the public. A single TUK is given by mothers accompanying young, in which situation it seems to be a contact note analagous to the soft clucking of a farmyard hen with chicks. A single TUK, repeated at intervals, is also a frequent call of females in flocks of mixed sexes long before courtship begins – when drakes are noticeably silent. Calls 5, 6 & 7 are sometimes given in flight.

8. KER KER KER

This somewhat rattling call may be repeated a number of times by females when defending their individual spacing.

(Continued)

Appendix 9 (continued)

9. KWA KWI KWA KWA KWA — This is probably a distress call. The second note is the highest, the last three descending rapidly. It was only heard from a one-legged colour-ringed female at close range.

10. KUK UK UK — This distinctive guttural call uttered through a wide open bill was only heard when females gave the **Gesture of Repulsion** display.

DUCKLINGS

Downy Young

11. PEE PIP PIP PIP — These soft contact notes are heard from newly-hatched downies before they are dry as well as from older downies.

12. PEE PEE PEE — These louder plaintive notes are the distress calls which carry some distance. They are frequently given in the first two weeks or so after hatching, especially when downies are handled or seized by other water birds. In the latter situation the note becomes shriller and conveys urgency whereupon the mother goes to the aid of her youngster.

13. SWEET SWEET SWEET — This harsher or sharper version of No. 12 call has been heard from ducklings aged about 18 to 23 days. It reminds me of the usual call of the Wood Sandpiper when on migration. To my ears it can be heard over a greater distance than the previous note. When about three weeks old or over ducklings are less susceptible to cold and wet weather but are still vulnerable to predators. The additional carrying power of this penetrating call may allow a mother to be alerted to a duckling's distress over greater distances and may have important survival value.

Partly feathered or feathered young aged about 5 to 9 weeks

As ducklings approach the flying stage the bond between them and their parent weakens. As feathers replace down many are deserted by their mother. Since feathered young are more able to look after themselves they no longer need the contact and distress calls of earlier weeks and become less vocal. The calls that they do give begin to resemble those of adults.

14. KWEE KWEE KWEE — This soft croaking version of No. 13 was given by a duckling aged 6 to 7 weeks with primaries just through and small amounts of down still on the rump and nape.

15. KUK KUK KUK — These two soft calls were heard from 7 to 8 weeks old
16. KAR KAR KAR — ducklings. The first was a short note and the second a longer one.

17. KAR KWI KAR KWI — This oft repeated call was given by a 7 to 8 weeks old which had all the characteristics of a young female. It was the youngster's version of an old female's distress call.

18. KWIL KWIL KWIL or KWILP KWILP — This soft liquid call from ca. 7 to 8 weeks old ducklings (once from a bird about 4 weeks old) is probably the early stages of the adult male's WHA WA WHEW call. Several ducklings of a brood of Pochard of similar age gave the plaintive piping KREE-YOU* of an adult male Pochard. A change to adult calls probably occurs in the final stages of fledging or soon after.

19. KWERK — These two soft single calls were the only ones occasionally
20. TUK — heard when ducklings aged 6 to 8 weeks were handled for colour-ringing.

*This is the third call of the adult male Pochard as suggested by Cramp and Simmons (1977).

APPENDIX 10

A LIST OF *AYTHYA* AND OTHER HYBRIDS, CONSIDERED TO INVOLVE TUFTED DUCK PARENTAGE, OBSERVED IN ST. JAMES'S PARK AND ELSEWHERE BETWEEN 1963 AND SEPTEMBER 1984

Aythya crosses, totalling a minimum of seven males and two females, are additional to ones observed in the Park in earlier years and recorded in *A Study of Certain Aythya Hybrids* (Gillham *et al.*, 1966) to which reference should be made. Also, eight hybrids seen in other parks or counties are referred to. All of the following birds were watched at close quarters.

MALE HYBRIDS

'Lesser Scaup type'

1 on March 23, 1968.	
2 on April 16, 1968	Both were seen in different Pochard courting parties.
1 from April 29 to June 21, 1968	This one was paired to a female Pochard.
1 from March 15 to June 10, 1969	This male occurred in Pochard courting parties on April 9 and May 7. It was temporarily paired to a female Pochard on April 14.
1 on April 10, 1970	This bird was associating with Pochard.
1 from April 25 to May 10, 1976	When photographed on April 29 and May 8 it was associating solely with Tufted Duck.
1 from April 20 to April 29, 1984	When photographed on April 21, this hybrid was a member of a Tufted Duck courting party. It assumed one of the two **Sneak** postures of a male Pochard on one occasion and, later, gave the triple WHA WA WHEW call of a drake tufted with accompanying wing-and-tail flick. Its voice, however, sounded slightly different, having the wheeze of a Pochard about it.

All of the above adults in breeding plumage (probably totalling only four different birds) had black bill tips typical of this hybrid. Those seen in 1968, 1969 and 1970 had a distinctive blackish area at the base of the bill, while the one seen in 1976 had but a negligible amount of black visible only at the closest quarters. The 1968 birds, and the one seen in 1976, had narrow white areas on their bills immediately behind the black tip as in the male Tufted Duck and some 'Scaup types'. The 1984 bird had no dusky markings at the base of the bill but possessed a distinctive white line behind the black bill tip. Its side panels differed from most other 'Lesser Scaup types' I have seen through being slightly darker than usual.

A male considered to be an American-Eurasian equivalent of the 'Lesser Scaup type' was photographed in another London park in 1983. It differed from others I have seen on five main points: (1) its black bill tip was fan-shaped as in a normal male tufted and not 'Mr. Moon'-shaped like other 'Lesser Scaup types'; (2) there was a distinctive green gloss on the cheeks contrasting with a purplish gloss on the forehead, crown, and nape; (3) the markings of the mantle were coarse like those of the Lesser Scaup and Scaup; (4) the eyes were golden yellow like an old male tufted and not amber like other 'Lesser Scaup types'; (5) the side panels were pure white.

A 'kink' in the nape, as in others of this hybrid type, was a flush crest. These crest feathers came to a sharp point when the bird stretched forward. A white band on the bill, behind the black tip, was as noticeable as in nearby male Tufted Ducks which the bird matched in size.

As this hybrid was pinioned I made some enquiries and learned that it had been purchased as a true Lesser Scaup about 1980. This male, which was probably a cross between a Tufted Duck and a Lesser Scaup, more closely resembled the latter than a 'Lesser Scaup type' hybrid.

(Continued)

Appendix 10 (continued)

'Pochard type'

One seen on May 14, 1970, differed from a similar male observed in 1962 through not having any suggestion of a crest. Moreover, it was the first example to be seen at close range, when its bill tip was found to be exactly like that of a 'Lesser Scaup type'. In all probability this distinctive hybrid is a variation of the 'Lesser Scaup type'.

'Scaup type'

An immature on October 14, 1970, resembled one seen early in 1960 but had a narrow white band immediately behind the fan or triangular shaped black bill tip. An adult in full breeding plumage was seen on June 5, 1980. This drake possessed a short bushy crest and its mantle appeared darker than either a male Scaup or Lesser Scaup in breeding plumage. Its bill had the usual fan-shaped black tip with a narrow white line behind the nail.

As the feathers forming the crest looked disarranged this hybrid has not been compared with four other 'Scaup types' at the end of this appendix. Three of these four are additional to the two 'Scaup types' referred to above.

Probable tufted × Mallard cross

One seen on December 17 and 18, 1966, and on June 7, 1967. In winter this hybrid, the size of a female Wigeon, superficially resembled a male Tufted Duck in plumage but sat higher in the water with its stern well up like a surface-feeding duck. Its head was peaked indicating a flush crest.

HEAD AND NECK: Crown and forehead glossy black with strong green reflections. Neck blackish with purple sheen.

UPPER BREAST: Brownish-black with purple sheen at sides but medium brown with blackish barring in the centre.

TAIL AND TAIL-COVERTS: Whole stern area blackish-brown.

FLANKS: Shape as in a male tufted but not pure white due to grey vermiculations which were fine and even.

WINGS: No wing bar visible in flight. Primaries were short of tail tip by about two inches.

LEGS AND FEET: Yellowish-orange.

BILL: Long and narrow. Distal two-thirds blue-grey shading to yellowish-grey at base. Bill tip similar to that of a 'Scaup type' hybrid with an almost white line behind the black.

EYES: Dark reddish-brown.

ECLIPSE PLUMAGE: On June 7, 1967, it resembled a small male Mallard in eclipse without any tufted characteristics whatsoever.

ASSOCIATES: Seen mainly with Mallard.

DISPLAY: Seen engaged in mutual head-pumping with a female Mallard.

Probable tufted × Rosy-bill crosses

One photographed on April 9, 1984, was reported by other observers at intervals until early May. In size and general appearance it resembled a male Rosy-bill except for the following main differences:

TAIL, CLOSED WINGS, BACK AND MANTLE: Paler, and a more brownish-black. The wing coverts, scapulars and mantle were finely speckled with grey and black. There were some dark green reflections on the wings and the tips of the primaries were buffish-brown.

UNDER TAIL-COVERTS: These appeared dark except for a distinctive white spot beside the outermost tail feathers.

HEAD: A slight but distinctive crest on the nape.

BILL: A slightly swollen pinkish-red 'shield' on the forehead adjoining the pinkish base of its broad bill. The rest of the bill was slate-grey with a faint yellowish tinge shading to white behind a black tip which resembled that of a typical adult male Tufted Duck.

EYES: Deep orange.

LEGS AND FEET: Pale yellowish-grey.

(Continued)

Appendix 10 *(continued)*

A second adult male cross, probably of the same parentage, was photographed in the Park between July 21 and August 9, 1984.

It was distinctly smaller than a drake Rosy-bill, being about the size of a male Baer's Pochard, to which it bore a strong superficial resemblance. Comparison with the last-named species was afforded by the arrival of a full-winged drake Baer's Pochard which stayed for at least ten days from July 28. This male hybrid could also be confused with a drake 'Baer's Pochard type' cross.

Details of this hybrid are as follows:—

HEAD AND UPPER BREAST: A darker brownish-black than the rest of the upperparts, especially the head. A minute crest sometimes visible on the slightly peaked nape. A pale brown neck-ring was noticed on the first date after which this plumage feature quickly disappeared.

TAIL, CLOSED WINGS, BACK AND MANTLE: Brownish-black with some dark green reflections on the wings. Tips of primaries buffish-brown.

UNDER TAIL-COVERTS: Pure white like those of the Rosy-bill and Baer's Pochard.

FLANKS: Shape of side panels closely resembled those of an adult male Tufted Duck. Evenly and finely vermiculated with grey-brown appearing darker than in the previous hybrid. Like the Baer's Pochard, the flanks and under tail-coverts were separated by blackish-brown feathering.

LOWER BREAST AND BELLY: These underparts were similar to the flanks but paler.

BILL: The bill shape of both this and the previous hybrid resembled that of a Tufted Duck. Colour a bluish-slate shading to a pinkish tinge at the base. A slightly swollen pale pinkish-red shield on the forehead, adjoining the base, was less conspicuous than in the previous hybrid. The Tufted Duck-like black fan-shaped tip, darkest on the nail, was bordered by a bluish-white line.

EYES: Orange.

LEGS AND FEET: Pale buffish-yellow.

DISPLAY: Seen to give the **Headthrow** posture of a drake tufted.

FOOD: Both this hybrid and the male Baer's Pochard were seen feeding on strands of a filamentous alga, a food which Tufted Ducks were never seen to eat.

ASSOCIATES: This hybrid and the male Baer's Pochard were never close companions, nor did they associate closely with other ducks. Both arrived at, and left, the feeding points independently, almost always at different times.

FEMALE HYBRIDS

Immature or adult female probably of tufted × Scaup origins ('Scaup type')
One photographed on October 31, 1975, was a long-necked bird with a mixture of Scaup and tufted characteristics. Head and bill shape like a Scaup but much smaller and more delicate. Head markings similar to a female Scaup in summer but the white areas were less distinct. The under tail-coverts were white. In size it was no larger than a female Tufted Duck.

Adult female probably of tufted × Scaup origins ('Scaup type')
An adult female photographed in Sussex in the winter of 1983 was associating with an old female Scaup which it matched in size. The main points of difference were: (1) it lacked the female Scaup's greyish speckles and vermiculations on the upperparts, thus more closely resembling several nearby female tufted in colour; (2) the smaller white facial mask was like that of some female tufted; (3) nape feathers slightly elongated giving the appearance of an extremely short but distinctive crest; (4) the size of the dark bill tip was similar to the bill end of a female Tufted Duck but only the nail area was black. The rest of the fan-shaped tip was a paler greyish-black. This was a striking feature when female Scaup, Tufted Duck and the hybrid were together; (5) early in May this bird had a noticeable amount of white on the under tail-coverts.

Adult female probably of tufted × Pochard origins ('Pochard type')
One photographed on June 24, 1978, had a mixture of tufted and Pochard characteristics. In general it resembled a small delicately built female Pochard the colour and size of a female Tufted Duck. The face markings were those of a female Pochard at the same time of the year. This hybrid's eyes were dark. Neither this nor the female seen in 1975 associated closely with other ducks.

(Continued)

Appendix 10 *(continued)*

DISCUSSION

My observations on adult Scaup, Tufted Duck and Ferruginous Duck in full plumage show that the black bill tips in these species are sometimes variable.

For example, a few male Scaup have the black extending a little over, and not confined solely to, the nail. Although covering a trifle larger area than usual, the black pattern retains the typical finger-nail shape. Similarly, an old female of this species had twice as much black on the tip of her bill as several other adults of her own sex on the same lake. Both adult male and female Ferruginous Ducks sometimes have mainly black bill tips in winter and spring. In the drake the black may be continuous but more often a tiny greyish patch intervenes on either side of the black nail.

The male Tufted Duck has two distinctive variations of bill tip, both differing from the normal fan or cone-shape. First, a few birds have a smaller amount of black on the bill roughly circular in pattern. This black is confined mainly to the nail and its immediate surroundings, and the white area may cover much of the distal edge. Second, a few others have the black flatter and broader through extending a little further along the bill tip than usual.

Differences in the bill patterns of adult male Pochard have been depicted in the paper referred to at the beginning of this appendix. In this species both the black at the base of the bill, as well as the central portion of the black tip, are variable. The general bill colour of certain species is subject to variation too. It is not uncommon for adult drake Pochard in full plumage to have an almost pure white band immediately behind the black tip. Similarly, old male Scaup in breeding plumage occasionally have the bill lead blue at the base shading to chalk blue at the distal end close to the nail.

Both the colour of the bill and the black patterning on the tip are still important points for the recognition of *Aythya* hybrids. Nevertheless, too much reliance must not be placed solely on bill characters, for other differences like size, plumage and eye colour are of equal value.

All male 'Scaup type' hybrids that I have seen have had pure white side panels. In contrast, all drake 'Lesser Scaup types' have had dirty white flanks similar to the Sutton Courtenay bird described by Perrins (1961).

Variations occur in the head-shape of 'Lesser Scaup types'. A proportion do not always have a profile matching the Sutton Courtenay bird which Perrins describes as "rather similar to that in the Ring-necked Duck." These somewhat round-headed birds only present a peaked head-shape when indulging in pre-nuptial display. Then the normally flush crest is elevated. The 'Baer's Pochard type' male also acquires a head-shape similar to a male ring-neck when displaying.

The following are some variations noted in four adult male 'Scaup type' hybrids in full plumage on water:

1. Ref. No. 24 in the paper referred to at the beginning of this appendix.
2. Seen in the London Area in 1971.
3. Seen and photographed in Sussex in 1981.
4. Seen and photographed in Sussex in 1983.

GENERAL COLOUR OF DORSAL AREA AND WINGS: 1 and 2 more like adult male Scaup in full plumage than 3 and 4 which were a much darker grey.

APPEARANCE OF WING LENGTH: 1 had noticeably short wings which did not cross at the tips. It was a shorter winged bird than the other three.

BODY SIZE: 1 and 2 were similar in size to adult male Scaup whereas 3 and 4 were the size of a male Tufted Duck.

HEAD SHAPE: 1 and 2 were without any suspicion of a crest and resembled male Scaup. 3 had a raised ridge of feathers on the crown producing the effect of a blunted crest similar to the mounted specimen shown in photograph 13 in the paper referred to at the beginning of this appendix. 4 had a much more distinctive pointed stand-off tuft which was permanently erect. This bird's head was more like that of a Tufted Duck than the others. It is possible that the crest of 3 takes several years to develop into one like that of 4.

SHAPE OF BLACK TIP ON BILL: 1, 2 and 3 had slightly smaller fan-shaped black tips than most adult male Tufted Ducks in full plumage. 4 had a finger nail-shaped black tip smaller than the other three but slightly larger than that of a normal adult male Scaup in full plumage.

APPENDIX 11

ABERRANT PLUMAGE

Tufted Ducks with slight inherited markings differing from typical adult plumages occurred more frequently than birds with major variations. Taking Mallard as a guide, the colouring of downy ducklings provided a useful yardstick to the potential frequency of distinctive mutants or variants in that species in St. James's. For example, plain unpatterned bright yellow ducklings grew into pure white females. Downies with blackish heads and upperparts and pale below turned into 'Dusky' adult females (*cf.* Lack, 1974). Thirdly, light-coloured downies, which were more fawnish-brown with buff patterning above and creamy buff below, became unusually pale fully-grown females. Adult females of these 'Dusky' or 'Pale' mutations were of annual occurrence in the Park. In the former the lighter feathering typical of normal adult females was much darker, while in the latter it was much lighter. It was not uncommon for a perfectly normal female Mallard to have a proportion of variant ducklings among her brood. 'Dusky' downies were commoner than 'Pale' ones. The degree of recurrence of distinctive variants among the Mallard population could, therefore, be gauged by the different colour phases of small ducklings. At Finsbury Park there were even more types of variant Mallard than in St. James's and interbreeding between variants was probably regular. One buff coloured female, with indistinct markings and showing white on the primaries and white on her tail-feathers, had six differently marked or coloured ducklings among her brood of nine. Only a single downy was normal while the remainder included one in unpatterned pale buffish-yellow down and one in unpatterned dusky down. The colour and patterning of some downies in other parks could also be linked with variant adult males.

In contrast, the apparent normality of the overwhelming majority of downy tufted ducklings observed closely on St. James's lake and in other London parks points to at least markedly aberrant birds being more exceptional in this species. Two greyish-coloured downy ducklings are described below, but apart from this couple, which reached maturity, only one other lighter than usual downy was seen during this study. The infrequency of variant Tufted Ducks is confirmed by the relatively few variant adults observed and which are described in subsequent paragraphs.

ADULT MALES

Partial albinism

Only one male with a large amount of white on the upperparts was ever observed. On March 20, 1963, this bird, which at a distance bore a superficial resemblance to a drake Scaup, had its closed wings, mantle and tail liberally streaked with white. Both its head and neck appeared normal. Two other males with much smaller amounts of white feathering were seen over the years, the most distinctive one having a noticeable amount of white speckling over parts of the back and mantle.

Isabelline feathering

In the years 1956 to 1958 inclusive, at least six different adult males were observed with varying amounts of pale buff feathering on the wings, mantle, back and tail (Gillham, 1959). From 1959 onwards males with buffish tails were of almost annual occurrence. In some birds decomposition of the tail-feathers was evident from the ragged appearance of the barbs and the spiky shaft tips. Few buff-tailed birds could reliably be considered as having this feathering unassociated with wasted tail-feathers. Incidentally, males and females with similar wasted primaries were occasionally recorded but such birds were never seen to fly.

ADULT FEMALES

Creamy-buff variety

Only one observed. In the breeding season of 1979 a most attractive pale creamy-buff female, paired to a normal male, was present on the lake. She was not seen in flight so it could not be confirmed that white marks near the tips of her primaries occurred on other parts of the flight feathers. At close quarters it could be seen that the pale plumage was faintly marked with brown. Her bill and irides were normal.

Grey-bodied variety

While catching ducklings for colour-ringing in 1965 two large grey-coloured downies of similar size

(Continued)

Appendix 11 *(continued)*

were obtained. Both were retained, temporarily, in a Duck Island pond enclosure to study their development as at that stage the possibility of hybrids could not be excluded. The palest duckling was pinioned, colour-ringed (No. 218), and released on the lake when about eight weeks old. She turned out to be a variant of this type. Her head, neck, bill and eye colour – in fact everything from the base of the neck upwards to the tip of the bill – were normal, but the rest of the body and wings were a pale slate-grey tinged pinkish in places. This female paired, nested and produced a brood in her first year and died when about eighteen months old. Her ducklings appeared normal.

Whitish-sided variety
The darker of the two grey-coloured downies was colour-ringed (No. 115) and returned to the lake full-winged. In adult plumage this bird proved to be a quite different variant from the previous one. On the many occasions when seen during ten-and-a-quarter years her size, bill, and eye colour were typical of an adult female. Superficially, she resembled a light-sided male tufted in eclipse. The whole plumage was a warm brown excepting the side panels, which were more like those of an adult male but tinted with buff and not brilliant white. In the breeding season the crown and forehead only were shot with purple and green. The drooping stand-off crest approached in length that of a first year male between April and September. In old age her winter plumage became much darker brown, thereby increasing the similarity to a light-sided male in eclipse. Once or twice this bird associated with females but it was mainly a loner which was never once known to pair. If judged solely on behaviour it could be classed as sexless. It is a matter of speculation whether this and the preceding female, which were so unlike one another, came from the same brood. The only other record was of a similar female, with slightly duskier sides, observed in Regent's Park on February 6, 1975.

Partial albinism
Females with an insignificant amount of white feathering were fairly frequent, the commonest feature being some white markings in the crest or nape feathers. Less usual were females with a few white feathers on the front or back of the neck or on the cheeks.

White Scaup-like facial patch
The white 'mask' of some female Tufted Ducks has confused and tantalised inexperienced bird-watchers for many decades. Over fifty years ago T. A. Coward (1929) was drawing attention to the transitional nature of the white frontal face markings in young tufted, a feature dealt with elsewhere in this book. In this section all that remains to be said on this subject is to stress that a few females retain a white frontal patch as a common characteristic *throughout their lives*, like the adult female Scaup. Colour-ringed female No. 213 was one such bird. She was seen at irregular intervals on some thirty dates in all months of the year except November over a period of ten-and-a-quarter years. The white facial patch developed when this female was between seven and twenty-eight weeks old and she was seen with it in ten months of the year from December 20, 1969, onwards. The blaze was absent in June 1970; dirty white on March 31, 1973, and on May 24, 1974; and indistinct on July 17, 1979. It was absent on October 18, 1973, yet clean and prominent on October 5, 1979, the last date on which this female was known to be alive. Her 'mask' was also a prominent white on October 31, 1970; September 21, 1971; August 24, 1973; January 11, 1976; January 18 and February 8, 1977; May 10 and September 15, 1978, and on April 17, 1979.

JUVENILES
Partial albinism
Of regular occurrence among St. James's reared tufted in the past twenty-seven years has been the presence of a small amount of white barring on the wings or mantle in some newly-fledged young. This was particularly noticeable on the coverts of the closed wings of swimming birds. There was no standard pattern, some having only a single narrow white mark on one wing while others had several bars of varying prominence in different positions. Unfortunately, only one juvenile with these white feathers was colour-ringed and followed through to maturity, when the markings were not present. In consequence there was no conclusive evidence from a larger sample that the white marks did not reappear frequently in adult plumage. It can be said, however, that after first noticing this feathering in ducklings in 1958, only one adult male was seen with similar white bars in comparable positions.

(Continued)

Appendix 11 (*continued*)

PLUMAGES SUGGESTING A CHANGE OF SEX

Plumage suggesting a sex change is known to occur in some species through hormonal imbalance with age. It is possible, therefore, that Tufted Ducks and Pochard in the following plumages may fall into this category.

Tufted Duck

Single birds with a mix of male and female characteristics occurred in St. James's in 1965, 1968 and 1969, and two in 1967. In addition one was seen in Finsbury Park in 1979. Sightings were on thirty-eight dates between April 5 and June 20. This variant is readily distinguishable in spring as it bears a superficial resemblance to some males moulting into eclipse.

The wings, dorsal area, rump and tail are blackish-brown and the sides a pale slatey-buff, broken by contrasting darker wavy vertical bars. The crest and irides are more like those of an adult male. The brown head is patterned with various-sized black blotches which are glossed with purple and bottle green, appearing a bronze colour at certain angles.

Only on two consecutive days was one of them thought to be paired to a male. Otherwise they kept to themselves.

Pochard

In this species there are two distinct variants with a mix of male and female characteristics, the commonest type bearing a stronger superficial resemblance to a female in winter plumage than the other. In 1980 alone, there were five of the 'female type' and one of the 'male type' in St. James's and one of the former in Finsbury Park.

Six of the seven in 1980 were almost identical, having the sides, mantle and wings pale grey, only a trifle darker than in an old male. The reddish eye colour was intermediate between an adult male and an adult female in the breeding season. The rest of the plumage, and bill colour, matched that of a female in transition from winter to summer plumage. The 'male type' had the same intermediate eye colour and, except for slightly reduced female face markings, more closely resembled an adult male.

Over the years most of these variants were easily recognised, especially between April and June. Some, however, had the grey parts mottled with light brown, making them look more like adult females in winter. Because of their presence in a similar plumage throughout the year, these distinctive Pochard baffled me for about two decades, and they must have puzzled other observers too.

Coloured photographs of these birds were sent to the Wildfowl Trust in 1979 and Professor Geoffrey Matthews tells me (*in litt.*) that he and his colleagues considered the Pochard to be males in the process of adopting female plumage. Naturally, confirmation from an examination of specimens freshly obtained in the field needs to be forthcoming.

All of these variants were loners. Though observed on several hundred occasions they were never seen in courting parties nor were they known to pair. On a single occasion one was seen scraping a nest bowl in the breeding season.

APPENDIX 12
BIRDS BREEDING IN ST. JAMES'S PARK
IN PERIOD 1961 TO 1984 INCLUSIVE

This list excludes pinioned or full-winged ornamental waterfowl which are referred to in Appendix 13. The following thirty-two species have been found breeding in the Park's 53 acres in the past twenty-four years.

CLASS I

Fourteen species each of which breed annually in numbers usually of six pairs or over. These are the established breeding birds:—

Canada Goose	Coot	Song Thrush
Mallard	London Pigeon	Blue Tit
Pochard	Woodpigeon	House Sparrow
Tufted Duck	Dunnock	Starling
Moorhen	Blackbird	

CLASS II

Eight species – usually not in excess of two or three pairs each – bred, or attempted breeding, or were present in the breeding season. These birds, because of their limited numbers, have a tenuous though better foothold than those in Class III:—

Herring Gull (since 1964)	Mistle Thrush	Magpie (since 1977)
Wren	Great Tit	Carrion Crow
Robin	Greenfinch	

CLASS III

Ten species, consisting mainly of single pairs of each, bred at least once and were seen occasionally in other breeding seasons. They were not proved to have nested regularly enough to be considered for Class II:—

Little Grebe (first breeding in 1983)	Tawny Owl	Coal Tit
	Pied Wagtail	Chaffinch
Great Crested Grebe (first breeding in 1984)	Spotted Flycatcher	Jay
	Long-tailed Tit (first breeding in 1983)	
Mute Swan		

NOTES

1. Strictly speaking the Canada Goose, through introductions as recently as the 1950s, should be grouped with the ornamental waterfowl. However, since by custom this species has, for some years, been included in the list of birds observed in the Royal Parks, it is placed in Class I. Breeding numbers of this species are controlled. Some persons may consider that the Greylag Goose should, henceforth, be treated similarly.

2. Of Class II birds, the Magpie is now the strongest candidate for elevation to Class I.

3. Of Class III birds a single pair of Pied Wagtails occurred most often. In several years it is probable that they nested just outside the Park boundary but fed regularly beside the lake.

4. By 1980 the shrubberies around the Park were the best since 1953 thus providing good cover for land-birds. The breeding season of 1969 followed drastic pruning of shrubberies which led to an unprecedented concentration of land-birds breeding on Duck Island. On May 3 that year there were at least 30 nests of the Blackbird, 5 nests of the Song Thrush, and 7 nests of the Dunnock in the untouched cover of this island.

5. London Pigeon, Moorhen, Coot, Blackbird and Great Tit have nested once or twice inside artificial nest sites placed on or near the ground for ducks.

6. The London Natural History Society welcomes all reports of birds observed in St. James's and in other Royal Parks in the London Area.

APPENDIX 13

NOMENCLATURE

BIRDS

Except for a few recent amendments English names of birds detailed below, which are on the British List, are as recorded in *The Status of Birds in Britain and Ireland* by the British Ornithologists' Union (1971). Taxonomic order of swans, geese and ducks, and English names of waterfowl not on the British List, are as published in the *Handbook of Waterfowl Behaviour* by Johnsgard (1965). Binomials only are given and reference should be made to the various works cited in the text to ascertain geographical races.

The following list includes wild birds referred to in the text and ornamental waterfowl in the St. James's Park collection in spring 1984. The latter may be identified by the preceding asterisk.

Little Grebe   Tachybaptus ruficollis
Great Crested Grebe   Podiceps cristatus
Cormorant   Phalacrocorax carbo
*Pelican species   Pelecanus
Grey Heron   Ardea cinerea
*Fulvous Whistling Duck   Dendrocygna bicolor
*White-faced Whistling Duck   Dendrocygna viduata
Mute Swan   Cygnus olor
*Black Swan   Cygnus atratus
Bean Goose   Anser fabalis
*Pink-footed Goose   Anser brachyrhynchus
*White-fronted Goose   Anser albifrons
*Greylag Goose   Anser anser
*Bar-headed Goose   Anser indicus
*Snow Goose   Anser caerulescens
*Ross's Goose   Anser rossi
*Emperor Goose   Anser canagicus
*Hawaiian Goose   Branta sandvicensis
Canada Goose   Branta canadensis
*Barnacle Goose   Branta leucopsis
*Brent Goose   Branta bernicla
*Red-breasted Goose   Branta ruficollis
Abyssinian Blue-winged Goose   Cyanochen cyanopterus
*Egyptian Goose   Alopochen aegyptiacus
*Ruddy Shelduck   Tadorna ferruginea
*Cape (or South African) Shelduck   Tadorna cana
*Shelduck   Tadorna tadorna
*Radjah Shelduck   Tadorna radjah
*Ringed Teal   Callonetta leucophrys
*Wood (or Carolina) Duck   Aix sponsa
*Mandarin Duck   Aix galericulata
*Australian Wood Duck   Chenonetta jubata
*Wigeon   Anas penelope
*Chiloé Wigeon   Anas sibilatrix
*Gadwall   Anas strepera
*Teal   Anas crecca
*Cape Teal   Anas capensis
*Chestnut Teal   Anas castanea
Mallard   Anas platyrhynchos
*Crested Duck   Anas specularioides
*Pintail   Anas acuta

(Continued)

Appendix 13 *(continued)*

*Bahama Pintail   Anas bahamensis
*Garganey   Anas querquedula
 Blue-winged Teal   Anas discors
*Cinnamon Teal   Anas cyanoptera
*Shoveler   Anas clypeata
*Marbled Teal   Marmaronetta angustirostris
*Red-crested Pochard   Netta rufina
 Southern Pochard   Netta erythropthalma
*Rosy-bill (or Rosy-billed Pochard)   Netta peposaca
 Canvasback   Aythya vallisneria
 Pochard   Aythya ferina
 Redhead   Aythya americana
 Ring-necked Duck   Aythya collaris
 Baer's White-eye (or Baer's Pochard)   Aythya baeri
 Ferruginous Duck (or Common White-eye)   Aythya nyroca
 New Zealand Scaup   Aythya novae-seelandiae
 Tufted Duck   Aythya fuligula
 Scaup   Aythya marila
 Lesser Scaup   Aythya affinis
*Eider   Somateria mollissima
 Long-tailed Duck (or Old Squaw)   Clangula hyemalis
 Common Scoter   Melanitta nigra
 Velvet (or White-winged) Scoter   Melanitta fusca
 Bufflehead   Bucephala albeola
 Barrow's Goldeneye   Bucephala islandica
*Goldeneye   Bucephala clangula
 Smew   Mergus albellus
 Red-breasted Merganser   Mergus serrator
 Goosander   Mergus merganser
*Ruddy Duck   Oxyura jamaicensis
 Australian Blue-billed Duck   Oxyura australis
 Musk Duck   Biziura lobata
 Sparrowhawk   Accipiter nisus
 Kestrel   Falco tinnunculus
 Pheasant   Phasianus colchicus
 Moorhen   Gallinula chloropus
 Coot   Fulica atra
 Wood Sandpiper   Tringa glareola
 Black-headed Gull   Larus ridibundus
 Lesser Black-backed Gull   Larus fuscus
 Herring Gull   Larus argentatus
 Great Black-backed Gull   Larus marinus
 Common Tern   Sterna hirundo
 Feral Pigeon (or London Pigeon)   Columba
 Woodpigeon   Columba palumbus
 Tawny Owl   Strix aluco
 Pied Wagtail   Motacilla alba
 Wren   Troglodytes troglodytes
 Dunnock (or Hedge Sparrow)   Prunella modularis
 Robin   Erithacus rebecula
 Blackbird   Turdus merula
 Song Thrush   Turdus philomelos
 Mistle Thrush   Turdus viscivorus
 Spotted Flycatcher   Muscicapa striata
 Long-tailed Tit   Aegithalos caudatus

(Continued)

Appendix 13 *(continued)*

Coal Tit	Parus ater
Blue Tit	Parus caeruleus
Great Tit	Parus major
Jay	Garrulus glandarius
Magpie	Pica pica
Carrion Crow	Corvus corone
Starling	Sturnus vulgaris
House Sparrow	Passer domesticus
Chaffinch	Fringilla coelebs
Greenfinch	Carduelis chloris

Notes on waterfowl in St. James's Park

In addition to the Park's mainly pinioned ornamental waterfowl a few birds originating from other collections fly in from time to time. Over the years full-winged escapees have included one or two Bean, Bar-headed, Snow, and Barnacle Geese. Among ducks Crested Duck, Baer's Pochard and Rosy-billed Pochard have also occurred. Some stayed for several years, unlike occasional Ferruginous Ducks whose irregular visits were usually fleeting ones.

Excluding Canada Geese, Mallard, Pochard, and tufted, the ornamental stock in recent years totalled about 300. Of approximately 225 ducks a little over ten per cent were full-winged, due largely to young birds having been reared in a wild state on the lake. These included two or three Ruddy Shelduck, Shelduck, Carolina Duck, Mandarin, Wigeon, Chiloé Wigeon and Pintail. Slightly larger numbers of full-winged Gadwall and Red-crested Pochard occurred in some years through influxes from elsewhere. Free-flying Greylags have increased to over two dozen in the past three years.

Always less easy to detect were one or two wild Wigeon, Teal and Pintail. Since the winter of 1980-81 up to twenty wild Shovelers have wintered. As their numbers exceeded the total pinioned birds of this species they were immediately noticeable in spite of the tameness of some of them.

At irregular intervals single wild Long-tailed Ducks and one or two Smew made brief appearances. Also there is one record of a male Ring-necked Duck. Occasionally the pinioned Cormorants have been joined by wild companions for several days.

Wild and pinioned waterfowl built up to a record 1,000 birds by June 1969 but, from 1970 onwards, the maximum has been nearer 750.

Full-winged hybrids, mainly of the genus *Aythya*, of which one parent was considered to be a Tufted Duck, are summarised in Appendix 10. Other crosses most frequently observed on the lake were: Canada × Bar-headed Goose; Cape Shelduck × Mallard; Ruddy Shelduck × Shelduck; Mallard × Red-crested Pochard; Wigeon × Chiloé Wigeon; and Red-crested Pochard × Rosy-billed Pochard. The second and fourth hybrids rank as probables.

Visitors to London with a special interest in ornamental waterfowl should visit Regent's Park. Here the collection includes a number of species not seen in St. James's. Moreover, excellent views may be obtained of wild Herons on their nests.

FISH

The following fish have been introduced into St. James's Park Lake in the past twenty-five years:

Eel	Anguilla anguilla
Rainbow trout	Salmo gairdneri
Perch	Perca fluviatilis
Common carp	Cyprinus carpio
Crucian carp	Carassius carassius
Goldfish	Carassius auratus
Gudgeon	Gobio gobio
Roach	Rutilus rutilus

BIBLIOGRAPHY

Adams, R. G. (1947). Mating behaviour of Wigeon and Red-breasted Merganser. *Brit. Birds* 40: 186-187.

Armstrong, Edward A. (1942). *Bird Display and Behaviour.* London.

Ashley, Maurice (1977). *General Monck.*

Atkinson-Willes, G. L. editor (1963). *Wildfowl in Great Britain.* Nature Conservancy Monograph Number Three. HMSO publication. London.

Baker, Leslie (1972). Mortality among wildfowl at Kew. *London Bird Report* 36: 84-85.

Bannerman, David Armitage (1958). *The Birds of the British Isles.* Volume 7. Edinburgh.

Bauer, K. M. and Glutz von Blotzheim, U.N. (1969). *Handbuch der Vogels Mitteleuropas.* Volume 3. Frankfurt.

Bent, Arthur Cleveland (1923). *Life Histories of North American Wild Fowl.* Part I. Dover Edition published in 1962. New York.

Bezzel, Einhard (1968). Die "Balz" von Tafel-und Reiherente (Aythya ferina und A. fuligula). *Vogelwelt* 89: 102-111.

Bezzel, E. and E. von Krosigk (1971). Zum Ablauf des Brutgeschäftes bei Enten. *Journal für Ornithologie* 112: 411-437.

Boase, Henry (1954).Movements and numbers of Tufted Duck in E. Scotland. *Brit. Birds* 47: 65-76.

Boyle, Geoffrey L. (1968). Foot-paddling by Pochards. *Brit. Birds* 61: 308.

Breed, W. G. (1962). Movements and breeding of Tufted Duck at Hall Place, Leigh, 1957-1960. *The Kent Bird Report* Number 9: 48-52.

Carbonell, Montse (1984). Young Tufted Duck riding on adult. *Brit. Birds* 77: 318.

Coats, Peter (1978). *The Gardens of Buckingham Palace.*

Coward, T. A. (1929). *The Birds of the British Isles and their eggs.* Second series: Fourth edition. London.

Cramp, S. and Simmons, K. E. L. editors (1977). *The Birds of the Western Palearctic.* Volume 1. Oxford.

Cramp, S. and Spencer, R. (1964). The birds of the gardens of Buckingham Palace. *Proc. of S. Lond. Ent. & Nat. Hist. Soc.* 1963: 40-45.

Cramp, S. and Teagle, W. G. (1952). The Birds of Inner London, 1900-1950 *Brit. Birds* 45: 433-56.

Cramp, Stanley and Tomlins, A. D. (1966). The birds of Inner London, 1951-65 *Brit. Birds* 59: 209-233.

Dementiev, G. P. and Gladkov, N. A. editors (1952). *Birds of the Soviet Union.* Volume 4. Moscow.

Driver, Peter M. (1974). *In search of the Eider.* London.

Dzubin, Alex (1955). Some evidences of Home range in waterfowl. *Trans. Twentieth North American Wildlife Conference:* 278-298.

Erskine, A. J. (1971). *Buffleheads.* Canadian Wildlife Service Monograph Series – Number 4. Ottawa.

Evelyn, J. (1641-1706). *Diary.*

Fitter, R. S. R. (1945). *London's Natural History.* London.

Folk, Čestmir (1971). A study on diurnal activity rhythm and feeding habits of Aythya fuligula. *Acta Sc Nat Brno* 5 (12): 1-39.

Fraser, Antonia (1979). *King Charles II*. London.

Frith, H. J. (1967). *Waterfowl in Australia*. Sydney.

Gardarsson, A. (1979). Waterfowl populations of Lake Mývatn and recent changes in numbers and food habits. *Oikos* 32: 250-270.

Gillham, E. H. (1951). Aerial courtship display flight of some surface-feeding ducks in winter quarters. *Brit. Birds* 44: 135-136.

Gillham, E. H. (1951A). Down-stripping by Sheld-duck away from nest site. *Brit. Birds* 44: 103-104.

Gillham, E. H. (1957). Notes on Tufted Ducks in St. James's Park, London. *Brit. Birds* 50: 2-10.

Gillham, E. H. (1957A). Field notes on the white feathering at the base of the bill and white under tail-coverts in the Tufted Duck. *Brit. Birds* 50: 389-393.

Gillham, E. H. (1958). Further notes on the Tufted Duck in St. James's Park, London. *Brit. Birds* 51: 413-426.

Gillham, E. H. (1959). Variations of plumage colourations in the Pochard and the Tufted Duck. *Bull. B.O.C.* 79/5: 87-88.

Gillham, E. H. (1960). Remarks on the female plumage of the Tufted Duck and a comparison with the Ring-necked Duck. *Bull. B.O.C.* 80/8: 140-141.

Gillham, E. H. (1961). Mallard feeding from dead birds. *Brit. Birds* 54: 357-359.

Gillham, Eric, Harrison, James M. and Harrison, Jeffery G. (1966). A study of certain *Aythya* hybrids. *Wildfowl* 17: 49-65.

Glegg, W. E. (1935). *A history of the Birds of Middlesex*. London.

Harris, John, Bellaigue, Geoffrey de, Millar, Oliver (1968). *Buckingham Palace*.

Harrison, J. G. (1977). Tufted Duck carrying its young. *The Kent Bird Report* Number 24: 98-99.

Harrison, James M. and Harrison, Jeffery G. (1960A). "On varieties of the Tufted Duck, with an account of an unrecorded type of variation." *Bull. B.O.C.* 80/2: 25-28.

Harrison, James M. and Harrison, Jeffery G. (1960B). Further remarks on Female Plumages of the Tufted Duck. *Bull. B.O.C.* 80/8: 141-142.

Harrison, James M. and Harrison, Jeffery G. (1961). Variant winter plumage of the female Tufted Duck. *Bull. B.O.C.* 81/6: 103-105.

Havlín, J. (1966). Breeding success of the Pochard and the Tufted Duck in Czechoslovakia. *Bird Study* 13: 306-310.

Hilden, O. (1964). Ecology of duck populations in the island group of Valassaaret, Gulf of Bothnia. *Ann. Zool. Fenn.* 1: 153-279.

Hochbaum, H. Albert (1944). *The Canvasback on a Prairie Marsh*. Washington.

Homes, R. C. editor (1964). *The Birds of the London Area*. Revised edition. London.

Homes, R. C. (1976). Twenty-five years of duck counts in the London Area. *London Bird Report* 39: 62-74.

Hori, J. (1963). Three-bird flights in Mallard. *The Wildfowl Trust 14th Annual Report*: 124-132.

Hori, J. (1966). Observations on Pochard and Tufted Duck breeding biology with particular reference to colonisation of a home range. *Bird Study* 13: 297-305.

Hudson, W. H. (1898). *Birds in London*.

Johnsgard, Paul A. (1965). *Handbook of Waterfowl Behaviour*. London.

Johnsgard, Paul A. (1968). *Waterfowl: Their Biology and Natural History*. Lincoln, Nebraska.

Keymer, I. F., Smith, G. R., Roberts, T. A., Heaney, S. I. and Hibberd, D. J. (1972). Botulism as a Factor in Waterfowl Mortality at St. James's Park, London. *The Veterinary Record.* Jan. 29, 1972: 111-114.

Kortright, Francis H. (1943). *The ducks, geese and swans of North America.* Washington D.C.

Lack, David (1974). *Evolution illustrated by Waterfowl.* Oxford.

Larwood, Jacob (1872). *The Story of London Parks.* London.

Laughlin, K. F. (1974). Bioenergetics of Tufted Duck (Aythya fuligula) at Loch Leven, Kinross. *Proc. Roy. Soc. Edinb.,* B74: 383-389.

Lebret, T. (1948). The "diving-play" of Surface-feeding duck. *Brit. Birds* 41: 247.

Linduska, Joseph P. editor (1964). *Waterfowl Tomorrow.* Washington.

McKinney, F. (1965). The Comfort Movements of Anatidae. *Behaviour* 25: 120-220.

Mendall, Howard L. (1958). *The Ring-necked Duck in the Northeast. University of Maine Bulletin* 60/16: June 20, 1958.

Millais, J. G. (1913). *British Diving Ducks.* London.

Montier, David, editor (1977). *Atlas of Breeding Birds of the London Area.* London.

Newton, I. and Campbell, C. R. G. (1975). Breeding of Ducks at Loch Leven, Kinross. *Wildfowl* 26: 83-102.

Ogilvie, M. A. (1975). *Ducks of Britain and Europe.* Berkhamsted, Hertfordshire.

Oliver, P. J. (1980). Moulting Tufted Ducks and Pochards in the London Area. *London Bird Report* No. 44: 80-84.

Oliver, P. J. (1983). Winter wildfowl counts in the London Area – 1947/48 to 1981/82. *London Bird Report* No. 47: 97-105.

Olney, P. J. S. (1963). The food and feeding habits of Tufted Duck. *Ibis* 105: 55-62.

Osborne, K. C. (1972). The Need for caution when identifying Scaup, Ferruginous Duck and other species of the *Aythya* genus. *London Bird Report* 36: 86-91.

Parr, D. (1974). The effect of sailing at Island Barn Reservoir. *Surrey Bird Report,* 1973.

Payne-Gallwey, Sir Ralph (1886). *The book of duck decoys.* London.

Pedroli, Jean-Carlo (1982). Activity and time budget of Tufted Ducks on Swiss lakes during winter. *Wildfowl* 33: 105-112.

Pentelow, F. T. K. (1965). The Lake in St. James's Park. *London Naturalist* 44: 128-138.

Perrins, Christopher (1961). The "Lesser Scaup" problem. *Brit. Birds* 54: 49-54.

Peterson, Roger, Mountfort, Guy and Hollom, P. A. D. (1974). *A Field Guide to the Birds of Britain and Europe.* Third Edition. London.

Player, P. V. (1971). Food and feeding habits of the Common Eider at Seafield, Edinburgh, in winter. *Wildfowl* 22: 100-106.

Ripley, Dillon (1959). *A Paddling of Ducks.* London.

Rogers, John P. (1964). A decoy trap for male Lesser Scaups. *The Journal of Wildlife Management,* 28/2: 408-410.

Rogers, Michael J. *et al.* (1982). Report on rare birds in Great Britain in 1981. *Brit. Birds* 75: 492-494.

Rolls, Julian C. (1983). Probable bigamy by Pochard. *Brit. Birds* 76: 232.

Savage, Christopher (1952). *The Mandarin Duck.* London.

Sharrock, J. T. R. *editor* (1976). *The Atlas of breeding birds in Britain and Ireland*. Tring, Hertfordshire.

Simmons, K. E. L. (1968). Foot-paddling by Pochards. *Brit. Birds* 61: 308-309.

Simms, Eric (1974). *Wild Life in the Royal Parks*. HMSO publication. London.

Sowls, Lyle K. (1955). *Prairie Ducks*. Washington.

Stow, John (1603). *A Survey of London*.

Taylor, D. W. *et al*. Eds. (1981). *Birds of Kent*. Meopham, Kent.

Ticehurst, N. F. (1909). *A History of the Birds of Kent*. London.

Tomlinson, David (1977). A feathered United Nations: The wildfowl of St. James's Park. *Country Life* Nov. 10, 1977.

Tuite, C. H. and Owen, Myrfyn (1984). Breeding waterfowl on British inland waters in 1980. *Wildfowl* 35: 157-172.

Van der Wal, Reinder J. and Zomerdijk, Piet J. (1979). The moulting of Tufted Duck and Pochard on the Ijsselmeer in relation to moult concentrations in Europe. *Wildfowl* 30: 99-108.

Veselovsky, Z. (1951). The postembryonic development of the Tufted Duck. *Sylvia* 1/13: 1-19.

Vinicombe, Keith (1982). Identification of female, eclipse male and first winter male Ring-necked Ducks. *Brit. Birds* 75: 327-328.

Walpole-Bond, J. (1938). *A History of Sussex Birds*. London.

Ward, Cyril (1912). *Royal Gardens*. London.

Weller, Milton W. (1957). Growth, weights, and plumages of the Redhead Aythya Americana. *The Wilson Bulletin* 69: 5-38.

Weller, Milton W. (1959). Parasitic Egg laying in the Redhead (Aythya americana) and other North American Anatidae. *Ecological Monographs,* 29: 333-365.

Weller, Milton W. (1965). Chronology of pair formation in some Nearctic Aythya (ANATIDAE). *The Auk* 82/2: 227-235.

Whitton, Brian (1979). *Rivers, lakes and marshes*. The natural history of Britain and Northern Europe series. London.

Willughby, Francis (1678). *The ornithology of Francis Willughby*. London.

Witherby, H. F., Jourdain, F. C. R., Ticehurst, N. F. and Tucker, B. W. (1948). *The Handbook of British Birds* Volumes 3 & 5. London.

Yarker, B. and Atkinson-Willes, G. L. (1971). The numerical distribution of some British breeding ducks. *Wildfowl* 22: 63-70.

Bird Life in the Royal Parks reports

In the text all reports published or printed by HMSO on bird life in the Royal Parks are, for convenience, lumped together under the above title. They were, in fact, published as follows:—

Reports of the Committee on Bird Sanctuaries in the Royal Parks (England) for 1928 onwards.

Bird Life in London (1939-47, 1948 and 1949).

Bird Life in The Royal Parks (1950, 51-52, 53-54, 55-56, 57-58, 59-60, 61-62, 63-64, 65-66, 67-68, 69-70, 71-72, 73, 74, 75, 76 and 77).

Anas Fuligula prima Gesn.

Facsimile of a drake Tufted Duck in Willughby (1678)

Female feeding by up-ending

Pair feeding with heads submerged

Downy Pochard feeding by skimming

A brood female foot-paddling to stir up food for her young

A variant (white) female Mallard and brood which includes one bright yellow downy

Turf damaged in wet weather by feeding Mallard
(Tufted Ducks never cause damage like this)

The *probable origins* of hybrids
mentioned herein rank no higher
than educated guesses until these
crosses are found to be *exactly* like
others of proven parentage

Male 'Lesser Scaup-type' hybrid

A male hybrid probably of Rosy-bill × Tufted Duck parentage
resembling a Rosy-bill drake

A male hybrid probably of Rosy-bill × Tufted Duck parentage
resembling a Baer's Pochard drake

Female 'Scaup-type' hybrid at onset of post-nuptial wing-moult in November
(note elongated feathers in vicinity of nape)

The female 'Scaup-type' hybrid of the previous photograph in winter plumage
(note slight crest)

Female Scaup with a normal black bill tip and (bottom) a female Pochard

Female Scaup with a larger than usual black bill tip (March)

Female with a white 'mask' (December)

Male Ferruginous Duck with a larger than usual black bill tip
(note tail down low swimming posture)

Male with a smaller than usual black bill tip

Male with a normal black bill tip

INDEX

Aggressiveness, behaviour, bill colour and markings etc., refer only to the Tufted Duck. Subjects relating to other birds are not indexed separately but can be found among the page numbers against individual species. Page numbers of photographs are given in heavy type at the end of each subject, species or place.

Abyssinian Blue-winged Goose, 124
Acknowledgments, ix, x
aggressiveness (*see also* behaviour, pursuit, rape), 49-57, 70-75, 80, 81, 86, 89, 90, 99-105, 113, 121, 122, 124, 126-129, 151, 152, 157, 210, **66, 91, 175-177, 226**
Australian Blue-billed Duck, 23
Baer's Pochard (or Baer's White-eye), 51, 270
Bahama Pintail, 105, 210
Barnacle Goose, 125, 187
Barrow's Goldeneye, 152
behaviour
  brood female attacking own young, 129
  communal calling warning, 87, 216
  defence
    of brood by female, 115, 117, 124, 126, 127, 151-153, 163, **226**
    of female by male, 71-77, 80, 89, 90, 99, 100, 125, 210, **174-176**
    of individual spacing, 49, 53, 54, 99, **66, 91**
    of nest, 86
  gesture of repulsion, 104, 105, 218
  homosexual, 68, 81, 82, 102, 248
  male guarding female, 75, 76, 212, **178**
  male threatening own female, 90, **177**
  pre-flight, 50, 67, 136, **92**
bigamy, 114, 115
bill colour and markings
  of adult female, 21, 22, 161, **14, 291**
  of adult male, 20, 157, 158, 160, 271, **13, 139, 255, 292**
  of duckling, 133, 134
  of juvenile, 41, 134, 135
biology, some comparisons between two eight-year periods of, 229
Bird Keepers in St. James's Park, 6, 8, 32, 35, 38, 58, 83-86, 106, 117, 120, 148, 151, 153, 181, 191
birds breeding in St. James's Park, list of, 275
Black-headed Gull, 34, 126, 128, 150, 170, 179, 182
Black Swan, 126, 127
Blue-winged Teal, 191

boats, effects of, 34, 35, 166
breeding
  age of females, 88, 217
  range, 27
bridge over St. James's Park lake, 37, 49, **61**
broods (*see also* young)
  amalgamation of, 121, 122, **221**
  behaviour on reaching water of, 112, 113
  drake attendance on, 111, 112
  duration of bond with parent, 131-133, 260-264
  family life of, 111-133
  feeding behaviour of, 115, 116, 133
  hatching dates of, 111, 230
  left alone by mother, 113-115
  nursery areas for, 31
  overland travel of, 31, 118, 120, **222-223**
  return to nest of, 113, 114
  sizes, 112, 233
  splitting of, 114, 121-123
  two in one season, 107
Buckingham Palace lake and gardens, 1, 8, 9, 10, 30-32, 36, 38, 39, 43, 44, 106
Bufflehead, 99, 100
Cake House feeding point, 37, 184, 185, **60**
Canada Goose, 6, 7, 69, 80, 87, 125, 126, 149, 152, 275, 278
Canvasback, 23, 52, 75, 132, 160
Carolina (or Wood) Duck, 84, 117, 127, 128, 210
Chiloé Wigeon, 58, 103, 106, 124, 182, 187, 188
clutch size, 85, 216
colour ringing and recognition of individual birds, 2, 35, 38
Common Scoter, 52
Coot, 19, 69, 80, 82, 85, 86, 106, 112, 116, 117, 126, 128, 129, 132, 149, 153, 154, 170, 187, 214, 275
copulation
  attempted and successful, 55, 67, 68, 77, 202, 203, **173**
  behaviour preceding, 213
  interspecific, 67, 68

post-copulatory display, 66, 77, 102, 205, 206, , **173**
precopulatory display, 66, 77, 101, 204, **98, 171·173**
Cormorant, 5-7, 126, 150, 151, 153, 278
courting parties
loose associations, 50-53
close-knit, 50-54, 58, 100, 199, **92·94**
courtship
aerial, 52, 53, 100
display postures, 50-53, 89, 99, **93, 94, 98, 171, 172**
interspecific, 54
nuptial, 73-75, 100, 211
prenuptial, 49-67, 77
soliciting, 55, 67, 202, 203, **98, 171, 172**
unmated males harassing pairs and unattached females, 54, 57, 77, 89, 99, **95**
Department of the Environment, 1, 3, 7, 31, 39, 149, 153, 180, 181
disease, 147, 148, 180
Duck Island in St. James's Park, 6-8, 37, 38, 43, 58, 78, 83-85, 105, 106, 117, 119, 123, 136, 148, 150, 151, 153, 154, 157, 169, 180, 189, 191, 273, 275, **63**
eggs
carrying of, 81, 106, 112
colour types of, 85, 86
covering of, 105
dimensions of, 85
eating of, 81, 183
examination of contents of left-over, 228
left in nest after hatching, 105, 112-114, 228
span of laying season of, 76, 88
eggshells
carrying of, 106, 112
eating of, 183
remains in nest after hatching, 114
Eider, 23, 100, 128, 130, 187
escape movements
of brood female, 130, 152
of flightless adults, 166
of young, 119, 120, 127, 128, 151, 152
eye colour
of adult female, 21
of adult male, 20
of ducklings, 133, 134
of juveniles, 41, 135
sexing ducklings by, 134, 135
evening flight, 43, 170
feeding
diurnal, 169, 170, 182-184

methods, 115, 133, 182-188, **285, 286**
nocturnal, 43, 169, 170
underwater, 23
feigning, 130, 131
Ferruginous Duck (or Common White-eye), 22, 23, 25, 51, 54, 271, 278, **291**
Finsbury Park, London, 35, 45, 71, 120, 166, 184, 272, 274
fish stocks in St. James's lake, 180, 181, 278
fixations, 58, 59, 103, 124, **98**
fledging
period, 133-136, 235
success, 136-138, 229, 231, 232
flight, age attained, 135, 136
flightless period of post-nuptial moult
of adult females, 131, 159, 160-163, 165-167, 209, 236-239, 260-262, 265, **142, 145, 257**
of adult males, 157-160, 162, 164-167, 235, 236-239, **140, 255, 256**
food
from public, 2, 32-34, 43, 115, 170
types of, 115, 169, 170, 181-188
foster parents, 123-125
fountain basins, Kensington Gardens, London, 31, 118, **65**
Gadwall, 112, 130, 182, 186, 210, 278
Garganey, 87, 130, 187
Goldeneye, 55, 118
Goosander, 55, 118, 152
Great Black-backed Gull, 128
Greylag Goose, 152, 187, 275, 278
Herring Gull, 69, 80, 121, 124, 127, 149-154, 275, **251**
home range, 71-73, 109, 245-247
hybrids, 24-26, 54, 163, 210, 268-271, 278, **145, 146, 287·289**
Hyde Park, London, 1, 8, 9, 30, 32, 36, 39, 45-47, 106, 120, 136, 147, 164
identification
of incubating females, 104, 218, **219**
of laying females, 89, 217, **219**
of pairs, 50, 57, 73
of unmated birds, 82, 89
of young, 133
incubation
behaviour during, 104, 105, 218
egg losses during, 105
males waiting during, 88, 89, 105
period, 104-105
Inner London, definition of, 30
Kensington Gardens, London, 8, 9, 30, 32, 33, 36, 39, 44, 46-48, 106, 115, 118, 136, 147

Lesser Black-backed Gull, 121, 127, 128, 154
Lesser Scaup, 19, 25, 52, 54, 75, 100, 268, 269
life expectancy, 154, 155
loafing spot, 72, 73, 80
locomotion, 22-24, 118-121, **14, 17, 18, 139-141, 222, 223, 251, 253, 258**
London Area, definition of, 27
London Natural History Society, 26, 28, 29, 47, 71, 275
loner females, evidence of nesting by, 81, 82, 89, 114, 217, 249, 250
Long-tailed Duck (or Old Squaw), 23, 100, 130, 278
Long Water, Kensington Gardens, London, 9, 31, 34, 36, 38, 39, 42, 44, 45, 47, 48, 53, 115, 147, 148, 159-160, 162, 164-166, **64**
Mallard, 19, 54, 55, 58, 68, 82, 84, 87, 99, 100, 102, 103, 105, 112, 116-118, 121, 123, 125-128, 130-134, 149, 152, 163, 170, 182, 183, 186, 191, 206, 210, 214, 269, 272, 275, 278, **91, 96, 98, 220, 221, 226, 251, 286, 287**
Mandarin Duck, 84, 127, 187, 210
Moorhen, 85, 86, 106, 126, 150, 153, 187, 214, 275, **226**
moulting waters, 164-168
movements, 41-43, 69, 157, 164-168, 194-197, 208, 209, 239
Musk Duck, 23
Mute Swan, 7, 8, 118, 149, 152, 184, 275
natal area, attachment to, 109
nests
  casualties to, 105-108, 227
  construction of, 79, 80, 84, 117
  disappearance of eggs from, 106
  down colour in, 85
  dump (multiple clutches), 86
  location of, 78, 84
  material used for, 84, 85
  maintenance of, 106
  parasitism of, 86, 87, 89, 114
  proximity of, 214
  token building of, 82, 83, 117, 215
  use of vacated nests by others, 84, 214
nesting
  areas, 78, 83, 84
  cover, 79-81, 83-85
  success, 107, 108, 227
nest sites
  artificial, 6, 79, 83-85, 190, 191, 214, 215, **178**
  elevated, 84
  natural, 79, 83-85, 214, 215
  search for, 58, 72, 76, 77, 79-82, 213, **177**

underground, 84, 214
New Zealand Scaup, 51
nomenclature, 276-278
pair formation
  behaviour, 49-68
  chronology, 56-58, 200
  dissolution of pair status, 68, 105, 207
  duration of bond, 58, 68, 109
  fixed, 52, 55-58, 241-244
  interspecific, 55, 58, 59, 124, **171, 224, 225**
  temporary, 55, 56, 58, 114, 115, 241-244
pairs
  percentage of, getting a brood to water, 138
  percentages of, in some small populations, 201
Palace end island in St. James's Park, 37, 83, 106, **62**
Pelican, 6, 7, 69, 149-153
piniomed and full-winged introductions, 2, 3, 7, 27, 29, 30, 32, 35
Pintail, 55, 74, 100, 105, 107, 130, 210, 278
plumage
  aberrant, 35, 163, 272-274, **145**
  of adult female, 19-22, 41, 160, 161, 163, **14-16, 141, 142, 144, 145, 219, 253, 257, 258**
  of adult male, 20, 41, 157, 158, 160, **13, 139-141, 255, 256**
  of downy young, 133-135, **144, 226, 251, 252**
  of partly-fledged young or juveniles, 41, 163, **143, 253, 254, 256**
  sex change, 274
  white or whitish 'mask'
    in adult female, 21, 161, 163, 273, **92, 174, 219, 226, 257, 258, 291**
    in adult male, 158
    in partly fledged young and juvenile, 135, 158, 273, **143, 252**
  white spot beside base of lower mandible in adult female, 21, **219**
  white undertail-coverts
    in adult female, 21, 158, 161, **258**
    in adult male, 158, **140**
    in partly-fledged young and juvenile, 135, **254**
Pochard, 19, 20, 23-25, 32-33, 43, 50-52, 54, 58, 67, 74, 75, 77, 81, 82, 85-88, 98-100, 102, 105, 106, 109, 111-113, 115, 117, 118, 120, 121, 123-125, 127, 129, 130, 133, 134, 149, 157, 158, 162, 163, 166, 170, 183, 185-187, 206, 210, 214, 267, 268, 270, 271, 274, 275, 278, **96-97, 176, 224, 225, 285, 290**

Index

population
  of Britain, 27, 167
  of Inner London, 190
  of London Area, 27-29, 190
  of St. James's group of waters, 30-32, 42
  of St. James's Park, 2, 29, 30, 41, 42, 193
predation
  of eggs, 83, 105, 106, 112
  of young, 149-154
predators and killers, 83, 87, 105, 106, 112, 121, 124, 127, 128, 149-154
pursuits
  aerial, 52, 53, 56, 73, 74, 90, 101
  on land, 71, 73, 80, 81, 86, 98, 99, 116, 117
  over the water, 72, 89, 90, 99-101, **175, 176**
  underwater, 56, 90, 101, **to air 176**
rape
  attacks on females, 100-102
  attacks on males, 102, 103
  definition of, 101
  interspecific, 102, 103
  males raping own females, 102
  reactions to rape attacks, 102, 259
  time-span of rape attacks, 70
recreations authorised on the St. James's group of waters, 2, 34, 35
Red-breasted Merganser, 23, 55
Red-crested Pochard, 54, 58, 67, 68, 87, 99, 100, 102, 103, 105, 123, 125, 186, 210, 278, **220**
Redhead, 52, 75, 85, 86, 89, 99, 100
Regent's Park, London, 9, 38, 45, 46, 148, 273, 278
renesting, 107-109
resting postures, 22, 24, **59, 144**
Ring-necked Duck, 19, 25, 53, 72, 77, 99, 107, 114, 127, 129, 157, 160, 191, 271, 278, **15, 255, 256**
ringing recoveries, 44-46
Rosy-bill (or Rosy-billed Pochard), 52, 68, 100, 134, 210, 269, 270
Round Pond, Kensington Gardens, London, 9, 31, 34-36, 38, 39, 42, 44, 45, 47, 48, 53, 67, 147, 159, 160, 162, 164, 166, **65,**
Ruddy Duck, 102, 152
Ruddy Shelduck, 186
St. James's Park, history of, 3-8, **11, 12**

Scaup, 19, 25, 55, 160, 161, 163, 268-272, **98, 171, 257, 258, 290**
Serpentine, Hyde Park, London, 9, 34-36, 38, 39, 42, 44, 45, 47, 48, 53, 109, 120, 147, 148, 159, 160, 162, 164-166
sex ratios, 46, 47, 71, 198
sex segregation, 46-48
Shelduck, 55, 77, 83, 84, 112, 118, 125, 126, 129-131, 150, 179, 185-187
Shoveler, 55, 74, 112, 130, 186, 278
Smew, 55, 278
Southern Pochard, 106, 210
study area
  acreage of, 39
  advantages of, 1
  depth of water areas in, 39
  sketch-maps of, 36, 37
tameness, in London Area, 1, 2, 32, 33
Teal, 24, 55, 74, 130, 131, 278
unmated birds, 69-71, 74, 82, 115, 193
voice, 49-52, 74, 87, 104, 116, 187, 266, 267
water area preferences, 34, 37, 48, 72, 73, 164, 165, 179, 245-247
White-winged (or Velvet) Scoter, 52
Wigeon, 54, 55, 87, 127, 187, 210, 278
young
  abandoning parent or foster-parent, 132
  agility of, 115, 118-121, 130
  attacks by, 127
  attacks on, 112, 113, 117, 129, 132, 149-153
  back transport of, 118
  brooding of, 116-118, **220**
  communal defence of, 124, 125, 127
  crash-diving by, 130
  departure of free flying, 136
  dropping to ground from a height, 119, 120
  greeting ceremony of, 129
  growth and development of, 134
  human being stroking, 129
  mortality of, 111, 112, 120, 121, 136-138, 147-155
  newly-hatched reaching water, numbers of, 234
  rearing themselves, 133
  wing exercising, 136, **254**